MW00368549

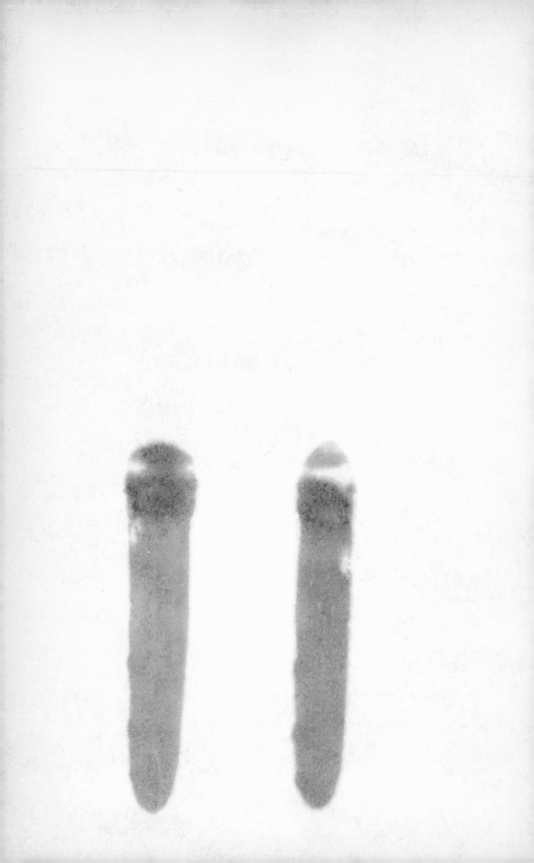

SCIENCE AND IMMORTALITY

Science and Immortality

The *Éloges* of the Paris Academy of Sciences
(1699–1791)

·CHARLES B. PAUL·

UNIVERSITY OF CALIFORNIA PRESS

Berkeley · Los Angeles · London

University of California Press
Berkeley and Los Angeles, California
University of California Press, Ltd.
London, England
Copyright © 1980 by
The Regents of the University of California

Library of Congress Cataloging in Publication Data

Paul, Charles B.
    Science and immortality.

    Bibliography: p. 181
    Includes indexes.
    1. Scientists—France—Biography.   2. Académie des
sciences, Paris.   3. Eulogies.   I. Title.
Q141.P375   509'.2'2   80-17208
ISBN 0-520-03986-6

Printed in the United States of America

*To Oliver Loud, who first showed me the conjunction
between science and other human activities, and to
Roger Hahn, who has encouraged me to
uphold that vision.*

Contents

Preface

Until fairly recently natural science was almost universally viewed as an objective, passionless, and value-free mode of knowledge. Concurrently, the scientist was (and to some extent still is) depicted as the embodiment of objectivity, of renunciation of pleasure and profit, and of selfless dedication to the mental and material improvement of humanity. For over two centuries scientists and laymen alike have clung to the belief in a superior breed of men engaged in a high moral venture. It need hardly be asserted, however, that the persistence of a belief is no proof of its validity. What, therefore, accounts for the widespread diffusion of this myth in media of communication as diverse as films, advertisements, novels, textbooks, and scientific popularizations? A partial answer to this question is given in this book.

In France at least this mythologization of scientists first assumed official form in 1699 with the *éloges* or eulogies penned by Fontenelle in honor of the recently deceased members of the Paris Academy of Sciences. He had transmuted an uncritical encomium inherited from antiquity into a semi-biographical narrative and had elevated scientists to the rank formerly held by generals and statesmen. Hence, the two-hundred-odd *éloges* that he and his successors Mairan, Fouchy, and Condorcet wrote between 1699 and 1791 can be studied as detailed accounts of scientific activity in eighteenth-century France, a collective biography of a new breed of savants, and specimens of a literary subgenre worthy of serious esthetic inquiry. Yet the *éloges* are much more than Lives and Works of the scientists of pre-Revolutionary France. By their felicitous style and great popularity, Fontenelle's *éloges* initiated a new tradition of extolling the moral virtues of the post-Renaissance sciences and their practitioners.

No overall study has hitherto been undertaken that encompasses all the eulogies written in the eighteenth century by Fontenelle and his three successors. Several volumes, however, would have to be written in order to do justice to the *éloges* as media of scientific popularization, biographies of over one hundred scientists, descriptions of more than one thousand scientific investigations, and idealized portraits of the investigators. Instead, the intent of this study is at once both less and more ambitious. The first five chapters show the inconsistencies that resulted from the secretaries' attempts to blend biographical accuracy with moral hagiography and from their inability to maintain historical impartiality towards scientific explanations that affronted their most cherished beliefs. Chapter 6 traces the virtues informing the idealized portraits of the eulogized scientists to a number of older and nonscientific traditions: pastoral literature, Plutarchan biography, Renaissance Humanism, and especially Stoic philosophy. The book concludes with the argument that by virtue of a semantic shift in the term "philosopher," the very virtues that have been attributed to the natural philosopher or scientist over the past two centuries had once been largely the property of the idealized Stoic (or Socratic) philosopher.

This book is heavily indebted to Orinda Outram's penetrating analysis of the eulogies penned by Cuvier between 1797 and 1832 and to Roger Hahn's magisterial study for its nonpareil bibliography and for many subtle *aperçus* on the stresses imposed upon the Paris Academy of Sciences from within and without. Yet, however supplementary to Outram's two articles on Cuvier and however complementary to Hahn's *Anatomy of a Scientific Institution*, neither of their works nor this one has exhausted the topics under discussion. Among subjects still awaiting examination should be included analyses of the *éloges* composed for the Académie de Médecine and the Académie de Chirurgie (eulogies modeled after those of Fontenelle), critical biographies of Fontenelle's successors Mairan and especially Fouchy, and a literary and intellectual inquiry into the image of the scientist in the nineteenth and twentieth centuries and in countries other than France.

Acknowledgments

The composition of this book over a period of seven years has been facilitated by the assistance offered by a number of individuals and institutions and lightened by two trips to France, in 1972 and 1974. I therefore wish to extend my sincere thanks to the Bibliothèque Nationale for enabling me to read separate printed editions of the *éloges* and sundry rare books. I am especially grateful to the staffs of the Bibliothèque de l'Institut and of the Archives of the Paris Académie des Sciences for their patience in meeting my requests to peruse all the manuscripts of Condorcet and countless issues of the *Mercure de France* and the *Journal des Sçavans* and to pry into the *plumitifs*, registers, and *dossiers* of the pre-Revolutionary Academy. I also would like to thank Professor Roger Heim of the Muséum National d'Histoire Naturelle and the Academy of Sciences for his kindness in providing me gratis a copy of Condorcet's *éloges* of the earliest Academicians.

Closer to home, I am grateful to San Jose State University for granting me a sabbatical leave in 1974, the Library of Congress for sending me copies of the four drafts of Condorcet's *éloge* of Benjamin Franklin, Karen Reeds of the University of California Press for reminding me of the value of concision, to Sheila Berg of the same press for efficiently steering the book through production, and Mary Lou White for her forbearance in typing and retyping my not-so-clean manuscript. Above all, two persons deserve my utmost gratitude: my mentor Roger Hahn, who encouraged me through these seven years and directed me to material in Parisian libraries, and my wife Janina, without whose patient understanding of the erratic summons of diligence and inspiration this book would never have been completed.

Except where specified, all translations from the French are mine.

C. B. P.

Introduction
Science and Eulogy

The fame of scientists is immortalized in ways denied to other men. They
are privileged to have stellar phenomena named after them, either because,
like Tycho Brahe, they discovered them, or because, like Edmund Halley,
they mathematically plotted their course, or because, like Copernicus, they
established a new astronomical system. They alone are remembered in
association with body pathologies like Addison's disease or with anatomical
parts like the Eustachian Canal or the Fallopian tubes. And they alone,
because of a particular discovery or special formulation, are entitled to be
remembered in connection with scientific laws or formulae or units of
measurements, as were Kepler, Newton, Boyle, Darwin, Volta, Watt, and
Ampère. These are the special ways by which the scientific community
discharges its eternal debt of gratitude to its most illustrious members. The
world at large is content to discharge its debt to scientists (if at all) in a manner
befitting illustrious men in all areas of achievement. Scientists share with
artists, politicians, and generals the appellation of streets, avenues, and public
squares. They also share with them entries in various biographical collections
of prominent persons. Finally, as members of learned academies, distinguished scientists, like other distinguished specialists, earn the additional
honor of a posthumous eulogy. And if they are members of more than one
academy, they are honored more than once.

It was Bernard Bovier de Fontenelle (1657–1757) who by his eulogies of
scientists first bridged the gap between the scientific community and the world
at large. Since his European reputation rested on a diversity of talents (bel
esprit, litterateur, philosophe, and apologist for science), he himself was
posthumously honored, not only by the three leading French academies of
which he was a member, but also by academies he had never been associated
with in any capacity. More importantly, he elevated the academic *éloge* from
an uncritical encomium to a semi-critical biography. As the first writer of
éloges for the Paris Academy of Sciences, he set the example for his imme-
diate successors in the eighteenth century—J. J. Dortous de Mairan, J. P.
Grandjean de Fouchy, and the Marquis de Condorcet—by transforming an

unctuous and hackneyed rhetorical device into a serious literary, biographical, and historical genre. The two-hundred-odd *éloges* written by these four men between 1699 and 1791 provide an evolving record of scientific activity in eighteenth-century France, a collective biography of the leading scientists in France and abroad, an important segment of French intellectual history, and a disclosure of the strengths and weaknesses, the intents and biases of the four secretaries.

THE EULOGY AND SCIENTIFIC POPULARIZATION

As a biographical record of over two hundred practitioners and patrons of science, the *éloges* of the old Academy of Sciences acquainted laymen with a discipline that was at once esoteric by its novelty and forbidding by its terminology and methodology. Hence the *éloges*, aside from the other functions they performed in the service of science, also served as a public relations organ in the same manner as journals, textbooks, public lectures, literary dialogues, scientific expositions, and *cabinets de physique* and *d'histoire naturelle*.

As a medium for the propagation of science among the educated public, the scientific *éloge* could not have arisen at a more propitious time than during the Enlightenment. While science had advanced most dramatically in the seventeenth century and while man's physical environment was to be most radically transformed during the nineteenth, the century in between, as Preserved Smith puts it, was marked

> by the resolute and successful effort to transfer the scientific spirit to other intel-
> lectual fields and to propagate it among ever larger strata of the population. . . .
> It did more than any other period both to bring under the reign of natural law the
> social disciplines, philosophy, religion, law, education, and even literature and
> art, and also to propagate the scientific spirit among the masses.[1]

The success of scientific popularization in eighteenth-century France was immeasurably helped by the fact that by that period French had well nigh replaced Latin as the learned language. Moreover, as Hélène Metzger has argued, since French prose as it was codified by the mid-seventeenth century was shaped for the convenience of the *honnête homme* who aspired to the ideals of universality, clarity, total intelligibility, and unambiguous abstraction, this Neoclassical prose was a perfect vehicle for scientific language with similar aspirations.[2] Thus the literate public, Metzger reminds us, could now read in the vernacular its philosophy in Descartes, Malebranche, and Régis, its physics in Rohault, its chemistry in Lémery, its cosmology in Fontenelle, and its natural theology in Pluche—and if pressed for time, digests of these and other scientific works in the *Journal des Sçavans*.[3] This supports Metzger's contention that in the eighteenth century

> the science that is taught, the science that is popularized, the science that is 'with-
> in reach of everybody,' is also on the level of the science being created. The new-

est discoveries, the latest theories on any subject whatever enter immediately into
the public domain and arouse discussions which everyone believes himself author-
ized to take part in, even if his lack of scientific training fails to endow him with
any competence or authority.[4]

Metzger's equation of the quality of the working sciences with that of
sciences within reach of everyman is contested by Louis Basso. "Popularization will never create a genuine science," he argues, since in order for the
layman to understand science with the same degree of sophistication as does
the professional, he would cease to be a layman. If the distinction between
layman and professional is to have any validity, Basso contends, a compromise has to be reached that can be stated in the form of another equation: the
smaller the distance between "popular" science and "working" science, the
smaller the lay public, while inversely, the larger the lay public that
understands science, the greater the distance between the two versions of
science—a universal public for science being impossible.[5]

Put into mathematical terms, Basso's reasoning is flawless. But it is based
on invalid premises, and is therefore faulty: the aim of scientific popularizers,
even of such *hauts vulgarisateurs* of yesteryear as Buffon, Nollet, Macquer,
or the writers of the *éloges*, or of today like Jeans, de Broglie, and
Schrödinger, is not to convey to the lay public the total spirit, methodology,
working habits, and terminology of the scientific community. Their aim is at
once less precise and more ambitious: it is to win over the general public to
the cause of science, to convert it to the rightness of its procedures, principles,
achievements, and applications, and to entice into science bright young men
and women who otherwise might pursue more lucrative, more traditional, or
more prestigious careers. It is furthest from the mind of the vulgarisateurs that
the whole public become a band of "elect": it is sufficient that intelligent
people endorse the work of the elect, support them if need be, remove the
obstacles that hinder their work, and do everything feasible to spread the good
news of science to the whole community. Hence it was not a travesty for the
eighteenth-century scientists and their spokesmen, as it appears to Basso, to
hold that the means of scientific publicity should include "the creation of
popular courses, the publication of cheap treatises aimed for a wide circulation, or . . .any other method."[6]

To convey the essence of scientific activity is not an impossible task; but
the ability to transmit faithfully the scientific matter and spirit to laymen is
reserved for a select few. As Voltaire, himself a fine practitioner of the art,
put it: to expound the abstruseness of science within the comprehension of the
intelligent layman requires the avoidance of the pitfalls of pedantry, novelty
for novelty's sake, misplaced wit, farfetched similes, and all without the
sacrifice of either clarity or precision.[7]

Voltaire, indeed, was ideally suited to expound on the rules of scientific
popularization, on the most effective rhetorical devices to convey the essence

of the growing science to the growing number of literate people eager to learn about the latest scientific discoveries. He had mastered nearly all the literary genres current in his time, he had written a popular exposition of Newton's natural philosophy, and he never ceased to advocate Newtonian empiricism and Lockean epistemology. It is therefore not surprising that in 1741 and 1743 Voltaire sought to fill the post of perpetual secretary of the Paris Academy of Sciences vacated first by Fontenelle, then by Mairan, and presented as his credentials a memoir on mechanics he had written. Though he soon renounced the ambition to become what he called "*le premier ministre de la philosophie*,"[8] Voltaire's bid for that position testifies to the prestige acquired in the midcentury by science, the Paris Academy of Sciences, and the *éloges* written by its *sécrétaire*.

THE INSTITUTION OF THE *ÉLOGES*

By 1741 the duties expected of the secretary of the Academy had been in its statutes for forty-two years. At the bequest of its presiding officer, the abbé Jean-Paul Bignon, and as a consequence of the semi-stagnation of the Academy for over a decade, that body had been completely reorganized in 1699. A new table of organization had been implemented and new functions had been assigned to all its members. The new *Règlement*, framed by Bignon's uncle, the *Sécrétaire d'Etat* in charge of the various academies, Louis Phélipeaux Pontchartrain, specified the new functions of the sécrétaire. He was to attend the meetings of the Academy on Wednesdays and Saturdays, keep a register of the substance of whatever had been "proposed, debated, examined, and resolved," collect from the speakers a summary of their observations, and at the end of each December publish extracts of the Academy's registers or an "*Histoire raisonnée* of the most remarkable deeds performed in the Academy."[9] To fulfill these obligations, the sécrétaire yearly published two volumes: one, the register of its proceedings and the other, a volume entitled *Histoire et Mémoires de l'Académie Royale des Sciences à Paris*. The latter primarily contained the more significant *Mémoires* written by the members, which in turn were preceded by an *Histoire*, that is, a collection of the secretary's precis of most of these *Mémoires*. Near the end of the *Histoire* proper of nearly every volume published under the ancien régime, however, were inserted *éloges* of members who had died during the year (and, in some cases, even earlier).

Nowhere in the règlement is there any mention of *éloges* or of their biyearly reading. Yet, from 1699 to 1791 (two years before the demise of the old Academy of Sciences), 193 *éloges* of deceased members were composed for public reading by the four *sécrétaires perpétuels*: Fontenelle, Mairan, Fouchy, and Condorcet. The origins of this tradition, though nowhere described, are not difficult to surmise. For one thing, the *éloges* were read at the two yearly sessions open to the public, one on the first working day after the two-week Lenten recess, i.e., the day after Easter, and the second on St. Martin's day, which followed the long recess between September 8 and November 11.[10] These two public sessions were most propitious to present science in its brightest hues; not surprisingly, therefore, these biyearly readings assumed the proportions of a vogue. As Roger Hahn says, "Accounts of these gatherings always stressed the majesty of the event, and newspapers generally reported them as they would other significant social affairs."[11] Indeed, even in his old age Fontenelle orally tested his *éloges* at the salon of Madame de Lambert and made corrections in them before presenting them officially at the Academy of Sciences.[12]

Furthermore, Fontenelle, by his composition of these eulogies, undoubtedly attempted to correct an oversight of his predecessor, the abbé Jean-Baptiste Duhamel. It must have seemed odd to him, if not to others, that while the Academy itself had paid no homage to its deceased members between 1666 and 1698, its de facto organ of publicity, the *Journal des Sçavans*, had occasionally inserted brief obituaries of Academicians in its columns. Besides, it was high time that the Academy of Sciences, thirty-three years after its foundation, set about commemorating its members when its rival institution, the Académie Française, had been composing *éloges oratoires* since its creation in 1635. Finally, Fontenelle must have been moved to write *éloges* by the sheer weight of a tradition that had honored eminent men since the days of ancient Greece.

THE PANEGYRICAL TRADITION

As a subject of rhetoric, the eulogy can trace its critical tradition to classical Greece. Although almost half "of the *Iliad* and more than two thirds of the *Odyssey* are devoted to speeches by the characters," it was not until the Age of Pericles, with the development of democracy, that oratory and rhetoric gained ascendancy in the public sphere. In Athens, oratory "was considered not the result of skill with the tricks of rhetoric, but a by-product of deep understanding of political affairs combined with intense patriotism. The orator clarified great issues of policy, stimulated heroic courage in times of crisis, cowed the enemies of the state when on foreign embassies, and encouraged virtue in times of peace."[13]

The ability to speak well also became a prerequisite for a successful career. Accordingly, the demand for instruction in public speaking attracted a group of new teachers, the Sophists, for whom the study of rhetoric was tantamount to "the study of style, a literary technique." Rejected by Plato on "philosophical and pedagogic grounds," rhetoric was rescued by Aristotle, who provided it with a "theory of the emotions (as in his *Poetics*), typology of characters, and detailed examination of style." It is he who is usually taken as the authority for the division of oratory into three genres, the deliberative (political), the judicial, and the demonstrative. The latter is further divided into subgenres like academic discourses, funeral orations, satirical speeches, and eulogies—all having as their final aim the praise or blame of a particular person. Both Cicero and Quintilian, who refined the aesthetics of demonstrative oratory, dwelled at length on its ethical content. Cicero required his orators to stress their subjects' possession of the Platonic virtues of wisdom, fortitude, temperance, and justice, while Quintilian taught that "rhetoric must be connected with the study of poetry and philosophy" and that within "philosophy, the emphasis is upon morality."[14]

Definitions of virtue also varied with the political circumstances during which the eulogies were delivered. Originally, the panegyric (literally "a general assembly") had been a speech "delivered before a mass audience" at the festivals of ancient Greece antedating the fifth century B.C. The purpose of these orations, like the Panhellenic festivals at which they were given, had been "the desire to promote domestic peace and national unity." Temporary solidarity among the Greeks during the Persian Wars gave rise to funeral orations over fallen Greek soldiers. This practice was continued by the Athenians during the Peloponnesian Wars, as is testified by Pericles' famous oration, but with the gradual extinction of freedom in the Mediterranean world during the Hellenistic era, the deliberative and judicial genres of oratory gave way in importance to the demonstrative genre. Finally, with the establishment of the principate in Rome, the rulers, whether dead or alive, tested the panegyrists' ability to disentangle just praise from obsequiousness. Pliny the Younger, whose address to the Emperor Trajan became a model of its type during the Renaissance, justified "his servile flattery of Trajan with the argument that in it 'good princes might recognize what they have done; bad, what they ought to have done.' "[15]

From the very beginning mimesis informed the ethical intent of demonstrative oratory. The fallen dead served as models to the beleaguered survivors, good rulers served as checks to the excesses of evil rulers, and, in general, the panegyric, as Isocrates put it, was designed to " 'eulogize in prose the virtues of a man' in order to stimulate 'emulation for virtue' among the young." The ethical aim of these panegyrics was also a commonplace in rhetorical aesthetics. The Sophists, as well as Euripides, Aristotle, and Menander dwelled on nobility of soul, "an intellectual nobility of good men which does not depend on birth."[16] Cicero stressed the four cardinal virtues discussed in Plato's *Republic*. Others selected two of these virtues, *sapienta* and *fortitudo*, and made them the core of their moral philosophy.

The establishment of imperial government in Rome discouraged the practice of praising an individual's courage and wisdom. Instead, orators perfected the art of praising the ruler's courage and literary culture, an epideictic practice that reappeared during the Renaissance in the writings of Castiglione, Ariosto, Rabelais, Spenser, and Cervantes.[17]

Fontenelle and his successors drew upon the large stock of *topoi* (plausible arguments) that the Greeks had bequeathed to the rhetorical tradition. As E. R. Curtius tells us, every "oration (including panegyrics) must make some proposition or thing plausible. It must adduce in its favor arguments which address themselves to the hearer's mind or heart. Now, there is a whole series of such arguments, which can be used on the most diverse occasions. They are intellectual themes, suitable for development and modification at the orator's pleasure." The Greeks had fashioned a whole "science" around these topoi.[18]

Because Fontenelle dispensed with the formal exordium (or opening of the speech) aimed at seducing the audience into hearing the remainder of the discourse, he also dispensed with the many topoi of mock humility that had figured in it.[19] Instead, he amply resorted to the "outdoing" topos to extol the superiority of the moderns over the ancients in positive knowledge and the moral superiority of scientists over other men. Temporally, this topos can be expressed in two ways: either the subject "is praised as having put all the greatest works of the past in the shade" or, inversely, "not only the past deserves praise; later men and the very latest should be praised too."[20]

The study of rhetoric, though far from extinct in the Middle Ages, assumed a preponderant role in the theory and pedagogy of the Humanist movement of the Renaissance. As is well known, the Humanists eliminated or denigrated the curriculum of medieval advanced education—theology, metaphysics, medicine, law, mathematics, and Aristotelian physics—and widened and elevated the core of secondary instruction. The curriculum of this *studia humanitas*, in P. O. Kristeller's words, "came to stand for a clearly defined cycle of scholarly disciplines, namely grammar, rhetoric, history, poetry, and moral philosophy, and the study of each of these subjects was understood to include the reading and interpretation of its standard ancient writers in Latin and, to a lesser extent, in Greek."[21]

Since nearly all Italian scholars from the beginning of the fifteenth century on obtained such a humanistic education, they diffused the studia humanitas, with its stress on the dignity of man on earth, "into all areas of Renaissance culture . . . ." As secretaries to princes or municipalities or as teachers of humanities in secondary schools or universities, they put into practice the fundamental precepts of Humanism. They taught "oral and written expression by means of rules and models" largely taken from antiquity.[22]

The panegyric played a critical part in the studia humanitas because of the diffusion of what may be called the Petrarchan theme. Countless variations on this theme—the emphasis on the dignity and privileged position of man in the universe—found their way into a number of genres, all designed to give praise to both general and particular man. Thus Pico della Mirandola extolled the intellect and will of the new Renaissance man, Machiavelli presented Cesare Borgia as the savior of Italy, Vasari conferred immortality upon painters, and Cellini heaped praises upon himself.[23]

All this panegyrical activity had a host of apologists. They revived the ancient justifications of literary praise on ethical and mimetic grounds. Lorenzo de'Medici argued that it was the task of poets to confer immortality upon great men. The influential critic Scaliger stated that "good fame is the reward of wise men." Valla went one step further and insisted that "hymn and epic—praise of gods and heroes—surpasses all other forms of poetry." Minturno and Campanella insisted that "the basic poetic emotion is emulation (*aemulatio*), and emulation is the struggle to live up to the virtues of those who have been praised by poets." The theme of praise and imitation as the informing principles of the major literary genres was most fully developed by Pontanus, in a dialogue on poetics written at the end of the fifteenth century. Both history and poetry, he says, use demonstrative as well as deliberative oratory and both poetry and oratory "have praise in common."[24]

RHETORIC AND EULOGY IN FRANCE

Neoclassical rhetoric, especially demonstrative oratory, appeared in France during the last years of the fifteenth century. By the middle of the following century it had taken the place previously held by dialectics and was to hold sway in and out of schools for another two hundred years. Although Aristotle's *Rhetoric* had first been translated into French in 1654, the schoolmasters of eloquence and elocution uncontestably were Cicero and Quintilian. Indeed, "it was in Quintilian that most of the modern treatises derived the essence of their lessons."[25] Since rhetoric "was a mark of social ascension, a key to relatively privileged sorts of employment and thus an integral part of the established order,"[26] this classical subject became a required course in secondary schools. Whether in Latin or in French, rhetoric taught students "the faculty of discourse, the art of developing an idea, [and] to speak and to write." It also imbued graduates of *collèges* with a common style of speaking and writing, a style found in writers as diverse as François de Sales, d'Urfé, Descartes, and Bossuet, or in genres as varied as remonstrances, legal briefs, and eulogies.[27]

In all secondary schools, whether run by Jesuits or not, memorization and the emulation of "illustrious and devout men" were the rule. Indeed, students in both the Jesuit and Oratorian collèges "were encouraged to relive the lives of the heroes." So pervasive was the theory of emulation that even behind the large number of grammatical rules the students memorized "lay hidden a rigid moral code. The rules themselves were precepts, usually drawn from Cicero and selected to illustrate some point of grammar, but also to convey a moral principle. Grammar and moral philosophy became the foundation of the curriculum, inextricably connected with and unfailingly enforced through the prohibition of French." Given these practices and the fact that classical literature largely meant Latin literature, the Roman world for the students of

seventeenth-century France was peopled with the heroes of epideictic literature—statesmen, emperors, and generals.[28]

In this stress upon the theory and practice of praise, emulation, and ethical
intent, the schools were but reflecting the intellectual currents that had swept
educated France since the early sixteenth century. With the revival of ancient
letters, the Petrarchian quest for personal immortality, and the Renaissance
monarchs' presumptions to imperial prerogatives, France was invaded after
1500 by memorials to the dead. This invasion turned into a full-scale occupation under Richelieu and Louis XIV to the point where "French eloquence
especially gained distinction with eulogies and funeral panegyrics."[29]

Until the seventeenth century the eulogies were all of the kind that
d'Alembert, in his article on "Éloge" in the *Encyclopédie* that he and Diderot
edited, named *éloges oratoires*. Himself a member of the Academy of
Sciences and a secretary of the Académie Française, d'Alembert was ideally
suited to expound on the sharp differences between the eulogies delivered at
these two learned bodies. The oratorical eulogies, derived by the Académie
Française from the mainstream of the epideictic tradition, are defined as
"praises extended to someone . . . in consideration of his excellence, his
rank, or his virtues, etc. . . . . pronounced in academies and literary societies
in honor of the members it has lost." These eulogies are purely panegyrical,
unconcerned about biographical detail, and either silent or euphemistic about
the subject's defects. "One confines oneself to praising his [the subject's]
talents, his wit in general . . . without entering into any detail of the
circumstances of his life."[30]

This omission of precise biographical information accounts for two major
contrasts between the eulogies delivered at the Académie Française and those
delivered at the academies established under Louis XIV and Louis XV (the
academies of *Inscriptions et Belles-Lettres*, of sciences, of medicine, of
surgery, etc.). In the former the newcomer composed and delivered a eulogy
in honor of the deceased member whose seat he had just taken. In the latter
(following the precedent set by Fontenelle for the Academy of Sciences) the
secretary composed and read the eulogies of nearly *all* the members who had
died during his tenure of office. These eulogies were of the type that
d'Alembert called *éloges historiques*, for they gave "in detail the entire life of
an academician, from his birth until his death."[31] In contrast, adherence to
the long tradition of honoring princes in panegyrics minimized the biographical element of the *éloges oratoires*. Fewer than three pages are devoted to a
summary encomium of the late Academician; the bulk of these eulogies
celebrate the glory of the reigning monarch and that of Cardinal Richelieu, the
founder of the Académie Française.

Thus Fontenelle broke with a long-standing rhetorical practice of maxi-
mizing praise and minimizing concrete biographical details. Instead, he
followed the minority tradition initiated by Aristotle. The encomium, the

latter had written, should stress the subject's noble deeds, should heighten these deeds "to make the praise more emphatic," but should above all be devoted "to a summary of the life of the man being praised."[32]

Fontenelle also appropriated the *éloge historique* from its originator Charles Perrault, the instigator of the famous Quarrel of the Ancients and the Moderns and a brother of one of the founders of the Paris Academy of Sciences. It was Perrault who had first honored in the vernacular men famous for other than political, ecclesiastical, or military deeds—artists and scientists like Pascal, Mersenne, Racine, Lully, and Poussin. Artists, writers, scholars, and scientists had been eulogized from the sixteenth century on, but the eulogies had been given in Latin, had contained fewer than three pages, and had been sparse in biographical substance.

The precedent of praising, in a language comprehensible to the hoi polloi, eminences in talent as well as in earthly power was not to the liking of many. As if to compensate for this breach of gentlemanly etiquette, Perrault also initiated the precedent followed by subsequent writers of *éloges historiques* of "suppressing low and puerile details, unworthy of the majesty of a philosophic eulogy." As d'Alembert explains it, since these eulogies are histories, they are "rightly memoirs useful to the history of letters: thus the truth must be its main characteristic. Yet that truth should be mitigated, and at times even silenced, since one is composing a eulogy and not a satire; but it should never be disguised or altered."[33]

One can well sympathize with the critics' objections to this new type of encomium. Perrault had challenged a two-thousand-year-old tradition that had denied that a virtuous commoner, "who has spent sixty years in improving himself and in enlightening his country, might well deserve some gratitude on the part of humanity."[34] He was fully persuaded of the merits of his contemporaries, imbued with a strong faith in utility as a merit deserving of the highest praise, assured of the march of progress by nonmilitary and nonpolitical achievements, and delighted by the rise of academies as testimonials of these achievements. Yet, however much they anticipate the *éloges* of the Paris Academy of Sciences in their intention, Perrault's one hundred eulogies do not resemble them in either substance or style. In A. L. Thomas's words, each of Perrault's eulogies "is but a very short notice, containing facts with dates, and almost wholly devoid of reflections . . . The style is almost bereft of wit; its worth resides in the subject matter, that is, the extent and precision of information. . . ."[35]

THE NEW *ÉLOGE*: BIOGRAPHICAL OR PANEGYRICAL?

In a fundamental sense, the *éloges historiques* composed in honor of the new sciences and scientists violated some of the most entrenched principles of the epideictic tradition. They admitted into the ranks of "immortals" men whose main distinction rested on their contributions to positive knowledge or human comfort. In addition, the *éloges* of the Paris Academy of Sciences simultaneously discarded the more fulsome hyperboles of the oratorical eulogy and the professions of mock humility that had been standard topoi since antiquity. Most radically, of the seven divisions of the conventional encomium[36] they retained only the peroration and transformed the remainder of the eulogy into a detailed Life and Works.

Yet, far more than the secretaries realized, the *éloges* they composed still displayed some of the major characteristics of the genre. The ostensible intent of the eulogies still remained the bestowal of immortality upon men whose mortality was being commemorated. These men were still exhibited, especially in the perorations, as embodiments of virtue and wisdom worthy of imitation. Tributes to enlightened rulers, past and present, were still extended though rarely with the servility of the traditional panegyric. The outdoing topos was still employed, not so much in praise of the scientists as of the undertaking they were engaged in. And despite their faith in science as a catalyst for future progress, they usually held up the wise men of the past as moral models.

The *éloge*, like many other literary genres, addressed itself to new issues in terms partly borrowed from the past. Yet this attempted fusion of ancient with modern intentions led to a fundamental paradox. How is it that an epideictic genre could successfully imprint a heroic image of the scientist upon contemporaries and many generations thereafter when that very same image, upon closer inspection, turns out to be flawed and at times obfuscated by contradictory images? While all the secretaries, following the precedent set by Fontenelle, discarded some of the traditional features of the panegyric and attempted to make the mystery of the new sciences comprehensible to humanistically-trained audiences, they did not always successfully mesh biographical veracity with mimetic didacticism, for reasons discussed in the succeeding chapters. Some of these reasons are stylistic and rhetorical, others are philosophical and ideological. As the first chapter will show, few secretaries possessed the skill to strike the proper balance among impartial *reportage*, stylistic finesse, and moral exhortation.

Chapters 2, 3, and 4 will draw on the secretaries' reports on *la physique* and natural history to illustrate the depth of their partiality. The eulogists' objectivity was tested beyond its limits when they were called upon to report on scientific interpretations that offended their own convictions. Partisanship, which surfaced sporadically in the *éloges* of Fontenelle and Mairan, informed the very substance of Condorcet's eulogies. Indeed, the latter are lay sermons on such cherished beliefs of his as the utility of science, the inevitability of progress, and the necessity for enlightened public service.

Yet, however biased in their reportage of some critical issues, neither Condorcet nor any of his predecessors lost sight of the ethical intent of their depictions. They all dwelled on the moral lesson that could be learned from observing the fortitude that enabled young men to overcome all obstacles in their quest for a scientific career. Chapter 5 will sketch a sociology of these men's class background, education, first infatuation with natural science, and career opportunities. As the secretaries interpreted it, experience with these obstacles strengthened the scientists' virtues, which, in turn, further ennobled their pursuit of science. Chapter 6 will consider the intimate link that the secretaries forged between science and morality. In particular, it will discuss the secretaries' motives for selecting moral values and trace these values to their sources: pastoral literature, Stoic philosophy, Renaissance Humanism, Enlightenment humanitarianism, and Plutarchan biography.

With these virtues at his disposal, each secretary, following a time-honored convention, had to heighten them in order to minimize, but not conceal, the defects possessed by the "virtuous" scientists they were eulogizing. To have ignored these defects completely would have made a mockery of the secretaries' profession as truthful biographers. Yet not to have offset these flaws with superior virtues would have cast doubt on their calling as eulogists. Such an unstable combination of biographical veracity and hagiographic morality was apparently redressed by the secretaries' retention of the peroration out of the conventional panegyric. Rhetorical convention had dictated that the peroration be a "set piece" for moral edification, but the secretaries did not intend this panegyrical conclusion to *appear* to be at variance with the historical truths imbedded in the remainder of the eulogy. This intention turned out to be successful to a degree these men could not possibly have imagined. Whatever faults the eulogized scientists displayed were redeemed by the activity they were laboring in. The overall impression gathered from this collection of two-hundred-odd *éloges* is of a new breed of men superior to the rest of humanity in mental acuity and selfless devotion, and engaged in an enterprise of the greatest possible benefit to mankind. No matter that a closer inspection of these eulogies reveals conflicts among these men for recognition from their peers and from posterity and conflicts within them between worldly ambitions and pursuit of nonworldly goals. As the Conclusion will attempt to show, the natural philosophers, by appropriating virtues that had traditionally been assigned to philosophers in general, bequeathed a hagiography that was to last until World War II.

·I·
Form and Style

Il avoit autant l'art de porter la justesse des Mathématiques, et la plus
exacte Métaphysique dans les choses de pur agrément, qu'il savoit re-
pandre la clarté et les grâces sur les matières les plus abstraites.
                                  —FOUCHY, *Eloge de M. de Fontenelle*

La simplicité, la vérité, l'exactitude font le principal caractère de ses
portraits. . . . S'il se présente à lui des réflexions fines, des images
heureuses, on voit que son sujet les lui inspire, et non qu'il ait
travaillé pour l'en orner . . .
                                  —CONDORCET, *Eloge de M. de Fouchy*

Beginning with the first secretary, Fontenelle, the *éloges* of the Paris
Academy of Sciences attracted large audiences because they were more than
repositories of biographical and scientific information of exclusive value to
practitioners, philosophers, and historians of science. They drew a large
number of laymen to the biannual readings and to the annual *Histoires* of the
Academy because Fontenelle brought to these eulogies his best skills as
raconteur, wit, historian, and philosophe. In honor of the new natural
philosophy and of the institutions that embodied it, he discarded the hackneyed format and platitudinous diction characteristic of the *éloge oratoire*
of the Académie Française; and out of respect for the lay listeners and readers,
he varied the biographical accounts of his subjects with rhetorical surprises,
philosophical asides, and a tone that ranged from understated irony to flights
of sublimity worthy of the best pulpit oratory of his age. Rarely has it been
given for a literary subgenre to originate under such fortunate auspices. Not
surprisingly, his sixty-nine *éloges* became the model for his eighteenth-
century successors to follow. However different in temperament, scientific
knowledge, and literary skill, Mairan, Fouchy, and Condorcet were to retain
the *general* format bequeathed by Fontenelle, deviating from it only to the
extent that the subject demanded it or that their own ability or parti pris
compelled them.

Fontenelle himself, however, almost totally dispensed with the conventional divisions of the eulogy. According to traditional rhetoric, the eulogy, as
a genre of demonstrative discourse, is divided into seven elements: (1) exordium, (2) proposition, (3) division, (4) narration, (5) confirmation, (6) refutation, and (7) peroration. None of the *éloges* of the Paris Academy of Sciences

opens with an (1) exordium to prepare the audience in such a way "that they will be disposed to lend a ready ear to the rest of our speech" and "to indicate the points on which the orator proposes to speak."[1] On the contrary, all but two of the 193 *éloges* abruptly begin with a brief recitation of either the subject's titles and genealogy or of his place and time of birth. Nor do these eulogies contain a (2) proposition or concise summary of the narrative and analysis of the discourse (except in occasional transitions). There are (3) divisions in parts, or listing in sequence the subjects to be covered, but they are rarely formal, and never follow one another without repetition, interruption, or circular development; only Fouchy occasionally resorts to formal devices to guide the reader or listener from one part to another. The heart of the *éloge*, of course, is the (4) narrative account or exposition of the facts of the subject's life and achievements. Yet there is no set disposition of the facts themselves, which are selected and arranged partly to follow the precedent set by Fontenelle, partly in conformance with the orator's rhetorical skill, but mainly to suit the subject's life, achievements, and character. And because, as both d'Alembert and Thomas remind us, these *éloges historiques* are designed to tell the truth but not the whole truth, they are sprinkled with stylistic devices to emphasize certain truths at the expense of others. The fifth and sixth elements of the traditional demonstrative discourse—(5) the confirmation and (6) the refutation—do not appear in any marked manner. Still, the majority of these *éloges* read like understated refutations of objections that might possibly be levelled against either the utility of science, the worth of the particular scientific achievements described, or the self-effacing character of the scientists themselves. It is only the last element of these *éloges*, the (7) peroration, that can be said to bear a close resemblance to the formal model bequeathed from antiquity.

FONTENELLE

In its main outline, every *éloge* written between 1699 and 1791 by Fontenelle and his successors follows a quaternary division: (1) the life preceding maturity; (2) maturity with its record of achievements, whether scientific, military, political, or scholarly; (3) the last years and death; and (4) a peroration, which sometimes included sundry matters such as the names of the family survivors, the last will and testament, and the honors received.[2] The peroration has forcibly and perhaps excessively struck the attention of the few commentators to have studied Fontenelle's *éloges* in some depth[3] (and his sixty-nine are the only ones, among the 193 publicly read in the ancient Academy of Sciences, to have been studied at all). These commentators elaborate on the collective moral portrait of scientists that the perorations depict, though they fail to point out that they sum up explicitly what is already implicit in the first three divisions of the *éloges*.

The format of the *éloges* written between 1704 and 1791 was roughly set with that of Viviani, Fontenelle's fourth eulogy, but at no time did he or any of his successors adhere but most generally to the above quaternary division. For the sake of both variety and fidelity to the subjects' lives and achievements, themes are distributed so as to break up lengthy discussions of particular motifs, even at the risk of violating chronological order. Likewise, the secretaries invariably put in asides to enliven, heighten, or amplify a discourse that may, at a particular point, appear too technical in a eulogy meant to be delivered to a lay audience. Some of Fontenelle's asides, indeed, could be extracted from the *éloges* and presented on their own as brief models of stylistic grace, historical insight, philosophical exposition, or scientific description. They include:

a lengthy description of Russia before and after the accession of Peter the Great to the throne;

a sympathetic portrait of the older d'Argenson as Police Intendant of Paris;

tributes to some of his colleagues' literary or oratorical gifts;

the importance of instruments in scientific research;

a parable on the utility and grand design of astronomy;

the utility of the crafts;

the abstruseness of algebra and its neglect in Fontenelle's day;

the nobility, necessity, and abstruseness of the science of geography;

the famous and eloquent parallel between Descartes and Newton;

popular credulity and fear of astronomers; and

a defense of Cartesian vortices.[4]

The above implies that Fontenelle's ingenuity in manipulating the placement of his themes is limited only by the density of his subject's life and achievements and by a formally overt obedience to the quaternary division. Though the main topics of an *éloge* are comprised of historical and biographical data, these topics are frequently treated like themes in a musical composition by placement, elaboration, modulation, repetition, variation, and emphasis. His *éloge* of the great mathematician Jakob Bernoulli is a case in point.[5]

The *éloge* of Bernoulli opens with the standard biographical notices of his birth, parentage, and education. These are followed by an account of his travels during which he studied Descartes's philosophy, and a discussion of Bernoulli the scientist working on the Cartesian problems of the paths described by comets and the weight of the ether (theme A). The next

passage—on his founding of a kind of experimental academy—is both
biographical and descriptive, and prepares us for the leitmotiv, his chief claim
to fame, namely his work in calculus. Fontenelle then gently leads us into this
forbidding subject by devoting one paragraph to Bernoulli's method and one
transitional paragraph to his appointment to a professorship at the University
of Basel, Switzerland. We now come to the exposition of the main theme (B),
nine paragraphs on his summation of mathematical series and his magnum
opus on integral calculus. This theme is then developed into two related
motifs, honor and envy: Bernoulli's outstanding work in analysis was
rewarded with membership in various European academies, which esteem
gave rise to his bitter rivalry with his no less gifted brother, Johann. Having
gone through all the variations on theme B, Fontenelle returns to theme A,
Bernoulli's devotion to Descartes. The description of Bernoulli's critical
edition of Descartes's geometry not only provides a formal unifying device
but also gives the secretary the perfect opportunity to discourse on his favorite
philosopher. The main subjects are brought to a close by a description of
Bernoulli's last illness and his death, which event leads not directly to a
peroration but to the papers on probability found after Bernoulli's death. Thus
the pattern of varying biographical elements with descriptions of Bernoulli's
mathematical work continues to the next-to-the-penultimate passages. The
éloge then ends with the expected peroration and, almost as an afterthought,
the sentence: "He married at the age of thirty and was survived by a son and a
daughter."

A reading of Fontenelle's *éloges* shows that he had mastered most of the
stylistic qualities of classical rhetoric:[6] clarity, propriety (the perfect adjust-
ment of thought and expression), precision, concision, grammatical correctness, purity of diction (especially in the most abstruse passages), nobility
("the avoidance of gross and trivial expressions and of low and repulsive
images"), and (his most underrated stylistic virtue) aural harmony. The test
of Fontenelle's success as a historian of natural science and scientists,
however, lies in his ability to present complex technical concepts and
procedures to a mixed audience of professionals and laymen. As a man of
letters *and* a publicist for science, Fontenelle was faced with a dilemma: how
to shape the limited vocabulary of Neoclassicism at his disposal in such a way
as to meet the requirements of both clarity and naturalness of expression on
the one hand, and fidelity to the technical facts of scientific activity on the
other. He had to forge a style that would prevent the lay audience from losing
sight of the specialized nature of scientists' labors and the scientists
themselves from forgetting their common bonds with humanity at large. He
solved this rhetorical dilemma by employing the old devices of variety,
imagery, and wit, all at the service of both scientific achievements and the
place of science in the enlightenment of humanity.

It is especially in the variety, invention, and fitness of his imagery that

Fontenelle towered above his successors. Unlike Mairan, Fouchy, and Condorcet, he came to the position of eulogist of scientists with thirty years of practice in the composition of pastoral verse, satire, diatribe, dialogue, scientific popularization, and other genres. Hence the profusion of personifications, analogies, and especially similes in his *éloges*. This readiness to draw upon a large stock of images can also be attributed to the continued vitality of a figurative tradition dating from the sixteenth century, a penchant for indirection, and, most frequently and most importantly, an earnest effort to clarify technical points by figures drawn from a tradition shared by all educated persons. Literary allusion was the contemporary writer's stock in trade, which stock was continually replenished at the storehouse of classical history and mythology. He put these allusions at the service of natural philosophers, whom he elevated to the rank formerly assigned to political, military, and ecclesiastical grandees.

Whether drawn from antiquity or not, the most common objects of Fontenelle's parallels dealt with his philosophy of science and were drawn from the characteristics of politics, geography, architecture, and the sciences themselves.[7] Note, for example, the following simile. Taking a term from mathematics, Fontenelle described the history of that science as advancing in "a kind of progression, whose intervals are at first extremely large and then naturally become smaller and smaller." The progress of science is assured; not so the perfectibility of the overall level of human intelligence. "In general, the number of thinking men is small, and one can assert that humanity resembles the human body in which the brain, and apparently a very small part of the brain, alone does the thinking, while all the other parts, much larger by their mass, are deprived of that noble function and act only blindly."[8]

Apparently because of this fact of human nature, Fontenelle felt that exhortations, arguments, diatribes, allusions, and similes did not suffice to win the public over to the cause of natural science. Hence his recourse to wit in all its diversity. Literary practice had taught him the correctness of Quintilian's appreciation of wit, namely, that it "serves as a simple seasoning of language, a condiment which is silently appreciated by our judgment, as food is appreciated by the palate, with the result that it stimulates our taste and saves a speech from becoming tedious." To Fontenelle, however, wit served much more than as a spice with which to whet his audience's jaded appetite. It also served to deflate dogma, to prick the bubble of conceit, to intimate the unspeakable, to display his own verbal ingenuity, to ridicule the detractors of science, and, by its very *jeu d'esprit*, to accentuate the highmindedness of the scientific enterprise. For however earnest the search for natural laws and however solemn the researchers, there was something about the very pursuit of science that partook of the nature of play, of almost childish delight. Such, indeed, was the conclusion that Fontenelle had arrived at when he depicted his lifelong friend Varignon at work: "He laughed with pleasure when talking about mathematics, and to see him, one would have thought that it was necessary to study it in order to be merry."[9]

So consistently did Fontenelle enliven his *éloges* with witticisms that one can find for each category of vice or defect a corresponding form of wit. He uses irony when the theologian-philosopher Duhamel is criticized for having refused to rule dogmatically on certain questions of epistemology: "He promised to amend, yet one must admit that he does not seem to have kept his word; it is a rare occasion when a philosopher has been accused of not being sufficiently positive." He mildly ridicules the courtiers to whom Sauveur had been assigned to teach anatomy: "It was said that the entire court came to listen to him, but I'm afraid that this is doing the entire court too much honor." He euphemistically describes Mazarin's miserliness: he, "who did not grant gratuities without cause, gave" Vauban "one that was rather reasonable." He makes a pun to shut the mouths of skeptics of scientific predictability: having observed the positions of a new comet on two consecutive nights, Cassini I boldly traced on a planisphere the curve that the comet was to take subsequently and predicted that after advancing in its orbit, it would temporarily make a retrograde motion—"These predictions found a large number of unbelievers, who maintained that the comet would escape the astronomer, and hoped until the very end that such would be the case, after which, when they saw that the comet had been perfectly submissive to him, they, like it, reversed themselves and said that Cassini's prediction had been but child's play." Finally, he engages in a cleverly phrased attack against the enforced ignorance of women, an attack whose full force is postponed to the last word: Carré's popularity as teacher of mathematics to women "had some of the seasoning of mystery, for they are obliged to conceal the knowledge acquired by their minds as much as the natural sentiments of their hearts, and their greatest science must always be to observe to the point of scrupulousness the external proprieties of ignorance."[10]

Stripped of their unique wit and figurative language, Fontenelle's *éloges* became the models for all subsequent hauts vulgarisateurs. Condorcet, Laplace, Arago, Claude Bernard, Louis de Broglie—all these scientists drew their inspiration from his felicitous style. "It was his glory," Leonard Marsak points out, that Fontenelle helped to create a scientific language "without creating monstrosities of jargon and style. And in addition, suppleness, clarity, and precision of exposition were to be the hallmarks of the new scientific language, not only to record the observations of nature, but to transmit them to laymen."[11] His was a language free from grandiloquence, but replete with wit, allusiveness, and suppleness, a style at once subtle, epigrammatic, flexible, and conversational. It was a style superbly suited to expound the difficult truths of science to an assembly of honnêtes hommes and *femmes*. This style influenced countless writers of the eighteenth century, notably Voltaire, Montesquieu of the *Persian Letters*, Melchior Grimm, and, to some extent, the scientist who was to succeed Fontenelle as Secretary of the Paris Academy of Sciences, Jean-Jacques Dortous de Mairan.

MAIRAN

The ten *éloges* that Mairan composed between 1741 and 1743 largely retain the formal features of Fontenelle's eulogies without partaking of their stylistic originality. Though they are crystal clear and occasionally succinct, his eulogies are bereft of any sense of humor, patent or ironic, and devoid of the heterodoxy that had made Fontenelle a byword for the philosophe. In his occasional attempts to match his predecessor's linguistic felicity, Mairan abused the rhetorical devices at his command, especially parallels and hyperboles. Rarely can he be accused of obscurity, vagueness, impropriety, or banality of syntax and diction; as rarely, however, is he to be commended for elegance of phrasing. He was a good journeyman: he had thoroughly absorbed the elements of rhetoric and had learned to adapt them to the matter on hand; when he labored to be a master, he most often relapsed into the worst excesses of an apprentice. He is always readable; he is rarely quotable.

Mairan's distinct superiority over Fontenelle lies elsewhere: in a working knowledge or an original productiveness in many fields of physics, astronomy, and mathematics. When he does not strive for the elegant or unusual turn of phrase, he compares favorably with Fouchy as a diligent, accurate, and sympathetic reporter of science. Unfortunately, none of the six native "working scientists" whom he eulogized in his three-year tenure of office— Petit *le médecin*, J. F. Boulduc, Bremond, Molières, Hunauld, and Louis Lémery—was of sufficient stature to call forth Mairan's wide-ranging knowledge of the sciences.

The *éloges* of Petit, Halley, and Lémery show Mairan's writing at its best: clear, smoothly-flowing, restrained in phraseology, detailed without excess, and never repetitious. On the contrary, the *éloges* of Hunauld, Bignon, and Polignac show him at his worst: garrulous, hyperbolic, unctuous, and overimpressed with titles and positions. Indeed, in two or three *éloges* the flattery is offensive by its sheer excess. A case in point is the *éloge* of the Cardinal de Fleury, late de facto ruler of France. Within twenty lines the account of his education is submerged under a wave of epithets: "penetration and amenity of wit, gentleness of manner, intelligence in and talent for literature," "erudition," "much knowledge," "much mental accuracy, a subtle and delicate discernment, a handsome memory, and a brilliant imagination." We emphasize Mairan's eagerness to extend flattery, not because it is so apparent, but because the other secretaries, while no less overtly submissive to throne and altar than Mairan, repeatedly insisted that courtly virtues and moral virtues are incompatible. That the court can be a snare for the honest man, Mairan was well aware; but in the same paragraph in which he depicted in dark colors the vices rampant at court, he absolved both Louis XIV and the young Fleury of any temptations for those same vices with which they were daily surrounded.[12]

FOUCHY

For a man who held the position of secrétaire of the Paris Academy of Sciences for a third of a century (1744-76), shamefully little is known of Jean-Paul Grandjean de Fouchy. The mystery of his life and character is compounded by Condorcet's cursory treatment of him in his eulogy and by the impersonality, technicality, and uniform style of the overwhelming majority of Fouchy's own sixty-four éloges. However deficient in literary ability, he also had to contend with an extraordinary revolution in science on which he had been charged to report. Condorcet's éloge of Fouchy[13] uses the very uneventfulness of its subject's life to paint a vivid tableau of that revolution: the accelerating tempo of research in most natural sciences, the rise of a number of new sciences, the professionalization and rapidly increasing complexity of them all, and a group of scientists who surpass in brilliance any group of Academicians eulogized by the other three secretaries. Fontenelle, writing in slower-moving times, frequently lapsed into generalities when it came to describing some achievements in natural history or the medical sciences. Condorcet, writing in more tumultuous times, erratically oscillated between first-rate analyses and overviews of scientific activity on one hand and tirades against or neglect of many of his colleagues' contributions on the other. Whatever faults can be charged against him, Fouchy can never be accused of lack of conscientiousness. Except during his last years in office, when old age and an increasing work load finally caught up with him, he painstakingly (almost too painstakingly) covered significant achievements by all his colleagues in all the sciences and in medicine. Though lacking in charm, finesse, or stylistic originality, the totality of his sixty-four éloges forms an invaluable guide to the history of science in the eighteenth century.

Yet, unlike the other three secretaries covered here, Fouchy rarely went below the surface of the events on which he reported. It is up to the reader to infer the significance of these events, to connect or compare them with one another, and to put them into the context of the Weltanschauung of the mid-eighteenth century. The rare commentaries in which Fouchy indulged[14] were as curt as his attempts at figurative language. He may have made a virtue out of a defect by dismissing imagination and a propensity to generalization as inimical to the spirit of reportage. More likely, however, this adherence to facts and to facts alone was his only escape from the impasse created by the accumulation of novel and startling scientific discoveries. Condorcet solved the problem by cavalierly dismissing the achievements of the lesser scientists; Fouchy, being both conscientious and diffident, seemingly felt that it was essential to keep up with the bare events of the scientific "revolution." In the nineteenth and twentieth centuries the problem was solved by dividing the task of reporting between two secretaries.

To keep abreast of the advancing technical times, however, is not tantamount to retaining the attention of the reader or listener accustomed to the grace and wit of a Fontenelle. In many of the *éloges* Fouchy simply overwhelms us with an accumulation of technical detail. In honor of Réaumur, one of the greatest scientists of the century, the secretary, almost without respite, devotes thirty-one paragraphs in near-succession to his scientific work.[15] No matter how imposing and productive a figure Réaumur cut in the world of science, this was an unfortunate format for an *éloge*, especially as it was read on the same public occasion as the *éloge* of Nicole, in which thirteen out of twenty paragraphs give a technical exposition of his mathematical achievements. The same uniformity of tone and monotony of structure prevail in the *éloges* of Hellot, Deparcieux, Pitot, and Buache.

Still, if one is willing to shut one's ears to the monotony and prosaism of Fouchy's writing, there is much to be learned from his technical descriptions, in which skill he was surpassed by none. Witness the excellent analyses of Helvétius' dissertation on the circulation of the blood, Maupertuis' argument for the flattening of the earth at the poles, the vivid narrative of the hazards and rigors that Chappe underwent in Siberia, and the eloquent tribute to Hales' quantification of air and organic systems. And, to cap them all, the *éloge* of La Caille, in which Fouchy is truly in his element in describing the life and achievements of an observational astronomer who was also his friend and student.[16]

CONDORCET

In both style and substance the *éloges* that Condorcet delivered at the biyearly public sessions of the Paris Academy of Sciences between 1773 and 1791 differ more radically from those of Fontenelle, Mairan, and Fouchy than the latter do amongst themselves.[17] Condorcet exaggerated or amplified features introduced by his three predecessors (his commentaries sometimes take up the bulk of his eulogies) and frequently introduced features of his own. To accommodate these commentaries and innovations, Condorcet expanded the *éloge* to a nearly unmanageable size. The 12,800 words that Fontenelle had devoted to Leibniz—a length not attained by either Mairan or Fouchy—were exceeded by Condorcet in his encomiums of Buffon and Franklin (13,000 words each), La Condamine (13,500) and d'Alembert (17,000).[18] This amplification can be attributed not only to the increasing complexity and proliferation of the sciences but also to Condorcet's frequent inability to concentrate on the subject matter, the deceased Academician. In his second "public" *éloge*, that of La Condamine, we first perceive a characteristic that became second nature to Condorcet, namely, lengthy disquisitions on political, social, economic, and educational institutions and customs that he deemed reasonable or unreasonable, relevant or outmoded.

The longest *éloge* ever written in the ancien régime was that of d'Alembert, Condorcet's mentor and friend. A good part of it, drawn from personal acquaintance, is devoted to his nonscientific *philosophie*, a two-page aside on the writing of *éloges* (d'Alembert was Secretary of the Académie Française), a brilliant verbal snapshot of Denis Diderot, and an unsparing yet sympathetic critique of d'Alembert's mathematical premises and scientific principles.

The most eloquent of all *éloges*, however, is that of Benjamin Franklin, the ideal scientist-humanitarian-inventor-philosophe-statesman.[19] As the diagram below reveals, eighteen paragraphs in the *éloge* are set aside to proclaim the perfect conjunction between Condorcet's and Franklin's principles (the first eighteen paragraphs under the rubric "Judgmental"); it concludes climactically with a fourteen-paragraph peroration, a fitting memorial to the man, his country, and the age in which he lived.

Éloge of Benjamin Franklin

Biographical	Descriptive	Judgmental
1−3,* Birth; ancestors		
		3, Religious persecution
4, Apprentice printer; essayist		
5, Obtains printer's job in England		
6−8, Readings and philosophical inclinations		
9, Buys printing shop		
10−11, Founds *Gazette*		9, Aside on generosity
	12−13, *Bonhomme Richard*	
14−15, Forms clubs		
		15, Clubs
		16, Eloquent plea for religious tolerance
17, Sets up various establishments		
	18, Plan to cultivate moral harmony	
	19, Plan to institute moral improvements	

*Numbers refer to the paragraphs in the *éloge*.

Biographical	Descriptive	Judgmental
20−22, Establishes plan for the military; pacifies the Quakers		
	23, Tolerance for religious laxity	
	24, One-fluid theory of electricity	
	25−26, Lightning conductor	
	27−28, Opposition to and acceptance of lightning conductor	
29, Member of Royal Society		
	30−32, Treaty with the Indians	
33, Plan for American Union rejected		
		34, Politics of reason
35−38, Work during the Seven Years' War		
		39−40, Comparative freedom in America
		41, Idyllic picture of America
42−44, Envoy to England		
45, Boston Tea Party		
46−47, Kangaroo court trial in England		
48, American Congress		
49−52, State constitution, Bill of Rights		
		49−52, The Bill of Rights
53−55, Proposes unicameral legislature		
		53−55, Unicameralism
56, Fails to bring Canadians over to the American side		
57−58, European friends & enemies of America		

Biographical	Descriptive	Judgmental
59–61, Envoy to France		
		62, Praise of Lafayette
63–64, Vergennes		
	65–66, Behavior as ambassador	
		67, Paradoxes in the state of France
		68, Attack on mercantilism
69–70, Last days in Paris		
71–74, Triumphant return to America		
75–77, Reluctantly approves U.S. Constitution		
78–79, Retirement; memoirs; death		
		80, Peroration: temperate & industrious
		81, Per.: theistic
		82, Per.: quality of scientific work
		83, Per.: applied science
		84–85, Per.: political views
		86, Per.: style of conversation
		87–89, Per.: political views
		90–91, Per.: fame at home and abroad
		92, Per.: connection between science and liberty, and
		93, Per.: between ignorance and slavery.

Stylistically, too, Condorcet is the most idiosyncratic of the writers of *éloges* during the ancien régime. Mairan's and Fouchy's syntax, diction, and imagery *formally* are not much different from Fontenelle's. Condorcet's style is a different matter altogether. By the time (1697) that Fontenelle had been admitted to the Academy of Sciences, he had purged his writing of the preciosity that had marked the literary productions of an earlier age; when Condorcet began writing his first *éloge* in 1773, Jean-Jacques Rousseau's major works had all been completed. Hence, Condorcet's panegyrical style displays the influence of both the neoclassical training he had imbibed in school and the pre-Romantic vogue that dominated his mature years. The apostrophes, hyperboles, and breathless interjections that mark some of his passages are as much tokens of the impact of the Age of Sensibility as they are of his impetuous and headstrong character. Mlle. de Lespinasse's sketch of him as "a snow-capped volcano" does not quite fit the Condorcet of the *éloges*. Except for his icy sarcasm, there is precious little coldness in the eulogies he wrote.

Though much of Condorcet's writing is still formally constrained by the concision and balance of the great French Neoclassicists, it is also suffused with the sublimity and moral rectitude characteristic of the pre-Romantics. Sympathy and understanding for misfortunes had been displayed by earlier eulogists, but not with the intensity and length of a Condorcet. These sentiments were most movingly expressed in the pathetic accounts of the paranoiac bouts suffered by the physiologist Exupère-Joseph Bertin and of the hardships and privations encountered by the botanist Joseph de Jussieu.[20] The facts alone should have sufficed to depict the harrowing perils Jussieu met in his wanderings in South America: epidemics, savage tribes, snowcovered mountains, starvation, a short bout of snow blindness, servants who robbed and abandoned him, and the news of the death of his brother Antoine, all leading to the loss of his own health, his self-esteem, and his memory. The conclusion of this pathetic life of a man who finished his days in France in senility, after an absence of thirty-six years, is made the more pathetic in Condorcet's telling, replete with such words as *pleurer*, *malheur*, *martyr*, *tendresse*, *sensibilité*, *douceur touchante*, and *reconnoissance*.[21]

The style of Condorcet's *éloges* cannot but reflect the character that in 1774 struck his intimate friends—d'Alembert, Julie Lespinasse, Turgot, and the Suards— as informed by an overwhelming passion for humanity, "an unselfish devotion to the public good which earned him the title *le bon Condorcet*, and an unrelenting rage in pursuit of this goal that threatened to rob him of his sobriquet almost as soon as he had earned it."[22] This rage at the obstacles that threatened to deflect the course of progress—ignorance, cupidity, selfishness, bigotry, frivolity, clannishness, envy, idleness, privilege, vanity—took many forms, from outraged indignation to cold sarcasm.

Lauding Trudaine de Montigny for maintaining an "incorruptible fairness" towards the various contending parties affected by the assessment and collection of taxes, Condorcet cuttingly added, "Fortunately, we do not live in either a country or a century where such an observation could be a eulogy." His irony is also evident in his defense of d'Alembert's appeal to Geneva to lift its ban on dramatic performances:

> M. Rousseau combated M. d'Alembert's opinion with the greatest eloquence and warmth; this writing against the theater, composed by an author who had written a comedy and an opera, enjoyed an enormous success, especially among fashionable people who are the most assiduous theatergoers. It seemed that they had waited to be fully assured of its total uselessness before they could enjoy it to the fullest.[23]

Condorcet even indulged in some Voltairean malice in the *éloge* of Etienne Mignot de Montigny, one of Voltaire's nephews. After flirting with the idea of joining the Society of Jesus, Montigny finally submitted to his father's contrary wishes. Condorcet remarks, "He understood that God did not require of a son that he abandon his father; of a savant, that he submit his works and his thoughts to the opinions of his superior; of a citizen, that he give himself to a foreign master; and that one could cultivate the sciences, serve humanity, live as an honnête homme, and be a Christian without becoming a Jesuit."[24]

At first glance, the substitution of the growth-maturity-decline-death sequence for the seven traditional divisions of the eulogy gives an overwhelming impression of sameness to the 193 *éloges* delivered between 1699 and 1791. This impression of formal monotony is reinforced by the secretaries' strict avoidance of the grandiloquence and hyperbolic imagery so pervasive in the *éloges oratoires*.

This impression is highly misleading. The *éloges historiques* of the Paris Academy of Sciences are alike only in the sense that Neoclassical plays are alike in being divided into five acts, in having protagonists and subsidiary characters, and in being written in Alexandrine verse, masculine couplets regularly following feminine couplets. These formal similarities, we are agreed, do not lead us to confuse Corneille for Racine or either of the two tragedians for Molière. Likewise, the chronological pattern initiated by Fontenelle and imitated by his successors permits, within wide limits, a great variety in formal arrangement, tone of voice, emphases, and selection of themes and topics. Stylistically, Fontenelle masterfully employed wit and imagery at strategic locations, Mairan strained hard to imitate his predecessor's inimitable style. Fouchy tainted his excellent technical reportage with the dullest kind of commentary, and Condorcet unpredictably alternated between sober overviews of a particular science and vehement or sarcastic tirades against instances of human resistance to progress. Ideologically, too, the secretaries differed widely from one another. Thus Fontenelle prescribed science as the sole remedy for man's hopeless addiction to credulity, Mairan frequently struck a judicial pose between contending scientific interpretations, Fouchy displayed his empirical bias in his deep distrust of any and all untested speculations, and Condorcet used the *éloges* to teach the philosophy of science and to preach the philosophy of the late Enlightenment.

Further variety was achieved in the *éloges* by the necessity of describing contributions that covered a wide range of sciences and in varying degrees of excellence. This blend of differing scientific achievements, differing styles, and differing predilections necessarily resulted in interpretations that violated the lofty ideal of impartial reporting. As the next three chapters will show, the secretaries were unable to conceal some of their most heartfelt beliefs, even with respect to what *appear* to have been uncontested truths.

·II·

Attraction and Affinity:
Fontenelle and Mairan

Les principes évidens de l'un [Descartes] ne le conduisent pas
toujours aux phénomènes tels qu'ils sont; les phénomènes ne conduisent pas toujours l'autre [Newton] à des principes assés évidens.
—FONTENELLE, *Eloge de Monsieur Neuton*

The *éloges* composed between 1699 and 1791 testify to the appearance or
rapid development of the sciences of electricity, hydrodynamics, mineralogy,
geology, and "genetics," and the new directions taken by mathematics,
chemistry, and taxonomy. They also record the reasons for and manner by
which theoretical understanding of nature was applied to the realms of
administration, navigation, the military arts, agriculture, the crafts, and commerce, and the uses to which the government put these applications in the
form of commissions and expeditions. Collectively, these eulogies further
reveal how that understanding of natural reality was unevenly modified by
some scientists' adoption of new principles, new methods, and the new
mathematics of analysis and probability theory, and how the resistance of
other scientists to these new views and procedures gave rise to acrimonious
disputes between the scientists themselves.

Disagreement with a particular interpretation or methodology, however,
was not reserved to the biweekly sessions of the Paris Academy of Sciences
nor to the treatises and mémoires published by its members. It informed the
very reporting of scientific activity by the secrétaires. True that the *éloges* repeatedly presented natural science and some of its procedures (mathematics,
observation, experimentation, and congruence between phenomena and general laws) as the surest (if not the only assured) means to certainty. True too that
the scientists themselves were exhibited, especially in the perorations, as the
embodiments of moral virtues sadly wanting in most of humanity.[1] Yet
neither the epistemological certitude of science nor the moral excellence
of the scientists placed some of their scientific interpretations beyond the
reach of the secretaries' criticisms. Thus, Fontenelle and Condorcet respectively exhibited Newton and d'Alembert as moral and scientific giants,
yet the first took strong exception to the Englishman's attraction at a

distance and the second, to the *Encyclopédiste's* stance against probability theory.

Indeed, Newtonianism versus Cartesianism, artificial versus natural taxonomy, preformation versus epigenesis, and the validity versus the invalidity of probability theory were among the most hotly-debated issues in eighteenth-century science. Unquestionably, some of the secretaries' views on these issues can be gathered from the separately-published works of Fontenelle, Mairan, and Condorcet. Yet, they are further elaborated in the *éloges*, which, however laudatory of the deceased scientists, disclose adverse comments and differing interpretations not found elsewhere.

FONTENELLE'S OBJECTIONS TO NEWTONIAN
ACTION AT A DISTANCE

When in 1686 Fontenelle published the *Entretiens sur la Pluralité des Mondes*, in which he expounded a Cartesian physics that had officially been deemed heretical, Mairan was only eight years old and Newton's *Principia Mathematica* was still one year away from publication. When in 1737 Fontenelle's rival in scientific popularization, Voltaire, published his *Eléments de la philosophie de Newton*, Fontenelle, Mairan, Saurin, and Molières were the only important Cartesians left in the Paris Academy of Sciences. In fifty years victory had swung over to Newton's theory of attraction. For over two decades the retreating Cartesians had been obliged to bring corrections and extensions to their explanations, while the advancing Newtonians displayed their power by showing that the Cartesian vortex theory "could not account for the precise form of Kepler's laws of planetary motion and was at variance with such astronomical phenomena as the movement of comets across the solar system."[2] That the final defeat of the Cartesian cause, however, was not a self-evident proposition can be gathered from a close reading of the *éloges* written by Fontenelle and Mairan, both confirmed supporters of the vortex theory well beyond 1737.

Holding steadfast to the belief that nature abhors a vacuum, Descartes had equated volume with three kinds of matter. The sun and fixed stars comprised the first matter, while the earth, planets, and comets made up the third matter. Whirlpools or vortices carried the satellites around their respective planets and also the earth and the other planets around the sun. "In the cosmic vortices heavy matter was drawn towards their centres, whilst light matter was dispersed towards their outer edges. Hence heavy objects fell towards the earth and fire rose upwards."[3] These vortices did not mutually destroy one another because they all turned in unison in a direction mutually convenient to all and by equal compression.

The vortex theory died hard in France because, unlike Newton's attraction at a distance, it was grounded in what the Cartesians deemed to be mechanical principles. As Fontenelle was to assert in *La Théorie des Tourbillons* (1752), there is no mystery in the effects inferred from the collision between vortices and the third matter. "We see very clearly that if body A in motion collides with body B in rest, something new is bound to ensue." If, on the other hand, it is said "that mutual attraction is an essential property of bodies, though not perceivable, the same could be said of sympathies, of antipathies, of everything that is opprobrious in the old Scholastic philosophy."[4]

Fontenelle's dismay at his colleagues' adoption of Newtonian attraction is conveyed most forcibly in his *éloge* of Saurin, penned one year after Voltaire's proclamation of Newtonian victory. It is interesting to note that in three separate passages the secretary accused his opponents of overconfidence and intemperance. In one of these, indeed, Fontenelle felt compelled to drive home Saurin's objections to attraction by adding scathing words of his own: "The conviction appears to be that the true Philosophers must exert all their efforts to preserve Descartes's vortices, *without which*, he says, *one would find oneself plunged anew into the old darkness of Peripateticism, from which Heaven preserve us*. It is clear that he is speaking of Newtonian actions [at a distance]." Having appealed to heaven for help in saving the modern world from the dark ages of Scholasticism, Fontenelle, as a last resort, appealed to French pride and patriotism: "Who would ever have thought it necessary to pray to Heaven to preserve Frenchmen from a too favorable bias for an incomprehensible system, they who love clarity so dearly, and for a System originating in a foreign land, they who have been charged with loving only that which is their own?"[5] Nineteen years earlier Fontenelle had had no need to appeal to piety or patriotism in his attempt to turn back the rising tide of Newtonianism. In his *éloge* of Montmort, he simply resorted to sarcasm when he applauded the latter for sending "the Attractions back to the void, from which they tried to escape." They deserve to be sent back to the void (*néant*, in this instance, standing for hell, the Newtonian vacuum, and the darkness of obscure meaning), because "there is no question that if one wishes to understand what is said, there are only [Cartesian] Impulsions; and if one does not care to understand, there are Attractions, and anything else one likes; but in that case Nature would be so incomprehensible to us that it would perhaps be wiser to leave it exactly for what it is."[6]

By treating Attractionism as either incomprehensible, absurd, foreign, or contrary to sound mechanical philosophy, Fontenelle attenuated the compliments he had paid to Newton in the famous parallel he had drawn between him and Descartes.[7] It has escaped most commentators that given the declining reputation of the latter, the compliment was addressed as much to him as to Newton. However, in passages surrounding that eloquent testimony to the two men's greatness, Fontenelle cannot deny the excellence of either the *Principia* and the *Opticks* on the one hand or of Newton's unusual mathematical skill on the other. Nor can he, as a biographer, deprive him of a fair estimate of his remarkable scientific achievements or of the predictive powers of some of his generalizations. Yet even in this *éloge*, Fontenelle cannot resist raising objections to Newton's addiction to terms like "attraction," which Fontenelle considered might lead the unwary reader to mistake for a mechanical cause.[8]

FONTENELLE'S ANSWER TO NEWTON'S QUERY

Attraction at a distance remained Fontenelle's bête noire, whether it appeared in mechanics, as with Newton's gravitational theory, in optics, as with Newton's conjecture in Query 31, or in chemistry, as with Boerhaave's attractionism or E. F. Geoffroy's affinities. They all feigned a hypothesis that to Fontenelle smacked of occultism and anthropomorphism.

In 1704 Newton published his *Opticks* and some years later, the appended *Queries*. The thirty-first *Query* of the 1717–18 edition has achieved some notoriety for its assertion of an analogy between the particulate nature of solid bodies acting upon one another and the presumed particulate nature of light corpuscles, moving in an aetherial medium, also acting upon one another by the same attractive forces. Newton asks, "Have not the small Particles of Bodies certain Powers, Virtues, or Forces, by which they act at a distance, not only upon the Rays of Light for reflecting, refracting and inflecting them, but also upon one another for producing a great Part of the Phenomena of Nature?"[9] To Fontenelle, the lifelong partisan of the mechanical vortex theory, the interrogative mood of Newton's statement was not the expression of a cautious conjecture, it was a subtle device to mask his genuine belief in attractionism. Newton's phrasing, the secretary declared in his eulogy, is not to be trusted, even when he

> quite distinctly declares that he presents this attraction only as an unknown cause and whose effects he only considers, compares and computes; and to save himself from the reproach of bringing to mind the *occult Qualities* of the Scholasticists, he says that he only establishes qualities that are *manifest* and very evident by the phenomena, but that in truth the causes of these qualities are *occult*, and that he leaves the search of them to other Philosophers. But were not what the Scholasticists called occult Qualities also Causes? They too beheld the Effects. Besides, did Newton think that others would find the occult Qualities he himself had not been able to find? Will the search of them be undertaken with high hopes?[10]

Note, first, Fontenelle's intentional interrogative rejoinder to Newton's interrogative conjecture and, second, the two fallacies masked as queries. The first fallacy is that of drawing the indirect yet illogical conclusion that since the Scholasticists described occult qualities as causes, Newton, who described attractive forces as occult qualities, *must* have thought of them as causes. The second fallacy, contained in the last two sentences of the citation, is Fontenelle's serious misunderstanding of the intent and meaning of hypothe-

sis, confusing as he does (perhaps knowingly for polemical purposes) the
testing of an unproven hypothesis with the establishment of its validity as a
natural law.

Fontenelle's barely-concealed indignation over Newton's imputing attractive forces to particles of light may have been exacerbated by the fact that this
untested imputation was appended to a work he could not sufficiently pay
homage to as "an excellent model in the art of undertaking Experimental
Philosophy." The *Opticks*, he proclaimed in the *éloge* of Newton of 1727,
was "as original, as novel, . . . as vast by the manner by which he treated a
special subject" as the *Principia*. In the *éloge* of Hartsoeker written two years
earlier, he had called its most original discovery—the prismatic nature of
white light—"one of the most beautiful discoveries of modern physics." It
was nothing less than the definitive treatise on the anatomy of light, for,
according to Fontenelle,

> if one wishes to interrogate Nature by experiments and observations, one should do
> it like M. Newton and in as skillful and persistent manner as he. Matters that by their
> very subtlety have almost escaped the notice of researchers he reduced to computa-
> tion, a computation that not only assumes good mathematical knowledge but even
> more a special kind of dexterity. The uses he makes of his mathematics have as
> much finesse as his mathematics has sublimity.

Possibly because he lacked that mathematical finesse and profundity,
Hartsoeker's 1694 claim to have been the first to assert that the differing
refrangibility of the constituent parts of white light derived from their differing
velocities is alluded to by Fontenelle without comment. It is to Newton that
the latter attributes the fundamental discovery of "the differing refrangibility
of red, yellow, green, blue, violet, and the infinite number of colors
in between, a property never before suspected and which one could not have
discovered by any conjecture." And whereas he dismisses as unheard-of
Hartsoeker's claim that the degree of deviation of a refracted light ray from the
normal is a function of its velocity, Fontentelle concludes his lengthy
description of Newton's mode of experimentation and multiple observational
discoveries with the enthusiastic claim that they form "a body of optics so
new that it can henceforth be said that this science is almost entirely the
creation of its author."[11]

FONTENELLE'S AVERSION TO CHEMICAL AFFINITIES

In 1768, eleven years after Fontenelle's death, Fouchy declared that "the
principle of affinities is so generally admitted among chemists today that to
simply recall a phenomenon is almost to explain it."[12] As Fouchy's
phraseology suggests, however, time has a way of simplifying what had once
been complicated and of smoothing over what had once been controversial.

He undoubtedly knew that his predecessor Fontenelle had as late as 1731 and 1738 expressed strong reservations about E. F. Geoffroy's chemical affinities for their presumed similarity to Newtonian action at a distance. As expressed by the historian of chemistry J. R. Partington, the arrangement of substances, including acids and bases, seemed innocuous enough. "At the head of a column is a substance with which all the substances below can combine. The latter are so placed that any substance replaces all others lower in the column from their compounds with that at the head of the table." Thus, in the column headed by acid of marine salt are found, in descending order, tin, regulus of antimony, copper, silver, and mercury, and in the column headed by silver are found lead and copper.

Fontenelle, however, saw more than met the eye. His *éloge* of E. F. Geoffroy runs to about 2,400 words but is largely devoted to extolling his subject's moral, administrative, medical, and scientific skills. He reserved only 95 words to his innovative theory of affinities, which he evasively criticized and deemed "a singular system." Without directly alluding to himself as a determined opponent of that theory, he made clear his opposition by his choice selection of pejorative epithets, an impersonal voice, and his use of the conditional mood in a number of clauses. Some men, he said, were pained by the affinities displayed in the table of 1718,

for they feared that they were disguised attractions, so much the more dangerous as skillful people have already been able to endow them with seductive figures, but at last it was recognized that these scruples could be overcome and that one could allow for [*admettre*] M. Geoffroy's table, which, if fully understood and carried to all the necessary precision, could become a fundamental law of chemical operations and a successful guide to those who work with them.[13]

In his last years of office Fontenelle resorted to plainer language to castigate the proponents of Newtonian attractionism. In his *éloge* of Boerhaave, the renowned Dutch physicist, physician, chemist, and popular teacher, the secretary at first elevated his polemic tone to suit his subject. He marvelled at the "rare and singular talents of a professor" capable of attracting students from the best universities at home and abroad and commended him for having reduced chemistry "to a simple, clear, and intelligible Physics."[14] Nevertheless, he deplored Boerhaave's partisanship of both attractionism and affinities. He says,

It must be admitted, however, that he acknowledged Attraction in this very pure and very luminous Physics or Chemistry, and, acting with greater frankness than is commonly done in this matter, he quite formally recognized that this Attraction is not a Mechanical principle at all. One might possibly hold it to be more tolerable in Chemistry than in Astronomy, because of the sudden, violent, impetuous motions so common in Chemical operations; but no matter what the occasion, has anything at all been said when the word Attraction is pronounced?[15]

On the surface, there was nothing in the table of affinities as briefly sketched by Partington to bring about Fontenelle's displeasure. The tabulated affinities represented but the results of countless laboratory experiments performed with chemical substances in varying combinations. There lurked beneath the surface, however, a number of assumptions that were bound to disturb the secretary's equilibrium. For one thing, the very word "affinity" smacked of an anthropomorphism inimical to a sound, self-induced mechanical physics. For another, though Geoffroy himself never used the word "attraction" in a chemical context, action at a distance was as much implied in the theory of affinities as was atomism. As Metzger summed up this issue, the law of universal gravitation, if applied to chemistry, had to presume a corpuscular philosophy.

> It immediately appeared, in fact, that the dissolutions, crystallizations, vaporizations, and precipitations that we observe in the laboratories are the results of very complex reactions whose totality escapes us. . . . In summing up by a single proposition the totality of natural phenomena, the law of universal attraction renders useless the luxuriance of details that the partisans of mechanical philosophy imagined to deduce from its principles. Like other doctrines that aspire to simplicity, however, the Newtonian synthesis clashed with the at-first disconcerting complexity of the facts observed in chemical laboratories.

The synthesis effected by Newton in physics was expressed as a function of the mass of the attracting bodies and the square of the distance between them; the synthesis as applied to chemistry was, by experimental duress, compelled to modify the latter variable by raising it to any power appropriate to the evidence. Nor was Newton's formulation of the law of universal gravitation of any help in determining "the reasons that lead one kind of substance to combine with a second rather than with any other kind of substance."[16]

Had Fontenelle been allotted the biblical span of six score years, his suspicion of the "Newtonian" basis of the theory of affinities would have been confirmed by Bergman's extension of Geoffroy's work to include the "terrifying number of thirty thousand experiments" and his substitution of the term "elective attraction" for that of "affinity." He would not have been reassured by Condorcet's apologia that either chemist's table met the scientific standards of being like "a précis of results" drawn from observation, by having reduced "the already large number of chemical facts to a small number of simple and general facts," and as serving "to explain several new phenomena, that is," of showing "their agreement with facts already known." Assuredly, generalization, simplicity, elegance, and predictability were highly desirable goals for both secretaries. Yet Fontenelle would have been scandalized by his successor's support of Bergman's use of the word "attraction" on the grounds that its effects, rather than its causes, "could be observed in all natural bodies." He would have been doubly scandalized by the Swedish chemist's use of the anthropomorphic term "elective" to describe the observed fact that this attraction varied according to the nature of the substance in the process of chemical combination.[17]

To Fontenelle, words like "attraction," "affinities," and "elective" had no place in natural philosophy because they denoted at worst occult qualities alien to a causal explanation of physical processes and at best, imprecise terms irreducible to a sound, commonsensical, mechanical description. It is also for failure to resort to natural explanations that Fontenelle categorically rejected Leibniz' explanation of the optical law of refraction. As he phrased it, Leibniz "believed that final causes could sometimes be of use; for example, that the ratio of the sine of the incidence and of refraction was constant because God willed that a ray changing direction from one point to another by two routes which, when added together, caused it to use less time than it would over all other possible routes," Deeming this principle a deplorable resurgence of Aristotelian entelechy, Fontenelle paid Leibniz a left-handed compliment. While this principle of least time is "certainly great and noble and worthy of its subject, . . . the essence of the Creator's wisdom seems even more above our feeble reach than does the essence of His power."[18]

MAIRAN THE MAVERICK CARTESIAN

As Fontenelle had done earlier, Mairan made it his duty to redeem the vortex theory from scientific oblivion. Indeed, about a third of his *éloge* of Privat de Molières, a partisan of a modified version of Descartes's and Malebranche's vortex theory, is devoted to a defense of that theory. As a practicing physicist, however, Mairan was more subtly aware than Fontenelle had been of the difficulties in weighing properly the merit of the Cartesian and Newtonian theories. Hence, he drew up, for all the world to see, a most exhaustive catalogue of the shortcomings inherent in both systems, but came up with a judgment that weighed heavily in favor of the former. Whatever its shortcomings, Cartesianism possessed what Newtonianism abysmally lacked, namely, an *"Explication méchanique, voies simples et méchaniques, et toujours de la méchanique"* (Mairan's italics).[19]

Mairan's inability to accept the nonmechanical premise of action at a distance may be attributed to his unwillingness to recognize the distinction between intelligible ideas and real objects, between the principles that underlie pure mathematics and those that derive from the laws of motion inherent in matter. He repeatedly attempted to disprove Newton's theory because it appeared to him as a mathematical hypothesis devoid of any reference to mechanical principles and another, if grander, of those occult qualities whose existence it was the aim of science to banish. It did not matter to Mairan, at least until the 1750s, that the vortex hypothesis had been shown by Newton to be inconsistent with Kepler's laws; it was a sound mechanical hypothesis, unlike Newton's mysterious action at a distance, and some other explanation could be offered to account for that inconsistency.

Mairan, however, proved to be an unreliable follower of Descartes. For while he preferred the Cartesian explanation of gravitation for its mechanical foundation, he also, by 1733, accepted "the Keplerian law of the periodic revolution of the planets about the sun, and the Newtonian principle that central forces operate according to the inverse square of the distance."[20] And, by virtue of both Malebranche's influence and his own experiments Mairan also preferred Newton's mathematical demonstrations in optics, especially on the composition of white light and the laws of refraction. According to Henry Guerlac, Mairan was very likely "the earliest in France to confirm by experiment the unalterability in the color of rays carefully separated by refraction."[21] Moreover, soon after 1714 Mairan showed himself to be familiar with the Latin version of Newton's *Opticks* and Malebranche's revised theory of colors. By 1712 Malebranche had superimposed the Newtonian "notion of the prior existence in a beam of white light of an infinite range of properties capable of producing the infinite range of colors" upon his own undulatory theory of color, first enunciated in 1699. By the latter theory, certain colors result from the differing frequencies of the pulses of the ether or subtle matter that makes up light.[22]

In 1722, 1723, 1738, and 1740 Mairan published four long mémoires, totalling about 120 quarto pages, on "Recherches Physico-Mathématiques sur la réflexion des corps," in which he argued that diffraction was only a species of refraction, and refraction a species of reflection. Hence he was faced with an apparent paradox: if refraction produces colors, as Newton had uncontestably demonstrated and he himself had confirmed, and if refraction was a species of reflection, why did reflection not produce the division of white light rays into colored rays? To resolve this paradox, Mairan felt compelled to throw his support behind Newton's theory of refraction while adhering to "Mechanism, and with the most solid and the most rigorous principles of Cartesian philosophy." For with Mairan, as with Fontenelle, Cartesianism did not mean so much the conclusions that the French philosopher had drawn from his reasoning as the fundamental method of reasoning itself: mechanical suppositions, experimental observation, intelligible terminology, and mathematical notation. Hence, Mairan was at pains to point out that his memoirs

have been composed in view of not adopting by necessity any physical system whatever on light. My intent was solely never to deviate from the clear idea of motion, in such a way that the hypothesis of *vibrations by impulse*, and even *attrac-*

tion—as long as they are experimental or the external effect of any cause whatever—are included therein by formulas uniquely related to that effect . . . .In short, I have claimed, in a strict sense, only a physicomathematical theory of the reflection of bodies, with its principal accidents, and reduced to an intelligible and known mechanism.[23]

He then showed that the different degrees of refrangibility of a ray of light and the differing colors created by such refrangibility could have been produced by neither the differing mass or thickness of particles of light, as Descartes had claimed, nor by the differing degrees of rotation of these luminary particles around their centers on any plane whatever. Hence, he concluded, the refrangibility of light is due to the differing velocity with which each of the rays of color moves, causing them to separate, or for the white light to break up into its constituent parts.[24]

MAIRAN ON HYPOTHESES

In his methodology of science as well as in his physics, Mairan too was a maverick. He was neither an unquestioning Cartesian nor an empiricist of the new school. And just as it is impossible to label Mairan with the name of any predominant school of scientific thought, so it is futile to seek consistency in a man whose active scientific career spanned over half a century and witnessed the co-existence of half a dozen philosophies of science. In 1719, 1722, and 1726, for example, he claimed *expérience* as the key with which to unlock the secrets of nature, either with or without *la raison* as a handmaiden. *"L'expérience* is the mother of physics. *La Raison* uses the facts that the former provides it for its guidance."[25] By raison Mairan meant reasoning from the facts provided by expérience, which itself subsumes what in English is denoted by both experience and experimentation. His is the statement of an experimental physicist schooled in that tendency of Cartesianism that permeated the work of such distinguished members of the first century of the Academy of Sciences as Huyghens, Claude Perrault, Cassini I, and Réaumur. The reasoning Mairan speaks of is Cartesian in that it must not only be confirmed by the test of sensory reality but must also meet the test of intelligibility. Mairan's stand on the proper alliance between raison and expérience, therefore, admits of no doubt. What does admit of doubt is his understanding of the place of hypotheses in the scientific method.

As late as 1729 Mairan penned the following note in an unpublished manuscript:

Hypotheses, fictions, and philosophical romances have been the weak foundation on which several persons have built their systems. Instead of their reason proceeding only after experience, their minds at first lost their way among a thousand fictions, after which they have explained everything [*ils ont ensuite rendu raison de tout*] by their hypotheses, without sufficient consideration as to whether they had not been belied by expérience.[26]

If this were Mairan's sole statement on hypotheses, it would occasion no surprise: it automatically follows from the previously-quoted statement about reasoning operating *only* after expérience, being validated solely by empirical evidence. By the above statement, therefore, hypotheses are classified along with fictions and philosophical romances among the chimeras of science. But there is a much longer statement, the preface to his work on ice, that is less peremptory about the meaning of hypotheses. That preface was published in 1716 and republished in 1749, at a time when leading philosophes had launched or were about to launch a wholesale attack against *systèmes* and what they deemed to be *hypothèses*.

It must be remembered that, contrary to common belief, Cartesianism by and large never denied the value of the test of expérience. The Cartesian method, as revealed in the early mémoires of the Academy of Sciences, was at once experimental and rational. Descartes, like his disciples, had held that the a priori understanding of the fundamental laws of nature "served to set definite limits to what is physically possible. But within the limits thus prescribed there still remain open for the physical universe practically infinite possibilities. All we desire is to explain the phenomena of the universe and know how these can be accounted for in terms of the fundamental principles that govern all natural happenings."[27] For decades Descartes's philosophy of science and his investigations had provided both substance and method to French scientists. There was, for one, the precedent of Descartes's own work in anatomy performed to elucidate the vexing question of the role of the senses and the brain in the distinction between primary and secondary qualities. For another, there was also a ready-made theoretical system in the hypotheses of vortices, mechanism, and dualism—systems or principles that Mairan retained until at least the late 1750s.

After nearly a century, however, that venerable tradition—reinforced by a profusion of discoveries in mechanics, optics, acoustics, and anatomy—was being challenged on all sides, especially by followers of Newton. The Newtonians claimed for themselves the monopoly of those precious scientific commodities—experimentation, observation, and fidelity to brute facts—and accused the Cartesians, whom they lumped together, of reverting back to occult qualities in the guise of final causes. The Cartesians, in turn, accused their opponents of resorting to these same occult qualities when they spoke of an action at a distance that could not be explained by any mechanical principle they were familiar with. Neither camp was spared the odium of that most heinous of eighteenth-century sins, scholasticism.[28]

Mairan tried to make the best of both worlds of science, selecting what he deemed the most solid features of both Newtonianism and Cartesianism. His was not Diderot's complaint that Newton's mathematics was too abstruse and his experiments too ingenious.[29] He had no objections to Newton's experiments, observations, and mathematics; it was simply a question as to whether it made any sense to rest the whole superstructure of science on observed data without the support of primary principles. It is because Mairan, like Fontenelle, Privat de Molières, and Jacques Cassini, hoped to save mechanism at all costs, that he publicly adopted features of Newtonian mechanics and optics without committing himself entirely to Newtonian science. Yet, it was not enough that the substance of correct physics, the hypothesis of vortices, was being increasingly discredited, but the very methodology of science as he saw it was also coming under heavy attack. Mairan, therefore, took the opportunity in 1749 to vindicate the Cartesian method once and for all. The republication of the *Traité sur la glace* was timed to coincide with the increasingly severe challenge posed by Newtonians to the Cartesian *esprit de système*.

To Mairan, the clamor against systèmes had all the earmarks of an intolerant campaign that would see no distinction between esprit de système and *esprit systématique*, between hypotheses and principles, or among self-evident principles, imaginary principles, and experimentally-tested principles. "System or chimera," he complained, "today seem synonymous terms in the mouths of many persons, otherwise skillful and noted for their works."[30] It is presently fashionable, Mairan continued, to condemn beyond appeal any book, any scientific law with the least tincture of systematization. This is sheer arrogance and pure nonsense, he argued. Sheer arrogance because abuses of the esprit de système are no more sufficient to condemn all systèmes out of hand than abuses of the spirit of experimentation are sufficient to ban all experiments. It is also pure nonsense because there are sound (methodical) and unsound (unmethodical) experiments, just as there are hypothèses, *soupçons*, and systèmes. All scientists, of whatever persuasion, have had to resort to some fluid or other hypothèse in their cosmology: even the great Newton had deigned to make use of soupçons or preliminary hypotheses in the optical work he discussed in the *Philosophical Transactions*. Newton's employment of a hypothesis, therefore, should prove an example to his followers. Unless we are definitely certain of having sought out every possible cause and have arrived at a final, uncontestable explanation, we have no right, as scientists, to reject systèmes *in toto*.[31] Mairan's conclusion is plain: all scientific work must be associated with a systematic method. Hence, when he condemns hypothèses in 1749, he means untested hypotheses. Hypotheses in the modern sense (i.e., soupçons) are essential to science, for they set the stage for and elucidate explanations of observational or experimental facts. Nowhere did he better set forth the prescription for the proper scientific method than in the *éloge* of the abbé de Molières, composed in 1742:

He has been reproached with an excessive love of systèmes. He could have answered—and undoubtedly believed it—that there were times in which too much trust had been placed in systèmes and not enough in the study of the facts; that, contrariwise, there are other times—and we are nearly in that position—in which the esprit systématique is not sufficiently cultivated and in which it seems to have shaken off the yoke of reasoning even when it is applied to facts alone. The true philosopher, the man for all times, who is not deceived by the dominant prejudice of his time and country, holds a golden mean between these excesses. He is aware that one will infallibly be misled by the esprit systématique without the aid of facts and expériences and without nature being investigated in nature itself; but he also knows that experiences remain imperfect, equivocal, solitary, and unfruitful, if that esprit, when equally applied to meditation and calculation, does not enlighten them, does not enliven them, and does not expand them almost to infinity by the new views it is capable of originating.[32]

To Fouchy, some scientists' hasty recourse to systèmes and first principles seemed almost an act of blasphemy, a prying into the secret recesses of God's mind. It suited what appears to have been his fideistic mentality to exhibit paragons of circumspection as the very models of scientific researchers. Thus he commends Stephen Hales for the "prudent and modest discretion with which he almost always contented himself to state the facts without permitting himself the slightest conjecture except where a precise calculation had converted it into a demonstration." So persuaded was Fouchy of the futility of seeking explanations where no evidence was forthcoming that he dismissed the quest for first principles or final causes as a chimera unworthy of scientific research. He agreed with Van Swieten that "the human mind is so limited as to be unable to go beyond certain limits. He scoffed at those who peremptorily sought to rise to first principles." Fouchy put the case against useless raisonnement in science most forcibly in his analysis of Quesnay's L'Art de guérir par la Saignée (1736):

Arguments take up very little room in this work; the few found therein are necessary to expound and to prove with precision the doctrine that must originate out of the experiments and observations given by the author; and he was so persuaded that nothing certain existed beyond the facts that the first causes he admits are ordinarily only the first general effects that he does not undertake to explain but that serve for him to explain an infinity of others.[33]

·III·
Generation and Taxonomy: the Secretaries' *Parti-pris*

Il faut commencer par classer les êtres, depuis la molécule inerte, s'il en est, jusqu'à la molécule vivante, à l'animal microscopique, à l'animal-plante, à l'animal, à l'homme.
—DIDEROT, *Eléments de physiologie*

Until the second quarter of the eighteenth century botany had been viewed as a branch of medicine known as herbalism and had been primarily approached from the standpoint of the collector and classifier of plants. Like botany, zoology was treated as a purely descriptive science whose proper function was the observation, enumeration, and classification of the external features of nonhuman beings. The physiology and internal anatomy of fauna were largely abandoned to the care of the medical anatomist. By mid-century, however, the biological sciences had shifted from nomenclature to the elucidation of the internal structure and functions of plants and animals. In A. R. Hall's words, they became less and less the preoccupation of the natural historian who "takes the whole rural scene for his province, and is primarily interested in creatures as individuals" and more and more the preoccupation of what the nineteenth century was to call the biologist, that is, one "predominantly concerned to answer specific questions."[1]

As recorded in the *éloges* of the scientists who died before 1792, pure description in botany gradually gave way to controversial issues in taxonomy and reproduction. Zoology was increasingly studied by anatomists and physiologists intent on proving or disproving the human body's kinship with those of other animal species and by microscopists puzzled by the functions of ovaries and sperms. All these living phenomena provided evidence or counterevidence for a number of debates that periodically raged through the century and which were not settled until after the demise of the ancient Paris Academy of Sciences. Partisanship in natural history was most deeply aroused over the sciences of taxonomy and generation. As they involved such philosophical and theological issues as mechanism, vitalism, Epicurean atomism, and providentialism, the secretaries felt compelled to express their most cherished principles in eulogies that were allegedly impartial.

As Elizabeth B. Gasking has superlatively demonstrated, the phenomenon of the sexual reproductions of animals has raised a series of vexing questions for centuries. These include "the contributions made by the different sexes," the order in which the parts appear in the embryo, the reason for and manner by which all "organisms seem to grow from structureless primordia into complex organic structures, each one being of a very definite kind," the degree of the offspring's replication of the characteristics of each of the parents, and the cause for the appearance of what the eighteenth century called "monsters."[2] The differing answers to these questions led to sustained controversies within and without the Paris Academy of Sciences and called for elaborate comments on the part of the four secretaries.

Two hypotheses were formulated in the seventeenth century to explain the growth of organisms "from structureless primordia into complex organic structures." The first hypothesis, epigenesis, was enunciated in 1651 by the famous anatomist William Harvey. It attributed the process of growth to an organization of parts by degrees. As Gasking felicitously puts it, "Harvey's account of development is of a simultaneous process of growth and differentiation. His model is not the sculptor but the potter who forms his pot by adding material to it and shaping it at the same time."[3] The rival hypothesis, first introduced into scientific literature by Jan Swammerdam in 1699, was that of preformation or *emboîtement*. According to the ovist version of that hypothesis, "The gradual appearance and apparent creation of the parts observed, as the ovum turned into the embryo and then into the adult, were simply due to an increase, in size and in hardness, of parts that were already present." In other words, the ovum contained "the ova of the next generation, and so on *ad infinitum* like Chinese boxes: in the ovaries of Eve were confined the future forms of all the human race."[4] This hypothesis was not fully disproved until the end of the eighteenth century since, as Gasking has exhaustively shown, it rested on the best inductive evidence available at the time.[5] Another version of preformation was put forward by Leeuwenhoek in 1679 when he suggested that the animalcules (sperms) he had discovered in semen through his microscope were the living embryos. The adherents of Leeuwenhoek's views, called animalculists, included C.J. Geoffroy, Boerhaave, and Hartsoeker, who from 1694 onwards "made repeated attempts to claim that he had, in fact, made the original discovery" of the spermatozoa.[6]

THEORIES OF GENERATION: FONTENELLE VERSUS HARTSOEKER

Apparently Fontenelle took Hartsoeker at his word, for in his *éloge* of the Dutch scientist, he remarked that he was "the first to disclose the most unexpected view in the world for *Physiciens* . . . —the hitherto invisible animalcules that will be transformed into men . . . ." So astounded was Hartsoeker by what he had seen that he attributed his discovery to mental derangement and did not resume his observations until 1677, when he had completed his formal studies with Cartesians who were "as infatuated with Descartes as the preceding Scholasticists had been with Aristotle." He saw these same animalcules, but differently-shaped, in a rooster and a pigeon. He and two of his friends, whom he had invited over to corroborate his observations, concluded therefrom that "all animals were born by invisible and hidden metamorphoses, in the way that all species of flies and butterflies grow out of perceptible and known metamorphoses." From further observations on a larger number of species, Hartsoeker inferred the animalcules' origin and role in the reproduction of these species. He surmised that they flew about in the air and that all the animals visible to the naked eye "confusedly took them in either by respiration or with food, [and] that from there those which suited each species betook themselves" to the male genitalia and thence to the female ovaries for their growth. Without endorsing Hartsoeker's hypothesis, Fontenelle argued that if it were correct that all animals developed out of sperms, it would follow that the number of sperms and therefore the number of all animals was limited and that "not all species are equally prolific."[7]

Without saying it in so many words, Fontenelle here was drawing a major conclusion out of the hypothesis of emboîtement that Hartsoeker had at first endorsed. Should any particular living form die without having reproduced itself, it would diminish the number of Chinese boxes for that particular species. Fontenelle's reticence in calling emboîtement by its right name and his sarcastic denunciation of Hartsoeker's teachers as Cartésiens outrés seem to point to the same inference: his more than likely rejection of that hypothesis. A witticism to the wise of his day may have been sufficient but it does not tell us the extent to which preformation meshed with both a modified Cartesianism and orthodox Christian piety. As Jacques Roger has shown in his exhaustive study of eighteenth-century biology, the préexistence des germes or emboîtement was accepted by Réaumur, Haller, Bonnet, Spallanzani, and others in that it endowed original genetic matter with a mechanical propulsion that compelled it, by the laws of motion, to eject fully formed and God-created living beings. To these scientists, the rival theory of epigenesis contained a basic flaw. It was heretical in implying the absurd possibility of spontaneous generation, the likelihood of Epicurean animated matter, and worse yet, a blurring of the distinction between the Cartesian realms of mind and matter and the existence of a self-created universe without God.[8] As a Deist, Fontenelle was not about to endorse a hypothesis that gave comfort to orthodox Christians; nor, however, did he dare risk the charge of impiety by speaking up on behalf of the suspect hypothesis of epigenesis. Because Hartsoeker, at one time or another, had quarrelled with Huyghens, Leibniz, Newton, Mairan, Homberg, and Jakob Bernoulli,[9] a reading of his éloge suggests that Fontenelle dismissed Hartsoeker's subsequent rejection of emboîtement in favor of a vitalistic version of epigenesis as another example of contentiousness without equal among Academicians.

Hartsoeker fashioned this vitalistic hypothesis because emboîtement, by causing God to have set lifeless matter into motion for eternity, could not explain Réaumur's experiments on the regeneration of the crayfish's legs.

Hence he inserted an *âme plastique* or *formatrice* into the crayfish, which soul
or spirit "enabled them to grow new legs," a spirit that also resided within
other animals and even man. Since the "function of these âmes plastiques is
not to reproduce these lost limbs," Fontenelle went on to say, Hartsoeker
"endowed them with the task of forming animalcules who perpetuate the
species."

By reiterating his contempt for Hartsoeker's vitalistic hypothesis, Fontenelle saved himself the labor of having to present the plausible objections the
Dutch scientist had raised against emboîtement, especially in a letter he wrote
to Jean Le Clerc, a Newtonian partisan of Natural Theology. The mechanical
formation of a single part of the animal's body, he wrote, "is no less
inconceivable nor less impossible than that of a whole animal, and it is no less
absurd to believe that God had made a new creation." Hence the necessity of
resorting to an intelligence, "which resides within the animal and whose loss
it repairs instantly." He subsequently attacked emboîtement on the grounds of
the inconceivable smallness of these "boxed" seeds. He argued that it was, on
the contrary, the âmes plastiques that maintain the health of all organic bodies
and that, omnipresent in the universe, explain such phenomena as orbital
motion and gravitation at a distance. However farfetched, this argument was
made in good conscience, since it was meant to show up the heresy of a
Cartesian mechanism (or rather, its Deistic interpretation) and the absurdity of
a providence intervening in every creature's movement. It would make more
sense as well as restore God to his majesty if he had endowed the entire
universe with a macroscopic soul of which the âmes plastiques were the
microscopic parts. Hartsoeker, as Roger points out, thus dealt Cartesianism a
double blow: he did away with the dualism between mind and matter and he
denied the existence of an independent, unextended spiritual substance. Rather
than meet head on the objections Hartsoeker had raised against emboîtement,
Fontenelle peremptorily dismissed his substitute hypothesis as a rebirth of
animism. He mockingly derided Hartsoeker as the author of a système he
would have preferred not to have created (given his opponents' strong
objections) but was too proud to discard.[10]

MAIRAN ON THE GENESIS OF "MONSTERS"

For a long time the preformation theory had held sway in the scientific
community: it supported the belief in the fixity of species, it meshed with
Cartesian mechanism, and it explained a host of biological phenomena. As the
eighteenth century went on, however, it increasingly was challenged by a
number of new scientific findings: "the discovery of animal regeneration, the
recognition of the intermediate character of hybrids, and the realisation that
variation was common and that novelty could appear."[11] The debate between
the proponents and opponents of emboîtement was especially prolonged over
the issue of "monsters" or unusually deformed organisms. For sixteen years

this issue pitted Louis Lémery first against Winslow and Du Verney (1724–30) and, after the latter's death, against Winslow alone. Partisans of the preformation theory, Du Verney and Winslow held that a monster originated in a seed that itself was monstrous. Lémery, on the other hand, held that two-headed children had been born out of totally separate embryos but "by diverse accidents of collision and pressure had adapted themselves on the remainder of one of their bodies."[12]

In his *éloge* of Winslow, Fouchy typically refused to take sides on this hotly-contested issue. Standing above the battle in 1760, he only remarked that "this dispute produced excellent mémoires from both of them [Winslow and Lémery], but it had the usual fate of disputes: each man stuck to his belief and the issue remained indecisive."[13] Thirty years earlier, Fontenelle, in his eulogy of Du Verney, had refused to take sides by the simple expedient of omitting this debate altogether. Mairan, in his *éloge* of Lemery, made up for his predecessor's silence by dwelling on this matter at some length. His account displays his attempt to strike a balance between the two opposing views. Yet it is clear from the concluding remarks that the preexistent creation of monsters was, in his eyes, an affront to both the infinite power and the goodness of God.

> The opinion [in favor of] of the originally monstrous seeds [*germes*] suddenly solved the possibly insurmountable difficulty of conceiving how the remains of two organized bodies composed of billions of organized parts could have produced a third body by this means. A difficulty that led someone in the Academy to say that one could as soon imagine that out of two pendulums crushed one against the other would be formed a new pendulum, or that the seeds themselves, monstrous or not, would have been formed in the bodies of animals only by wholly similar accidents [*hasards*]—which would prove too much and would invalidate the general system. But the common opinion also has the advantage in that those who reject it are constrained to admit that there are monsters and monstrous parts whose formation is visibly due to accidental contact, or at least that this explanation may have some merit without one having to trace it back to the egg. Plants provide other examples of it and it is here that the analogy in favor of the system of accidents is carried by M. Lémery to the highest degree of verissimilitude it is capable of. Another principle which he set forth but which cannot be used with too much circumspection is that nothing imperfect having left the hand of the Creator, there is no likelihood [*apparence*] that he had directly willed the creation of monsters by seeds destined to produce them. For, after all, our lights are too dim to permit us to decide the nature of perfection or imperfection in the Order of Nature and whether the monsters as we perceive them had been prepared with the world by the same wisdom that suffered them to be in it.[14]

FOUCHY *CONTRA* MAUPERTUIS

In the *éloge* of Maupertuis, published in 1759, Fouchy did not exhibit the kind of impartiality he was to display one year later in his eulogy of Winslow.

Lumping all of Maupertuis' achievements in natural history in one ragbag of a paragraph, he simply remarked that "we have from him a dissertation on the generation of animals, which he published under the title of *Vénus physique*; there are found in it conjectures that are as novel as they are bold, which since then have acquired great fame." A few pages earlier he had apologized for this peremptory treatment of "one of the most industrious of the Academicians and one of those who were most adept in selecting the subjects of their work." The relatively short space allotted to a eulogy, he claimed, did not permit him to expand on the multivarious achievements of his colleague.[15]

It is true that the inclusion of Maupertuis' pioneering investigations in and hypotheses on generation and heredity would have intolerably expanded what is already the fourth longest of Fouchy's sixty-four *éloges*. Still, the suspicion remains that more than lack of space explains this neglect of one of the great biologists of the century, noted for his empirical refutations of emboîtement, the application of the theory of probability to "genetics," experiments in animal breeding, the formulation of a particulate theory of heredity, and the enunciation of a "theory of organic evolution based upon mutation, natural selection, and geographic isolation."[16] From the totality of Fouchy's *éloges* and especially from that of Maupertuis it can be gathered that the secretary's reluctance to expound on the latter's biological views stemmed from a number of circumstances and parti pris. It is possible that Fouchy, unlike Buffon but like most of the great evolutionists and geneticists of the nineteenth century,[17] was not endowed with the hindsight that enables us to appraise the full importance of Maupertuis' revolutionary hypotheses. Furthermore, Fouchy probably preferred to dwell on those of his subject's achievements that had made him famous, if not notorious, in his own day: his espousal of Newton's action at a distance in a scientific climate then overwhelmingly dominated by Cartesian vortices, his leadership of the geodesic expedition to Lapland, and his assumption of the presidency of the Berlin Academy of Sciences. As a deeply pious man, too, he may very well have viewed Maupertuis' mechanistic version of epigenesis[18] as a challenge to the orthodox interpretation of the creation.

The best substantiated explanation for Fouchy's neglect of Maupertuis' biological achievements can be inferred from the very words and tone of voice of the *éloge* itself. It is one of the few eulogies in the entire corpus written between 1699 and 1791[19] where a secretary did not disguise his anger for a particular deed or moral trait of his subject. Delivered on April 16, 1760, in the midst of the Seven Years' War (1756–1763) and after the spectacular Prussian defeats of the French at Rossbach and Minden, this *éloge* was the occasion for a bitter tirade against Maupertuis' presumed betrayal of his *patrie*. He was accused *ex post facto* of having led "his too lively imagination" to accept in 1745 Frederick II's offer of a permanent position at the

Berlin Academy of Sciences. Fouchy climaxed four pages of indignation with a passage reeking of self-righteousness:

> The severity of the office [*ministère*] that I have the honor of holding at this moment does not permit me to commend the step he took. It would undoubtedly have been better to continue to render to his king and his patrie the services that they had acknowledged, honored, and rewarded. And the Academy is too well informed of the duties of a subject towards his prince and of a citizen towards his patrie to recommend this conduct as a model for imitation.[20]

However deficient in patriotic virtue, Maupertuis the natural historian deserved more recognition from Fouchy than the latter had been willing to grant him. The secretary cannot be entirely faulted for ignoring those genetic findings whose full import were not to be recognized for more than a century. Given the liveliness of the debates over the issue of generation, however, Fouchy could have been more specific about those conjectures of Maupertuis which he considered "as novel as they are bold." As Jean Ehrard has stated, Maupertuis had drawn up "an inventory of all the difficulties" inherent in emboîtement. Maupertuis claimed that this theory was not rational since it implied "a permanent appeal to miracles." He asked, "What is to be gained from believing that He [God] has formed" all beings simultaneously?. . . Is there any difference to God between the time we view as simultaneous and that which is successive?" He did not believe the theory was comprehensible, for, he asked "How could all these souls be contained one within the other since Creation has remained inactive for so many centuries?" Nor did he believe that the hypotheses of ovism and animalculism were empirically verified, since, on the contrary, experience teaches us "that children resemble sometimes their father, sometimes their mother, and sometimes both of their parents." The only rational, logical, and empirical view remaining, Maupertuis concluded, is that Descartes and most ancient natural historians were right in attributing the inheritance of traits to both parents and that most of his contemporaries were wrong in explaining heredity by the preformation theory.[21]

CONDORCET, HALLER, AND FINAL CAUSES

It goes without saying that philosophical and theological presuppositions and predilections play a critical role in yielding differing readings of the same observed phenomena. A superb illustration of this is Haller's interpretation of the growth of the chick as a form of emboîtement and Condorcet's contrary interpretation of it as a form of epigenesis. The secretary praises Haller for having selected birds' eggs for his study of growth, for they enabled him to

observe, step by step, the successive appearances of the animal's organs and
systems. He is quick, however, to seize upon his subject's weakness:

> As the vessels of the growing chick mingle with those of the yolk and form with
> them a continuous whole, and as these vessels of the yolk are observed in non-
> fertilized yolks, M. von Haller thought he could conclude thereby that the chicken
> existed wholly formed in the egg before fertilization. He did not doubt that the
> foetus was also wholly formed in the females of viviparous animals, and he viewed
> this observation as conclusive proof in favor of the system of the successive
> developments of seeds [i.e., emboîtement]. Yet he may have viewed it only as
> simple probability; he might possibly not have deviated, on this point alone, from
> the wisdom that made him impervious to the esprit de système, if reasons of a dif-
> ferent kind had not inspired him with a secret inclination for the belief in the devel-
> opment of seeds.

These reasons were grounded in Haller's fear that epigenesis, by its implica-
tion of the self-sufficiency of natural laws or of secondary causes, would
destroy one of the strongest proofs for the existence of providence or the first
cause. Condorcet was at a loss to understand how the same Haller who had
once rejected the hypothesis of emboîtement as an explanation for the creation
of monsters (a rejection nowhere elaborated in this éloge) was compelled to
bring back God as first cause to explain the inheritance of normal creatures.
Should he not, instead, have sought proof for the existence of a supreme being
in the "wisdom or goodness made manifest by the totality of" natural
phenomena rather than in the character of the forces that produce these
phenomena? After all, concluded Condorcet, the laws operating on matter are
uniformly constant and the phenomena resulting therefrom always present the
same regularity, whether they be the geometrical shapes assumed by salt
crystals or the more irregular forms assumed by animals.[22]

What Condorcet was expressing in 1777 was the view, almost commonplace by that time, that the disregard for final causes that had become a
scientific article of faith with the triumph of Newtonianism in the physical
sciences by the late 1730's was also an article of faith for biological scientists.
As Jacques Roger has painstakingly demonstrated, "The First Cause and its
mysteries were no longer of any concern to" the scientists of Condorcet's
generation. "The quest for final causes and God's intentions in the physical
universe became meaningless [sans objet], since forms had been produced by
the activity of nature and no longer were immediately created by a God-
mechanic." In the short and long run, the sciences most affected by this
intellectual revolution were geology and "genetics." Hence the rejection of
emboîtement, which implied the direct intervention of God in favor of
epigenesis with its assumption of the play of secondary causes. And epigenesis, like emboîtement, was an a priori principle. Whereas Haller attempted
to save theological appearances at all costs, Condorcet and the majority of his

contemporary natural historians attempted to save naturalistic appearances at all costs. As Roger puts it, "The new scientists preferred any kind of physical hypothesis to a metaphysical hypothesis which ran the risk of precluding any kind of research. . . . Inversely to emboîtement, epigenesis solved nothing but opened up all paths. . ." And of these paths, the most important proved to be that of evolution or transformism.[23]

FONTENELLE AND CONDORCET ON TAXONOMY: NOMINAL OR NATURAL?

Nearly every natural historian eulogized before 1792[24] thought it incumbent to pursue the age-old practice of herborization. Systematic trips in the wilderness, at home or abroad, were undertaken for a variety of purposes: curiosity about the wonders of nature, the need to collect medicinal herbs, the ambition to add new species to a botanical garden, enunciation or refutation of a particular taxonomic scheme, and the elucidation of the structure, functions, and utility of particular "exotic" plants. Some botanists, like Joseph de Jussieu, had been specifically commissioned to study the native flora of South America; others, like his brothers Antoine and Bernard as well as Tournefort, viewed their herborization as a form of postgraduate work.[25]

Tournefort was the model botanist. He collected plants in the Alps, Pyrénées, Catalonia, parts of southern France, and the Parisian region, and between 1700 and 1702 executed a royal commission to visit the Mediterranean area as far as Persia and to report on its natural history, geography, and customs.[26]

Tournefort's reputation, however, rested not so much on the vast number of plants he collected as on a system of classification he first postulated in 1694, in the *Elémens de Botanique, ou Méthode pour connoître les Plantes*. To Fontenelle, however, taxonomy owed its sole *raison d'être* to its being a mnemonic device. Such a system served the purpose of putting "order in the prodigious number of plants, sown so confusedly on land and even beneath the waters of the sea" and of distributing them "in genuses and species, which facilitate our knowledge of them and prevent the memory of botanists from being overwhelmed by the weight of an infinity of different names."[27]

But what kind of order was it, and by virtue of what botanical characteristics? As Fontenelle has it, Tournefort's system

consists in classifying [*régler*] the genuses of plants by the flowers and the fruit taken together, that is, so that all plants similar by these two parts will be of the same genus, after which the differences in either the root, or the stem, or the leaves will make up the different species. M. de Tournefort went even further. Above these genuses he has placed classes that are classified only by the flowers, and he was the first to have held this idea, which is more useful to botany than one would at first have thought. For he has found so far only fourteen different shapes of flowers that need to be imprinted upon one's memory.[28]

This classification, according to the secrétaire, is "a prodigious aid to the memory." Instead of the botanist having to select one out of 8,846 names whenever he sees a particular species of plants, all he has to do is look at the flower, which thus gives him the class of that plant, then look at the fruit, which gives him the genus, and once he knows both the class and the genus, it is easy for him to determine the particular species. "In this manner one is in the position of studying that plant in those authors who have mentioned it, without danger of attributing to it what they had said of another plant, or of attributing to another plant what they had said of this one."[29]

If, as Fontenelle alleges, Tournefort's taxonomy had been but a mnemonic device, it would not have been "attacked on several points by the famous English botanist and physician M. Ray." Tournefort's division of species into genuses and classes was not simply an attempt to abide by Descartes's second rule of method, "to divide each of the difficulties which I encountered into as many parts as possible, and as might be required for an easier solution."[30] According to J. F. Leroy, it was Cartesian in a much more fundamental sense: the clear and distinct ideas imbedded in the system of classification Tournefort had enunciated verified the existence of the very objects (classes, genuses, species) these ideas designated. Whereas Fontenelle had declared that the order read into nature had not been "established by nature, which has preferred a magnificent confusion to the scientists' convenience, and it is up to them to put, almost in spite of her, an arrangement and a system in plants," Tournefort's system of reference, in Leroy's words, "is stable and hierarchical, and *in nature*. Philosophers would designate it as a nature in itself [*en soi*] without any need for us to exist."[31]

One need not go as far as Leroy in associating Fontenelle's extreme nominalism with "solipsism." Still, it is difficult to place any other interpretation upon the very report that Fontenelle gave of the Tournefort-Ray debate: "One might say that the subject was hardly worth arguing over; for what was the issue at stake? To know whether the flowers and the fruit sufficed to establish the genuses, whether a certain plant belongs to this or that genus. One should make allowances for men, however, especially *savants*, for arguing seriously over trifles [*légers sujets*]." As the debate between these two leading natural historians was largely without bitterness, Fontenelle inferred that the issue of the debate was without much substance. In other words, Fontenelle attempted to reassure the naifs by attributing this debate to human frailty and the skeptics by referring them to the Paris Academy's *Histoire* of 1700 "where M. de Tournefort's system has been more thoroughly and more extensively discussed."[32]

Aside from his nominal stance toward the classification of organic beings, two other reasons may have impelled Fontenelle to misunderstand the intent of Tournefort's taxonomy. The latter had attributed the essences of plants to the mind of God and he had implied the existence of a taxonomic système. Fontenelle's distrust of that last term is evident throughout the *éloge*: he uses it either to describe a purely mental denotation of a taxonomic scheme or he dismisses it as an unsubstantiated, if not chimerical, belief. Hence, Fontenelle's failure to tell us that as a taxonomist Tournefort believed that nature was filled with "discontinuous and well-marked groups, using a few, or even only one characteristic . . . for the purpose of classification." In contrast to this so-called system of artificial classification, the "natural" system of classification that John Ray had adumbrated "saw the various animals and plants as so many links in a great chain of creatures, the gradations between them being insensible and continuous." Such a system "aimed to bring the diverse organic species into natural families, in which there was a continuity of creatures, as many characteristics as could be found being studied in order to establish the affinity of the organisms within a family." The characteristics that Tournefort had used to distinguish the various species, genuses, and classes, were deemed by Ray to be "accidents." According to S. F. Mason, "The true criterion, implied in Ray's paper of 1672 and stated explicitly in his *General History of Plants* (1686−1704), was one of common descent, presumed or actually observed."[33]

Although Tournefort was succeeded by Antoine de Jussieu as Professor of Botany at the Jardin des Plantes in Paris, it was his brother Bernard, as *Sous-démonstrateur*, who lifted that botanical garden out of the disarray into which it had fallen.[34] Although Bernard de Jussieu had supervised a new edition of Tournefort's *Elémens de Botanique*, some fifteen years later he took issue with his "artificial" method of classifying plants on the basis of both their flowers and their fruit.[35] It was only in the 1760's, however, that he posited a "natural" method of his own. This method is described and praised by Condorcet, who was at once critical of men like Fontenelle who had described botanical nomenclature "as a science of words" and of those botanists, "*peu philosophes*," who had attached supreme importance to "artificial" methods.

Jussieu had divided botanical characteristics into three categories. He dismissed as impermanent the characteristics that altered "with the climate, the age of the plant, [and] the nature of the soil that had nourished it." Among the constant characteristics, some appeared to him to be

superficial, so to speak, so that two kinds of plants that differed between them-selves solely by these characteristics presented the same phenomena in their genera-tion, their growth, their reproduction, and yielded similar substances in analysis, and that consequently, if such characteristics served as basis to a method, they would separate the plants that Nature had brought together or would bring together those that Nature had separated.

So much for Jussieu's reasons for classifying plants according to these fundamental and constant characteristics. Yet, by what presumption did Jussieu arrogate to his system the appellation of "natural," one of the sacred words of the Enlightenment? Jussieu's ascription of the term to his own taxonomic method stemmed from a view that, though more traditional than Buffon's evolutionary hypothesis, was no less current in his day. As Condorcet painstakingly points out:

> It was far from being the case that all the possible combinations of these character-istics were found in nature, from which he concluded that there were necessary relations between them, that their combinations had been regulated by laws, that the discovery of these laws should be one of the main objects of botany. He thought above all that the germination, growth, reproduction, and the nature of the products yielded by the chemical analysis of these plants were connected by laws of this kind. Therefore a botanical method founded on these laws and which would give at the same time the demonstration was no longer a more convenient simple nomen-clature, a kind of artificial memory, it became the foundation of a science. This order of plants, established according to the general laws of nature, appeared to M. de Jussieu the only true method by which to study them and he gave it the name of natural method.[36]

A number of assumptions prevalent in Jussieu's day underlay his belief in the perfect congruence between his nomenclature and the essence of nature's laws: the fixity of species as revealed by their reproduction in kind; the Cartesian correspondence theory of truth insofar as clear and distinct ideas of external objects guaranteed the existence of these objects; and a peculiar interpretation of the distinction between primary and secondary qualities (in which he differentiated between constant features and features altered by conditions "foreign" to the plants). Nothing on Condorcet's éloge indicates that Jussieu inferred an "insensible and continuous" gradation or a common ancestry between species possessing similar generative parts and processes.

The death of Bernard de Jussieu preceded by two months that of his chief rival Linnaeus, whose binomial system has become the cornerstone of modern taxonomy. Linnaeus laid the foundations of this taxonomy when, in his early twenties, he took a leave of absence from the University of Uppsala, to which he had just been appointed Professor of Medicine, in order to study the flora, fauna, and minerals of Europe at first hand. The outcome of his travels through Sweden, Denmark, Germany, France, the Netherlands, and England, and of his conversations with the leading botanists of his day was, in Condorcet's words, nothing less than "one of those great revolutions . . . . [in] the history of human thought." It was a milestone, the secretary went on to specify in great detail, by virtue of the scope of the evidence, the simplicity of the theory, the thoroughness of its application, and the enormous impact it had upon contemporary natural history. He did not deny, however, that the system Linnaeus put forth was artificial in the sense that his divisions within the animal and vegetable kingdoms were determined by one set of characteristics only, that of their reproductive parts.[37]

Linnaeus' elimination of all but one of the characteristics believed by Tournefort and Bernard de Jussieu to determine the divisions between species and genera enabled him to graduate his taxonomy along four levels—species, genera, orders, and classes—and to classify a much larger number of living forms than they had done. Such a streamlined taxonomy, however artificial, was additional testimony to Condorcet's belief in the necessary simplification of natural laws. Hence, the great pains he took to do justice to Linnaeus' "revolution." In three masterful pages he described with perfect lucidity the differing structures and functions of the reproductive processes of plants: the fine details of the pistils, the manner by which the pollen force their way into the stamena, the variation between species in the number of stamens and pistils and their position within the flowers, the existence of hermaphrodite flowers in some species, and the essential role played by the wind or insects in the reproduction of some plants. Condorcet concluded this section by enumerating those parts of the reproductive organs by which Linnaeus subdivided the plants into classes, orders, genera, and species, and labelled by means of the binomial nomenclature that had first been employed by a scientist of the preceding century.[38]

Like all great pioneers or systematizers in science, Linnaeus had his full share of detractors and critics. Some of them pointed to his occasional misnaming of a plant, others dismissed his work as that of a plodding collector, while still others devalued his system for its artificiality. Condorcet challenged Linnaeus' critics to come up with a better method. Despite its indubitable weaknesses, he argued, "no other method has brought together so many advantages; it is even possible that the presumed defects of this system are inevitable in any artificial method. Is it therefore necessary to banish them and to condemn oneself to feel one's way about simply because the torch given to us does occasionally go out.[39]

Condorcet's admiration for this "Newton of natural history" was such that he seems to have minimized Linnaeus's faith in the providential design of his taxonomy. While it is true that the secretary devoted two paragraphs to describing Linnaeus's; "great respect for Providence, a lively admiration for the grandeur and wisdom of His designs, a fond gratitude for His favors," it was not to his advantage to report that in the "fruiting organs of plants Linnaeus believed he could discern characters 'written by the hand of God' to aid man in distinguishing the genera." And since the pattern of nature disclosed by this "natural" method rested on "an absolute stability appropriate to its divine origin,'' it necessarily followed that the species of plants and animals had been fixed in both God's mind and in the world of matter once and for all since creation. Linnaeus did subsequently remark that he could not attribute the presence of fossils high on the mountains to the biblical deluge. This remark, however, was an obiter dictum, incidental if not detrimental to his natural theology. Even if Condorcet had been privy to Linnaeus' private convictions on this matter, a public reading in 1779 would not have been the occasion for casting doubt on the equation of Linnaeus' taxonomy with a static view of nature.[40]

·IV·
Science and Utility:
From Colbert to Franklin

And the king of Brobdingnag "gave it for his opinion, that whoever
could make two ears of corn, or two blades of grass to grow upon a
spot of ground where only one grew before, would deserve better of
mankind, and do more essential service to his country, than the
whole race of politicians put together."
      —LEMUEL GULLIVER, *Travels into Several Remote Nations*
                                        of the World, Book II

Thoughtful laymen at the turn of the seventeenth century might have grasped
the implications of the new scientific world view upon the formation and
development of their own ideas, but they might also have treated the new
natural philosophy as another, if improved, occupation for idle minds and, at
best, as the latest of a successive series of attempts at understanding the natural
world we live in. Moreover, they would have to have been convinced that
science was not a form of impiety, nay the greatest impiety of all, in seeking
to elucidate the laws of God. Otherwise, they might have wondered as to the
reason for Thomas Sprat, the first historian of the Royal Society of London,
devoting seventeen pages to arguing that experiments were "not dangerous to
the Christian Religion," not destructive of "the Doctrine of the Godhead,"
"not injurious to the worship of God," "not prejudicial to the Doctrine of the
Gospel," not subversive of "the Doctrine of the Primitive Church," not
hindering to "the Practice of Religion," and not challenging to "the Doctrine
of Prophecies, and Prodigies."[1]

Sprat's capacity to adjust natural science to orthodox religion probably
would have been less than persuasive had it not been further supported by the
most telling argument of all: science must be cultivated because it is "advantageous to [the] Maual Arts" and "to the Interest of our Nation."[2] While only
Fouchy, among the secretaries of the Paris Academy of Sciences before 1793,
presented natural theology as an argument for the cultivation of natural
philosophy, they all dwelled on its practical benefits to humanity. The theme
of utilitarianism runs through all their Academic writings, from Fontenelle's
*Préface sur l'utilité des mathématiques et de la physique et sur les travaux de
l'Académie des Sciences* (1699) down to the last *éloge* delivered by Condorcet
on November 12, 1791.

In concise yet eloquent language Fontenelle, in the *Préface*, demonstrated the connection between the observation of the Jovian satellites and improved navigation, the study of anatomy and improved surgery, the development of geometry and improved hydrography, the study of conic sections and improved ballistics, and the investigations of the cycloid and improved horology. The history of science since the Renaissance, he said, proves that most of what is called pure science "leads to or derives from" applied science or that "such and such a mathematical speculation that at first seems wholly useless will be applicable in the future."[3]

Indeed, the Baconian call for the fusion of the crafts and the sciences to their mutual advantage runs like an *idée fixe* through Fontenelle's *éloges*. For example, Des Billettes

> was particularly conversant with the arts, with that prodigious number of singular crafts that are unknown to those who do not work in them, not at all observed by those who work in them, neglected by the most universal *savans* who do not even know that there is something there for them to learn, and yet which are marvelous and delightful as soon as they are observed with enlightened eyes.[4]

Fouchy, however, was not as sanguine as Fontenelle on the feasibility of meshing theory with practice. As the only one of the four secretaries with a working knowledge of instruments and machines, Fouchy cautioned scientists against an overoptimistic thrust in the applicability of science to the crafts. As he pointed out in one of his few analytical comments on the utility of science, Pitot directed

> his views toward mechanics, and not only the theoretical and abstract part of that science, but toward the laborious application of its principles to machines in which the part played by physics entails at every step exceptions to nearly all the rules and which calls for genial efforts and continual vigilance in order not to be deceived in the performance.[5]

Fouchy's cautious words notwithstanding, utility increasingly permeated the scientific labor of the Academy, especially during the last three decades of the ancien régime. The *éloges* testify to the extraordinary variety of utilitarian achievements contributed by the French scientists: agricultural processes, medical improvements, mining techniques, the manufacture of ceramics and steel, weights and measures, and above all hydraulics, industrial tools and procedures, and military and naval technology.[6] The central government also hired a number of Academicians for both permanent and ad hoc positions and consulted them on matters regarding the common and private weal. Few of the scientific elect, accordingly, could resist the allurements proferred to them by command, prestige, profit, curiosity, flattery, or humanitarian zeal. To the extent that they devoted their energies to aggrandizing the national armies or navies or to enhancing the splendor of their rulers' settings, the scientists were correct in believing themselves candidates for a new aristocracy based on talent. As it were, their usefulness to the state certified the equality of men of the cabinet to men of the cloth, noblemen of the sword, and noblemen of the robe. If a bourgeois like Louvois bequeathed a title of nobility to his heirs by dint of making France the terror of Europe, military and other services rendered by scientists might also be rewarded with a handsome income or admission into the second estate.

COLBERT

During the first seventeen years of the Academy's existence (1666–1683) Colbert had set a precedent of government patronage that was to remain the ideal against which other rulers and ministers were judged by the secretaries. Colbert had founded the Academy, he had supported its efforts within all the powers granted him by Louis XIV, and he had, through the collaboration of such Academicians as Claude Perrault and Galloys,[7] enticed the brightest scientific luminaries to that institution. In return, he obtained from them services that the grateful Academicians were only too willing to perform. At first, Roger Hahn tells us,

> the Academy seems to have been directed toward long-range projects, such as help-ing to solve the problem of determining longitude at sea, the mapping of France's territory, the establishment of hydraulic theory useful for fountain construction, and the composition of treatises of mechanics relevant to military uses. Gradually, the Academy was also called upon to provide answers of a more particular nature, and to make pronouncements upon the merits of specific technical proposals offered to Louis XIV. The Academy's printed *Mémoires*, for example, refer to the examination of several projects to make saltwater potable, of a metal mirror to focus light rays for the production of high temperatures, and of a series of machines invented to perform human tasks mechanically.[8]

The close alliance between the Paris Academy of Sciences and the state that Colbert had strenuously encouraged remained the Academy's ideal at least up to the mid-eighteenth century. He remained the patron saint of those men unable to resist the accelerating pressure of rivalry with Great Britain, the population boom at home, and the beginning phases of the agricultural and industrial revolutions. As the example of Sweden amply demonstrated, how-ever, military prowess had little lasting value unless it was supported by an economy whose wealth was commensurate with the military effort expended. And the cultivation of public and private wealth necessitated an increasingly closer alliance between science and the state and between scientists and the new class of entrepreneurs. Hence, as Hahn has shown, the utilitarian projects that preoccupied a large proportion of the Academicians usually came from two sources: "One was the private individual who, for the sake of personal fame or financial gain, needed the company's formal and public stamp of approval. The other was the government, which was in constant need of professional judgments to make intelligent administrative decisions."[9]

The general impression gathered from various *éloges* by Fontenelle[10] is that Colbert was an anomaly for France in his understanding of the proper balance to be struck between pure research and utilitarian science and of the right amount of state support for that combined undertaking. Few French politicians had his intelligence, tact, or knowledge to draw a fine distinction between persuasion and authority and between the unanticipated demands of science and the peremptory commands of absolutist monarchy. Louvois is a case in point. Upon the death of his rival Colbert in 1683, he found himself in charge of functions far removed from those he had overseen at the War Ministry. Hence, he could be forgiven if, unfamiliar with the diffidence and scrupulousness of some scientists, he should have wished immediately to implement Philippe de La Hire's discovery of a new source of water supply for Versailles about ten leagues south of Chartres. Louvois, however, was not prepared for La Hire's explanation

> that before undertaking such a vast enterprise, it was best that he begin the levelling anew, since he might have been mistaken in some operation or in some calculation—a daring expression of sincerity, since it was apt to throw doubts on his knowledge in the mind of the minister. M. de Louvois, impatient to satisfy the king's wishes, maintained to M. de La Hire that he had not been mistaken, but the latter, persisting in his dangerous modesty, finally obtained the favor of not being held up as the model of infallibility. It so happened that he did not deserve it; in 1685 he began anew the levelling, which differed from the first only by one or two feet.

The minister later revealed his spite when La Hire, "exact to a fault and to the point of superstition, presented" to him accounts of his expenses in which even "fractions were not neglected. With an obliging contempt the minister tore them up without looking at them, and he had orders dispatched in round numbers, in which he had nothing to lose." This cold war between a minister and a scientist drew from Fontenelle one of his many warnings against the fundamental irreconcilability of scientists' quest for truth with the courtly quest for position and preference. Because "the spirit of the sciences and that of the court" are "exceedingly incompatible," La Hire refused to take advantage of his position as surveyor at Versailles. As Fontenelle says,

> As soon as he had given an account of the work he had been ordered to do, he only thought of returning to his study, which called him home forcibly; it was useless for the minister to retain him; he had nothing more to say to him. He was well aware

that silent assiduity leads to fortune, but he did not want fortune at such a cost, which effectively is high for whomever feels that he has better things to do.[11]

Obviously, it was not Louvois that Fontenelle exhibited as the model patron of science or the model leader of the nation as a whole. Instead, he repeatedly exhorted rulers and ministers to follow the examples of such public-spirited men as Peter I, Colbert, Leibniz, the marquis d'Argenson, and Vauban, who labored for the welfare of all and gave recognition and encouragement to talents like those of the savants it was his task to eulogize.[12]

Unlike Fontenelle, Fouchy was too conservative and too diffident to speak out on political issues that might be interpreted as subversive. Yet even he sometimes dropped his self-proclaimed role as conscientious reporter of science to upbraid worldly clergymen, frivolous courtiers, and civil servants neglectful of the common weal and of the interests of the republic of science. Thus he twice protested at the government's arbitrary treatment of three of his colleagues.

In 1755 the chemist Rouelle was commissioned to examine the gold coinage of the realm. Though he put his faith in a minister's promise to create a position for him as a reward for his labors, the position never materialized. That was only to be expected, exclaimed Fouchy. Rouelle "was apparently unaware that, to the shame of humanity, the best deserved rewards are obtained only by dint of solicitation."[13] Fifteen years earlier Hellot had been appointed general inspector of dye works. So pressing were the ministry's needs, however, that it transferred him to other commissions when he had only submitted two preliminary memoirs on the subject. Two years later Hellot was assigned the Academician Théodore Baron as his assistant, on condition that the latter give up the medical practice he had barely exercised for ten years. When a short time later, the ministry abolished Baron's appointment on the pretext of fiscal economy, he bitterly complained about his difficulties in resuming his medical practice. "He would have been more easily consoled," Fouchy commiserated, "if it had been only a question of his private interest, but he had lost valuable time in chemical experiments."[14]

These instances of cavalier treatment of scientists were offset in the *éloges* with numerous instances of devotion to the common welfare. Probably because his *éloges* covered a large number of public servants, Fouchy devoted much space to describing the offices they held and the qualifications of those who held them.[15] He was especially impressed by the second d'Argenson, who, in addition to inheriting his father's office of Intendant of Paris, simultaneously held the positions of War Minister and Postal Director, all the while finding time to listen to citizens' complaints for hours on end. Indeed, Fouchy held him up as the ideal public servant, as a bureaucrat who had not forgotten that his first and foremost duty was service to the public. Office holders, he felt, "far from overburdening" the public "with the weight of their authority, should, on the contrary, gladly present them with the sovereign's favors and, by their sensibility, soften as much as is possible the bitterness of necessary denials and the rigors of justice whenever they are compelled to resort to them."[16]

CONDORCET, PUBLIC SERVICE, AND LAISSEZ-FAIRE

However much they criticized, explicitly or implicitly, the indifference of some monarchs and ministers to their subjects' welfare or to the advancement of learning, neither Fontenelle, Mairan, nor Fouchy questioned the necessity of an absolute monarchy for France. At worse, an individual monarch failed to live up to the ideals of "father of his people," "patron of the arts," or "God's vicar on earth." Neither the political circumstances, the climate of opinion, nor their own temperaments prepared them to doubt the very principle of absolutism (however tempered) as it had been sanctified by long tradition or embodied at its most glorious by the Sun King Louis XIV.

By the 1770s, however, the Enlightenment had made such inroads into educated and official consciousness as to enable Condorcet to question the very necessity of absolutism. Instead, fortified with the examples of the enlightened ministries of Maurepas, Trudaine de Montigny, and his mentor Turgot, he presented as part of his liberal platform a modified Lockean version of representative government, a modified policy of laissez-faire, and a modified bill of rights. However, he never abandoned the ideal of the utility of science that had been proclaimed by Fontenelle and practiced by most Academicians.

In particular, the administrator-philosophe Turgot set forth a body of doctrine from which Condorcet developed a program that integrated politics, economics, pedagogy, and natural science into a grand vision of the regeneration of France. The premises underlying both Turgot's and Condorcet's programs go far to explain many of the views that the latter expressed in his *éloges*, which were written between Turgot's assumption of power under the monarchy in the early 1770's and Condorcet's assumption of power under the French Revolution in 1791. These views were reiterated whenever Condorcet deemed them appropriate and, in turn, the successes and failures of the public servants he eulogized (e.g., Camper, Duhamel du Monceau, Fourcroy, Franklin, Haller, Maurepas, Montigny, Praslin, Trudaine de Montigny, and Anne Robert Jacques, Turgot's younger brother) further sharpened his ideology. As K. M. Baker remarks, the first *éloge* that Condorcet composed as permanent secretary after the fall of Turgot from power "was that of the administrator who had been so instrumental in securing his claim to that position [of *Inspecteur des Monnaies*], Trudaine de Montigny, Turgot's closest administrative subordinate during his twenty months as Controller-General." He adds, "In a sense, the *Eloge de M. Trudaine* celebrated more than a man: it glorified an administrative ethic—a conception of the relationship between power and enlightenment that lay at the heart of Turgot's reforms—and it bore witness to the shattering of a brief moment in which everything had seemed possible."[17] Selected citations from this *éloge* not only support Baker's statement but, in many respects, anticipate the political views that Condorcet was to maintain until events during the Legislative Assembly (1791–92) compelled him to modify them somewhat:

> The true splendor of the throne only resides in monuments of utility to the people.
>
> The sovereign is bound to his people by anterior and sacred engagements.
>
> The happiness of the people has been . . . the only duty and the only true glory of sovereigns.
>
> People called to administration are in greater need of virtue and instruction than of skill and cleverness.
>
> It is fondly to be wished for that those who govern other men surpass them in enlightenment as they surpass them in authority: the order of society would thus approach the order of nature; by rendering obedience to reason rather than to power, man would thus not have relinquished any of his rights.[18]

Condorcet never questioned the necessity of infusing governmental policies with the proper dose of moral virtue and scientific method. And dismissing the fear that power would corrupt the intellectual, Condorcet, like many in his generation, "began to feel that direct public service was a duty for the philosophes."[19] Yet, as the selection from the *éloge* of Etienne Mignot de Montigny below reveals, far from all scientists were fit to tackle the complex and variegated tasks of administration. Montigny, Condorcet remarked,

> had been named *Commissaire du Conseil* for the Department of Commerce. This position, created in 1735 for M. Du Fay of this Academy, had for its aim to associate to the Administration a *Savant* who, trained in the scientific aspects of the arts and that aspect of the sciences immediately applicable to public utility, would be able to enlighten Administrators for whom the important functions they had been charged with since their youth would not always permit them to acquire that knowledge which they had once dismissed as useless. Often the questions to be resolved are too unimportant, are not susceptible of a sufficiently precise decision, do not directly relate to the sciences, and are too entangled in irrelevant considerations to be decided by the advice of a body of Savans. Sometimes, in more important matters, it is necessary to possess extensive knowledge to be able to determine precisely the nature of the question requiring consultation by a learned body, to judge whether that question deserves to be examined by it, whether that question has already been decided, either by that same body or by the consensus of all enlightened men. He who holds the position of *Commissaire du Conseil* is in

some way an intermediary between the *Savans* and the Administrators; he must be
able to speak both the language of the laws and that of the sciences.[20]

In keeping with his vision of a society ruled by an enlightened elite for the
welfare of all, Condorcet offered a short declaration of the rights of the citizen.
Citizenship entails reciprocal duties: it obliges all citizens "to sacrifice themselves for the welfare of the patrie" and, inversely, it entitles them to "hold
an opinion on public matters," which "right is inseparable from that of
expressing it."[21] It is because he deemed freedom essential to the integrity of
citizens and the greatness of nations that he never ceased to launch bitter
tirades against slavery[22] and what he deemed to be its associated evil,
mercantilism. Indeed, he inveighed against compulsion in its multivaried
forms. Sons should not be compelled to follow an occupation not suited to
their native talents; sons and daughters should not be compelled to marry
against the sentiments of their hearts; citizens should not be compelled to obey
laws they had neither understood nor voted for; and children should not be
compelled to learn subjects that were outmoded or incomprehensible.[23] Above
all, the *éloges* reveal Condorcet as an implacable opponent of all compulsion
in economic matters. As a physiocrat devoted to the principle of the single tax,
as a disciple of the free-trader Turgot, and especially as a self-proclaimed
spokesman for the welfare of humanity, Condorcet lavished praise on those of
his colleagues who effected significant progress in forestry, horticulture, and
agriculture. The near-monopoly Condorcet held on the reporting of these
achievements among the four secrétaires also testifies to the belated yet visible
changes that France was undergoing after midcentury in the agricultural sector
of the economy.

The model estate occupied by Duhamel du Monceau and his brother was
displayed by Condorcet as a standing reproach to the seeming backwardness of
the French realm. When it came to pronouncing the *éloge* of their nephew
Fougeroux de Bondaroy in 1791, Condorcet was moved by flights of rhetorical
sublimity to present that family as a model for revolutionary France to follow:

> . . .It seemed as if science, work, and virtue had selected this house for their eternal
> abode. It is there that one beheld, perhaps for the first time in France, wealthy land-
> owners occupied in diffusing abundance and enlightenment around them, in per-
> fecting at once farmers and farming . . . . Those who have given the example of
> these beneficial virtues when personal interest did not compel them to do so, those
> who have busied themselves with the instruction and needs of the common people
> when the people could but return naive and kindly blessings, those who have sacri-
> ficed the prejudices of pride to these pure enjoyments, [all] have some claim on our
> gratitude, and we should all be thankful to them for having displayed under a
> perverted and tyrannical regime the manners and virtues of liberty.[24]

What specifically had Duhamel du Monceau and his brother done to
deserve such a highminded encomium? In addition to his numerous contribu-

tions to naval technology, the health of sailors, metereology, chemistry, and the comparative study of animals and plants, Henri-Louis Duhamel du Monceau had devoted a good part of his life to the improvement of forestry and agriculture. He investigated "the laws of the growth of plants, the formation of barks and wood, the . . . phenomena presented by grafting, . . . the proofs for the double motion of the sap, and in large part at least, the influence of air, light, and soil on the development of the life and sustenance of vegetation." The theoretical principles he enunciated Duhamel then applied to the cultivation of wood needed for naval, architectural, and technical purposes, especially to the better care and greater fertility of fruit trees and grape vines.[25]

It was agriculture, however, which, according to the historian of eighteenth-century agronomy, André J. Bourde, became the chief preoccupation of Duhamel from the 1740s to his death in 1782. His experiments and extensive travels through the French countryside taught him improved methods of sowing, fertilization, and crop rotation. He also set an example to others by establishing on his estate "the cultivation of rhubarb, artificial pasture lands, and finally potatoes." Condorcet, however, completely omitted from his account Duhamel's and Buffon's abridgment of a commissioned French translation of Jethro Tull's *Horse-shoeing Husbandry* (1733). One of the landmarks of the English agricultural revolution, this treatise initiated advanced plowing and seeding techniques in its home country and, thanks to Buffon and Duhamel, in France as well. As if to compensate for this important omission, Condorcet launched into an extended defense of free trade in grains:

> Sacrifices can be expected out of beneficence or patriotism, but their activity is limited; these sentiments have a lasting power only over a small number of souls, for success can only be expected out of self-interest with respect to utilitarian methods that apply to all. Yet the owner of wheat fields, who several times a year risks his entire harvest from inclement weather and is frequently compelled to set up expensive precautions to preserve his commodity, has more to fear from the effects of restrictions all too often placed on the freedom of his sale (impediments that are the more pernicious to landlords and the common people) as that commodity is the more essential. Hence M. du Hamel, on this subject only, has broken the respectful silence that he had imposed upon himself on matters dealing with legislation; he has pleaded the cause of free trade in grains, because he believed it to be linked to the safety of subsistances, to the prosperity of agriculture. And he has pleaded for it courageously at a time when the prejudice he attacked had incensed on its behalf powerful partisans who would have found it surer and easier to take revenge than to reply to him.[26]

If the *éloges* of Duhamel du Monceau and Trudaine de Montigny express Condorcet's physiocratic faith at its most fervent, those of Mignot de Montigny and Vaucanson show him to have been a strong proponent of laissez-faire, of the industrial revolution, and of technological progress.

Indeed, the *éloge* of Montigny contains some of the most heartfelt expressions of Condorcet's beliefs. The death of one of Voltaire's nephews and a technologist par excellence elicited from the Secretary a Baconian profession of faith, a tirade against military barbarism and religious intolerance, a rejoinder to potential Luddites, and a paean to unlimited economic progress. The two full pages Condorcet devoted to Montigny's important contributions to the textile industry open with an exordium on the maximum benefit to be derived from the collaboration among government, industry, and science, and close with a peroration on the inevitability of industrialism. Montigny apparently deserved these encomiums, for his knowledge encompassed the sciences of mechanics and chemistry, the craft of textile manufacturing, and the art of government as practiced by himself as *Trésorier de France* and by his patron D. C. Trudaine, finance minister and director of the postal system. He also had the proper measure of firmness and moderation, except "when public utility demanded it" and "when the sight of injustice or oppression aroused his ardor."

An Englishman by the name of Holker, "who was very knowledgeable about the manufacture of all kinds of textiles," had rallied to the cause of the Scottish Pretender in 1745, had been captured at the battle of Culloden, and had escaped to France. There he suggested to Trudaine that he "employ him in establishing in France several branches of industry that England had a monopoly of and to perfect others in which France held such an inferior position as to exclude her from competition." This proposal, in Condorcet's view, served at once the rightful cause of free trade and the righteous cause of retribution. To test the merit of Holker's proposal, Trudaine selected Montigny to "examine the projects whose full utility and importance he had a presentiment of." Montigny's and Holker's combined efforts effected a minor revolution in the French textile industry. We owe to them, Condorcet jubilantly exclaimed, "our manufactures of cotton cloth and velveteen, the use of cylinders to calender fabrics, a better method of giving them the preparation to which they owe their brightness, the present-day perfection of our hardware and of our manufacture of gauze, and finally, the establishment of machines to comb and spin cotton and wool. . . ." Not everyone, however, was as persuaded of the ultimate benefit of machines that saved expenses and labor, and certainly not those who owed their livelihood to older forms of manufacturing. These objections Condorcet dismissed as retrogade and inimical even to the interests of the protesting laborers:

> A spurious humanitarianism opposed to the introduction of these machines should also have led to the rejection of the plow, vehicles of transportation, canals, mills, the printing press, of nearly all the arts. Besides, it is not difficult to sense that any saving in manual labor, far from diminishing working opportunities for the people, tends on the contrary to multiply these very opportunities, by increasing for all men

the quantity of objects of consumption, and consequently, that of their enjoyments and of their wealth. After all, once a nation has adopted machines of this kind, others no longer have a freedom of choice: they are compelled to imitate it, under the penalty of being condemned to a ruinous and humiliating inferiority in all the markets of Europe.[27]

In assuming that industrial progress would dispel workers' fear of technological unemployment, Condorcet was only voicing the laissez-faire liberalism of his age. Nothing in his artistocratic background and elitist position prepared him to understand, much less sympathize, with the wishes of the common people. No such excuse can be made for Vaucanson. He was born into an artisan's family, from which, it is true, he soon ascended to a higher social standing by dint of his extraordinary mechanical skills. His humble background and technical virtuosity, however, had in common that they prevented him from fully understanding the political and economic ramifications of the inventions he designed. Both the virtues and defects of being a *mécanicien* pure and simple were displayed at their strongest in the commissions he executed for the central government. In the early 1740's, for example, he was entrusted by Cardinal de Fleury with the inspection of silk manufacture, particularly "the most important, most difficult, and hitherto most defective" step, namely, "the preparations that silk must be subjected to before it is worked on." His examination revealed widespread unevenness in the finish of the silk, due to the absence of standardization "of all the spools and skeins in the same task and of the entire length of the thread that formed each spool or each skein." Vaucanson, therefore, was obliged to design not only new machines, "but even the instruments needed to execute with regularity and uniformity the different parts of these machines." To those critics who pointed to the fact that "the price of silk prepared by his method did not make good the expenses it entailed," Condorcet argued that it was sufficient that Vaucanson had rationalized and standardized a mode of industrial production: that's "all that could be expected from the genius of a Mécanicien." Let the manufacturers themselves reconcile economy with perfection and make the sacrifices that the interests of the trade demand!

The division of labor that Condorcet set up between the scientist in his laboratory and the manufacturer in his shop he also envisaged among the various workers collected into one large factory. If silk products are to reach the highest perfection and the lowest cost possible, he argued, they should be produced only in large workshops, "because it is there only that one can bring together all that is needed for perfection and for economy." Division of labor, "by matching each worker with a simple operation that he constantly repeats, enables him to perform better in the least amount of time."

Lower wages and the division of labor are not the only threats that the worker may face in the wake of technological progress: he can be dispensed

with altogether. Vaucanson had been consulted by the French government "in
a discussion in which was set off the uncommon intelligence that must be
possessed by a worker in silk fabrics. . . ." Vaucanson's retort to this
excessive claim was as telling as it was insulting: he designed "a machine with
which an ass turned out a fabric in floral pattern." This display of pettiness
was deemed by Condorcet a fitting, even if humorous, revenge against "those
same workers who, in a journey he [Vaucanson] had made to Lyon, pursued
him by throwing stones at him, because they had heard that he intended to
simplify their jobs"—a result to be expected from the introduction of new
ideas and devices. Indeed, Condorcet concluded, there is an overall moral to
be drawn from this entire episode, a lesson for workers, employers, and
statesmen alike:

> M. de Vaucanson considered this machine to be only a jest, and in this respect he
> was perhaps too modest. The labor of overseeing such tasks as can be made to turn
> by mills and of knotting broken threads requires less strength and intelligence and
> a shorter apprenticeship than are required by present-day jobs; and the severest
> economy of the strength and industry of men is at once an excellent principle in all
> the arts and one of the most certain maxims of an enlightened policy.[28]

BENJAMIN FRANKLIN

For want of wholehearted support from the French monarchy, Duhamel's,
Trudaine's, and Montigny's efforts on behalf of the single tax, agricultural
reform, and freedom of trade were bound to fail. The philosophes' last hope of
implementing their program under the auspices of absolutism came to an end
with the dismissal of Turgot from office in 1776. It looked as if the
philosophes had either to redouble their efforts, bide their time, or look to other
means or other regimes for the fulfillment of their program.

They did not have to wait long or look too far into the future, however. In
the very same year that Turgot was dismissed from office, a number of
circumstances joined to produce in reality what for so long had been but a
dream in Europe. In North America the conjunction of virgin territory, English
political institutions, the theory of natural rights, and the diffusion of
enlightenment demonstrated to Condorcet and his fellow reformers the
intimate link between progress in science and progress in liberty. And not
surprisingly, Condorcet's demonstration is a verbose variation of the famous
epigram coined by his mentor Turgot, namely, *Eripuit coelo fulmen,
sceptrumque tyrannis* ("He seized the lightning from the sky, and the
scepter from tyrants[11]").[29] The Paris Academy of Sciences, Condorcet began,

> hastened to admit in its ranks the savant who had wrested one of the secrets of
> nature and averted one of its scourges: it rapturously welcomed upon his arrival

the sage who had just taught a lesson of justice to tyrants and to men, that of depending exclusively upon their rights. It beheld with calm satisfaction one of its members unite the glory of having liberated two worlds, that of enlightening America and of providing Europe with the example of liberty. Forever free amidst all manners of servitude, the sciences transmit to their practitioners some of their essence of independence or either fly from countries ruled by arbitrary power or gently prepare the revolution that will eventually destroy it; they form therein a large class of men habituated to think on their own, to take delight in the search for truth and in the judgment of their peers; too enlightened to be unfamiliar with their rights, even when they are sufficiently prudent to silently wait for the propitious moment to recover them. If the sciences possess any utility unconnected with political revolutions and forms of government, if they do not surrender men to all the evils of ignorance at a time when they are still suffering those of servitude, if by making them bearable they adorn the chains of an enslaved people, they still contribute to making the recovery of liberty more rapid, more peaceful, and more assured. Let us compare the efforts of unenlightened centuries, so rarely crowned with lasting success and always sullied with wars, massacres, and proscriptions, with the successful efforts [i.e., the revolutions] of America and France; let us observe within the same century but at two different epochs the two revolutions of a fanatical and of an enlightened England, one will then behold on one side the contemporaries of Pym and Knox [sic] who, in boasting of their struggles on behalf of heaven and liberty, covered with blood their unfortunate fatherland so as to cement the tyranny of Cromwell; on the other, the contemporaries of Boyle and Newton establish with calm wisdom the freest constitution up to that time.[30]

Benjamin Franklin owed his enormous appeal in France to a curious blend of myths. He was venerated as the inventor par excellence, the scientist who had wrested lightning from the gods, the wordly philosopher posing as *Le Bonhomme Richard*, the moral paragon from a pastoral setting, and the crafty statesman fighting for "ancient" freedom against modern tyranny. Yet, incongruous as this mixture appears to be, the victory of the cause he represented seemed to endow this mixture with some validity. This victory also confirmed Condorcet's belief in the causal relationship between science, freedom, and education. Hence, it was more urgent than ever that the accelerated progress in the natural sciences should be accompanied by universal education in these same sciences and in civic virtue.

The dawn of a new era in France in 1789 was therefore auspicious for the launching of Condorcet's pedagogic reforms. In 1791 he presented his epoch-making proposals for a universal yet hierarchical education in five *Mémoires sur l'instruction publique*. There he attempted to fuse his ideal of a new aristocracy of talent with the ideal of a society composed "of individuals equal in their rights as men and their obligations as citizens." In addition, he urged that the traditional classical curriculum be replaced with "a program oriented towards the physical and moral sciences . . . . Even an elementary study of their methods would be sufficient to develop the critical faculties, freeing them from passion, prejudice, and the authority of superstition.'' Furthermore,

> the dissemination of scientific knowledge would at once accelerate the progress to be derived from the technological revolution and prepare men to accept more readily the social changes that would inevitably accompany industrial progress. At the same time, Condorcet regarded the very progress of the moral and political sciences, and the consequent improvement of the social art, as another argument for the primacy given to scientific studies.[31]

In short, social change is impossible without the development of men's critical faculties, which in turn is impossible without the dissemination of scientific knowledge. And, as he argued in sundry *éloges* written before 1791, that dissemination is impossible without the support of public opinion and the state. As late as 1783, for instance, he expressed his sympathy for a father who was appalled at seeing his son reject a remunerative career for one in erudition or science. What else can be expected of him, he rhetorically asked, when he knows that ''in the various classes of society'' under the ancien régime ''instruction and knowledge lead neither to honors nor to fortune?'' He adds, ''In this circumstance, as in so many others, the faults of individuals are the product of public institutions.''[32]

Nearly a hundred *éloges* penned by Condorcet and his predecessors Fouchy, Mairan, and Fontenelle bear out this contention of the widespread neglect of up-to-date instruction in the natural sciences. As the next chapter will show, however, even public indifference did not deflect some hardy souls from their pursuit of a scientific career.

·V·

Estate, Education, and Employment

Le hasard lui offrit dans le cours de ses études, quelques livres de Géométrie elémentaire, qui lui en inspirerent le goût, et les Eloges de Fontenelle, qui lui apprirent qu'une carrière paisible et honorée est presque toujours le prix du talent et même de l'amour des Sciences.

—CONDORCET, *Eloge de M. Bézout*, 1783

As the preceding chapters have suggested, the *éloges* are invaluable as detailed accounts of the history of science in France between the mid-seventeenth and the mid-eighteenth centuries. By themselves, however, these eulogies cannot be fully counted upon to provide a collective biography of the French savants who died before 1792. Frequently, the social class from which these scientists emerged is described only in the most general terms; in many cases, too, the early years and education of these men are slighted or completely passed over. Most importantly, the number of Academicians with scientific credit to their names and some significant biographical detail in their *éloges* (115 in all[1]) is too small to yield anything but the broadest generalizations on their estates, education, and employment. A prosopography of the scientific community in France between the 1660s and the 1750s would have to combine the biographical information contained in these official eulogies with other, more recent, sources.[2]

Nevertheless, the *éloges* cannot be so easily dismissed as depositories of useful biographical data. True that the secretaries never concealed the hagiographic intent of their eulogies, especially in the perorations (as will be shown in the last two chapters). Yet, however incomplete in vital statistics, the encomiums penned by Fontenelle, Mairan, Fouchy, and Condorcet are genuine *éloges historiques*: they truthfully record the lives of distinguished men while attempting to elicit the admiration of their lay contemporaries and the emulation of future generations of scientists. Hence, as historians and as moralists, the secretaries were compelled to draw attention to the disjunction between the scientists' contributions to society and the small rewards society accorded most of them. Fouchy and Fontenelle especially dwelled on the obstacles which the Academicians overcame to achieve whatever recognition and remuneration their contemporaries saw fit to grant them. As these obstacles particularly circumvented the designs of Academicians pursuing a career outside the old sciences of medicine and astronomy, certain generalizations can cautiously be drawn from the *éloges* with respect to these Academicians' class background, first infatuation with science, education, and careers.

Most prominently, four patterns emerge from an examination of these men's social, educational, and occupational status. First, better than half of the Academicians who practiced medicine and/or the allied fields of botany or chemistry also had fathers with equivalent or like occupations, in contrast to Academicians of other specialties who were bereft of a similar occupational inheritance. Second, many, if not most, of the scientists who pursued careers in mathematics, physics, or applied science did so in the face of paternal resistance, possible unemployment, and low social prestige. Third, the physicians and botanists and some chemists differed from their colleagues in having completed their higher education in a formal institution, namely, a medical faculty. Last, unlike the physicians, surgeons, botanists, and astronomers, the other Academicians rarely held positions corresponding to their special scientific abilities or interests. In family background, education, and employment, therefore, the physicians and to a lesser extent the astronomers comprised a nearly disparate group from the other "working" Academicians.

ESTATES

Table 1 shows that out of the fifty-one Academicians practicing medicine or related fields, twenty-seven had fathers or near relatives who also practiced in these fields. Table 2 reveals that the majority of the other scientists of the Paris Academy of Sciences did not issue from families with a scientific history. At least twenty-six of the sixty-four nonmedical scientists eulogized before 1792 could boast ancestors who were noble either by origin or by pretension and, except for Fouchy, La Caille, and Gua de Malves, who owned lands that assured them a steady income. In addition, twenty-three other mathematicians, physicists, and engineers were raised in families whose income derived from secure positions: for example a sinecure as court painter, a bureaucratic office, the teaching and practice of geography, and the pleading of legal cases or the keeping of legal records.

The remaining fifteen nonmedical scientists were born in the nonprofessional third estate, all with small means except for Jars' father, who was a mining entrepreneur. Yet, of these fifteen, nine were mathematicians and/or mathematical physicists, out of a total of twenty-two such specialists in the entire group presented in table 2. One might argue that the negligible cost of mathematical equipment—pen and paper—was within reach of the poorest peasant and that mathematics provided a better, even if unsteady, living than the less stable living of farming and trade in an era punctuated by financial panics, bad harvests, and wildly fluctuating prices. This argument, however,

TABLE 1

Occupations or Estates of Fathers or Near Relatives of Native
Scientists Who Practiced Medicine and/or Related Fields

Occupations of fathers or near relatives	The scientists' occupations					
	M.D.-botanists	M.D.-chemists	Other M.D.'s	Chemists without an M.D.	Surgeons without an M.D.	Total
M.D.-chemist		1				1
Other M.D.'s		3	11			14
Apothecaries	4	1	1	1		7
Surgeons			1		3	4
Chemist without an M.D.				1		1
Subtotal	4	5	13	2	3	27
Nobility	1	2[a]		1		4
Lawyers		3	2[b]			5
Bureaucrats	1		1			2
Danish Protestant minister			1			1
Tradesmen			2			2
Unspecified bourgeois	2		3			5
Other commoners			1	3	1	5
Subtotal	4	5	10	4	1	24
Total	8	10	23	6	4	51

[a]One ruined Saxon nobleman and one Catholic Jacobite.
[b]Lieutaud's maternal uncle was a botanist.

does not explain why four of these mathematicians—Saurin, Carré, Nicole, and Rolle—vehemently resisted their plebeian fathers' designs to prepare them for lucrative careers in the clergy or the bar. Bright young men from the lower classes and not-so-bright younger sons of the aristocracy could always find preferment or revenues from some ecclesiastical benefice, yet no amount of worldly good could lure these young mathematicians away from their insistent calling.

One would have even greater difficulty explaining why sons of well-to-do or of noble families pursued careers in a field that was deemed peculiar, wanting in social amenities, and bereft of luxurious appurtenances. The records are too incomplete for an accurate answer but sufficient accuracy can be obtained from passing remarks, indirect hints, and a few detailed accounts of some scientists' childhoods. As Suzanne Delorme has described it for those scientists eulogized by Fontenelle, many traumatic events determined the careers of a large number of these men, whatever their social background: precosity in some mathematical or scientific realm, disgust with a traditional feature of the school curriculum, and an illumination in the guise of a book

TABLE 2

OCCUPATIONS OR ESTATES OF FATHERS OR NEAR RELATIVES OF NATIVE NONMEDICAL SCIENTISTS

Occupations or estates of fathers or near relatives	The scientists' occupations					
	Mathematics with or without other sciences	Astronomy and geography	The new physical sciences	Instrumentalism or engineering	Three or more sciences	Total
Astronomers		3[a]				3
Geography tutor		2[b]				2
Surgeons	3					3
Prof. hydrography					1	1
Math. tutor	1					1
Mining entrepreneur				1		1
Subtotal	4	5	0	1	1	11
Nobility	4	5	4	7	5	25
Italian gentry		1				1
Bureaucrats	1			2	1	4
Lawyers	2[c]	1	1	2	1	7
Protestant minister	1					1
Artists	2					2
Tradesmen	1	1		2		4
Other commoners	4	1	1			6
Unspecified	3					3
Subtotal	18	9	6	13	7	53
Total	22	14	6	14	8	64

[a]Cassini II, Cassini de Thury, and G. F. Maraldi, respectively, the son, grandson, and nephew of the Italian-born Academician Cassini I.
[b]The brothers G. and J. N. Delisle.
[c]Parent's paternal grandfather was a lawyer; his father's occupation is unknown.

picked up by chance or a lecturer heard by happenstance.[3] The effect of such events on the careers of many scientists, however, is characteristic not only of many of the earlier members of the Paris Academy of Sciences but also of many who died between 1740 and 1791. The syndrome of revulsion-cum-attraction, accompanied by a rejection of one's father's career advice, affected only those who were trained to become landowners, lawyers, and especially clergymen—twenty-seven in all, an impressive number.[4]

A few examples will illustrate the lengths to which the young men went to pursue the educations and careers they had selected for themselves, usually against their fathers' wills. Both Ozanam and Tournefort obediently followed their fathers' wishes to study for the priesthood, but as soon as their fathers died, both returned to their first academic love: Ozanam to astronomy, which he had been studying secretly on his own since the age of ten, and Tournefort to botany and Cartesianism, which he had been secretly studying from books in his father's library. Montmort and Fontaine could not wait for their fathers to die: Montmort ran away from home to avoid studying for the bar and was permitted to openly declare his love for the sciences only when at the age of twenty-two he inherited a sizeable sum. Fontaine too ran away in order to avoid the study of law and found his career accidentally when he picked up a book of mathematics. Another mathematician, Carré, was not so fortunate as Montmort: he studied theology for three years as his farmer father requested but when he refused to join the holy orders, his father cut off all funds to support him. In preparing himself for a career not expected of the son of a glove-maker, Vaucanson found himself threatened by an even more severe penalty than had Carré: one of his uncles, hearing of his nephew studying science to embark upon the career of mécanicien, threatened him with a *lettre de cachet* to keep him away from the Parisian center of subversive studies. The lettre was apparently never issued, since Vaucanson continued his studies unabated.[5]

EDUCATION OF MEDICAL SCIENTISTS

Having rejected their family traditions in such occupations as landholding, state administration, jurisprudence, trade, and farming, how did these young men go about fulfilling their destinies in the natural sciences? What opportunities and what institutions were available to enable them to become full-fledged scientists?

Alone among all the Academicians described here, the medical doctors completed university training beyond the level of the Faculty of Arts. All the physicians, even those who subsequently devoted themselves to botany or chemistry, received their degrees from either the University of Paris or the University of Montpellier, and in some instances from both. Since, as is well known, the medical curriculum was still rooted in past traditions (Aristotelian, Galenian, and iatrochemical) and was largely expository and verbal, most of the Academicians with medical degrees attended many extra-university institutions. These included hospitals giving free medical courses, *écoles de santé* attached to the military and naval departments, private schools founded by either individuals or religious orders, and especially the Jardin Royal des Plantes in Paris, which possessed a cabinet of natural history, botanical and zoological grounds, and three teaching chairs, with many more for démonstrateurs.[6]

Moreover, an inspection of the medical training received by the twenty-three physicians without botanical or chemical ambition[7] reveals that some of them (e.g., Tauvry, Bouvard, and Claude [II] Bourdelin) were started in their careers by their fathers. Less fortunate scientists resorted to other means to make up for what formal institutions lacked in scientific instruction. Thus, Lieutaud taught himself anatomy while Littre learned his practicum by dissecting two hundred cadavers, which had been obtained by stealth by a friendly surgeon of the Hôpital de la Salpêtrière in Paris.

Self-teaching was especially the hallmark of the eight botanists and sixteen chemists eulogized between 1699 and 1787. The botanists,[8] all of whom possessed a medical degree, learned their craft mostly outside the medical faculties. Nearly all had either pharmacists for fathers or had become infatuated with natural history when very young; and they all rounded out their botanical education by taking extensive herborization trips or courses of botany at the Jardin des Plantes in Paris.

A chemist was even less enlightened than a botanist by the subjects he studied at the medical faculties, knowing as he did of the truly significant discoveries being made outside the university walls in pneumatic chemistry and in the understanding of calcination. But however oldfangled the chemical instruction required for a medical degree, the chemist could not so easily dispense with it. Without the degree, he was considered at best a skilled craftsman beneath academic contempt and at worst, one of the unwashed extracting industrial products by the sweat of his brow. Hence, until the chemical revolution of the 1770s, most chemists took, pro forma, a medical degree.[9]

In contrast to the M.D.-chemists, the six chemists who did not possess a medical degree[10] were all trained largely in chemistry and all but the amateur Milly came from plebeian families. Indeed, three of these Academicians sprang from *honnêtes* or *bonnes familles*, which were probably incapable of supporting their sons' medical educations. A case in point is Jean Hellot. The history of his career by itself paralleled so many strands from other scientists' lives as to almost read like a caricature. His father, who had been impoverished by John Law's Louisiana scheme, taught his son the humanities. While rummaging through the papers left by his physician grandfather, Hellot discovered the grandfather's chemical memoirs and thus became addicted to chemistry himself. He accordingly decided to become a chemist, no doubt preferring to model himself on his successful grandfather than on his unfortunate father, by zealously devoting all his spare time to medicine and chemistry. He continued his studies with his contemporary C. J. Geoffroy, who later was to marry one of Hellot's nieces. Since Hellot could not expect his family to support him, he assumed the position of editor of the *Gazette de France* while continuing his chemical studies on the side. And he rounded out his scientific education by visiting members of the Royal Society of London.[11]

EDUCATION OF NONMEDICAL SCIENTISTS

With the exception of the medical doctors, none of the French scientists who died before 1792 acquired most of his scientific skills within the four walls of a university. Nearly all the curricular reforms effected within the institutions of higher learning took place after the mid-eighteenth century, when all but half a dozen of our Academicians had already passed their twenties. Hence, the lonely odyssey in search of the latest and the best was not confined to young men instructing themselves in new sciences like electricity and magnetism; it also informed novices in older sciences like mechanics and mathematics.

Next to the medical doctors, the twenty-two mathematicians who died between 1699 and 1791 comprised the single largest group of working scientists within the Academy.[12] In its main outlines, the instructional history of these men follows the pattern followed by the other nonmedical scientists: instruction at home or more commonly rebellion against their fathers' occupational wishes; perfunctory attendance at the collège; an occasional illumination brought about by a copy of a book picked up by chance; and an enormous amount of self-teaching, sometimes with the aid of more experienced professionals (see table 3).

Neither the prospects of a brilliant legal career nor the security of an ecclesiastical office could lure Carré, Fontaine, Montmort, Nicole, Ozanam, Rolle, or Saurin from their determination to pursue the unworldly and insecure prospects of mathematics. Not that some of their fathers had not done their best to steer them in the right direction! Nicole's father was so zealous to see his son become a clergyman that he became his son's tutor (*répétiteur*) when his son attended the Jesuit collège in Paris; Saurin's father, a Protestant minister, trained his son to succeed him by teaching him everything—from the alphabet to the law and theology—except what the young Saurin was destined to excel in. Some fathers, however, were more fortunate. The court painter La Hire taught his son the elements of his art—drawing, perspective, and gnomonics. Both Camus and Clairaut were introduced to mathematics through ingenious devices: the former's appetite for geometry was whetted by toys and the latter's by learning the alphabet from figures in Euclid. Yet all this instruction proved insufficient, since a majority of the mathematicians in the Academy are known to have had to master their science on their own: Bézout, Fontaine, La Hire, L'Hopital, Molières, Ozanam, Camus (mechanics, astronomy, civil and military architecture), Lagny (Euclid and algebra), de Moivre (geometry, trigonometry, Huyghens' probability theory, Rohault's mechanics, perspective), Rolle (algebra, theory of numbers, analysis), Varignon (Euclid, Descartes, perspective), and the child prodigy Clairaut (Guisnée's analytic geometry at the age of nine and L'Hopital's calculus at 10!).

The intensity of these men's autodidactic labors might have flagged in some

TABLE 3

ACADEMICIANS' SCIENTIFIC EDUCATION BY SPECIALTY AND METHOD
OF INSTRUCTION

	Specialty					
Method of instruction	M.D.-botanists	M.D.-chemists	M.D.'s only	Chemists without an M.D.	Surgeons without an M.D.	Subtotal
From their fathers	2	0	3	2	1	8
From others in their childhood	2	1	3	0	2	8
On their own	2	4	8	3	1	18
University	8	9	23	1	0	41
Jardin des Plantes, Paris	3	1	3	1	0	8
Other institutions	1	1	0	0	0	2
Privately, from an Academician	4	2	3	2	1	12
Apprenticeship, practicum, or herborization	3	3	7	1	3	17
Outside France	0	1	1	0	0	2
Unspecified	0	0	0	1	0	1

	Specialty						
Method of instruction	Mathematicians	Astronomers and geographers	New physical scientists	Instrumentalists and technologists	"Universalists"	Sub-Total	Total
From their fathers	6	2	0	1	2	11	19
From others in their childhood	7	2	1	3	2	15	23
On their own	15	8	4	9	5	41	59
University	0	3	0	0	1	4	45
Jardin des Plantes, Paris	0	0	0	0	0	0	8
Other institutions	4	0	0	1	0	5	7
Privately, from an Academician	5	8	2	3	3	21	33
Apprenticeship, practicum, or herborization	0	3	2	3	0	8	25
Outside France	1	3	1	1	2	8	10
Unspecified	1	0	1	2	0	4	5

instances if they had not been sustained by aid received or requested from established scientists. Malebranche especially gave aid and comfort to novices in need of encouragement and advanced knowledge. When Carré's financial support from home came to an abrupt end with his change of career plans, Malebranche hired him as his secretary and for seven years gave him instruction in mathematics and metaphysics, as he did with Bragelongne, who, from the age of seventeen on, devoted his summer vacations to studying with Malebranche. Montmort, who had studied Malebranche from books as well as geometry and algebra from Carré and Guisnée, in turn taught higher mathematics to Nicole, who at the age of sixteen had been recommended to him by his Academic colleague Gamaches, and Nicole in turn taught mathematics to Maupertuis. Finally, de Moivre studied advanced geometry from Ozanam while Camus received from Varignon advanced instruction that he could not obtain anywhere else.[13]

Like mathematics, astronomy is one of the oldest of sciences, a traditional part of the quadrivium, and noted as a field for spectacular achievement since the mid-sixteenth century. Yet, because of its antiquity as a learned endeavor, its strikingly successful uses in navigation, and possibly the sublimity of its operations, a career in astronomy appeared both more respectable and more rewarding than did one in mathematics. Hence, none of the eleven astronomers under discussion,[14] especially the Cassinis, was faced with the obstacle of his father's resistance. Indeed, Cassini II had been tutored at home by the astronomer Chazelles, had taken courses in mathematics at the Collège Mazarin under another Academician, Varignon, and had joined his father, the Italian-born Cassini I, in scientific expeditions to England, Italy, and the Netherlands.

By their directorship of the Paris Observatory and by sheer weight of numbers, the Cassinis also influenced, directly or indirectly, the careers of most of the remaining astronomers who died before 1792, namely, Chazelles, La Caille, Chappe, Godin, and the two Delisles. They all benefited from an informal guild system in which novices learned their craft from masters, then passed on their knowledge to other novices. The Delisle brothers—Joseph-Nicholas and Guillaume—are an instance in point. Both had been taught at home by their father, a tutor in history and geography. Joseph-Nicholas studied mathematics on his own upon graduation from the collège, decided on his vocation when he observed the solar eclipse of 1706, was tutored in astronomy by two abbés, and completed his astronomical studies by taking practical lessons at the Dome of the Palais de Luxembourg from two Academicians, Jacques Lieutaud and Cassini II. In turn, Joseph-Nicholas taught what he had learned from the latter to Godin. For his part, Guillaume Delisle had been admitted to the Academy of Sciences in 1702 as an *élève* of Cassini I. He was, however, to make geography his vocation, though it was not until 1730, four years after his death, that a special seat was created by the Academy for bona fide geographers.

Just as the class of astronomy in the Academy, until 1730, had to accommodate the new science of geography, so the class of mechanics, until 1785, had to accommodate the old sciences of mechanics and optics and, with the group of *associés libres*, the new sciences of acoustics, electricity, magnetism, hydromechanics, and ballistics, as well as engineering, military and naval technology, and other applied sciences. The incongruity between the sciences officially recognized by the Academy's seating pattern[15] and the sciences in which great achievements were being made was matched by an incongruity between the "new" scientists' early schooling and their subsequent activities. They had to depend solely on self-instruction or private tutoring from the few older practitioners in their areas of specialization (see table 3). The scarcity of teachers (whether at home, in school, or elsewhere) was due simply to the first appearance of many of these sciences and the legitimatization of the others during the period—mid-seventeenth to mid-eighteenth century—in which our scientists were educated.

The six Academicians who largely worked in the new physical sciences were distributed over a wide range of classes in the Academy: they included the *honoraire* Chaulnes, the *associé libre* La Faye, and the working scientists Sauveur, Pitot, Nollet, and d'Arcy. Just as these men had been assigned seats in ways deemed appropriate by the Academy, so they had to find their specialized training in any way deemed appropriate by themselves alone. Sauveur is a good case in point. It is Fontenelle's contention[16] that Sauveur, being born deaf and learning to speak only with difficulty, naturally should have been repelled by the *rhétorique* taught at the Jesuit collège at La Flèche, have turned avidly to the study of mathematics and mechanics, for which he had displayed precocious talents. This distaste for nonscientific courses was apparently exacerbated by the course on Scholastic philosophy and theology he had to take in Paris to the point where he resorted to other forms of education: self-instruction in Euclid, taking Rohault's popular course on Cartesian physics, and traveling with the future *Hydrographe du Roi*, Coubard, at Brest. It was only by dint of his own efforts that Sauveur turned late in life to the study of the science which he termed *acoustics* and in which he made some outstanding contributions.

Like the physical scientists and the mathematicians, the technologists and instrumentalists[17] had obtained their technical training by any means available. They certainly did not turn to the traditional schools for instruction in engineering. The only—and striking—exception to this rule was the case of Antoine-Gabriel Jars. He was fortunate because, being the third youngest of all the Academicians who died before 1792 (being born in 1732), he could avail himself of the education provided by the Ecole des Ponts et Chaussées (civil engineering) set up in 1747 by Perronet and the Academician D. C. Trudaine. Indeed, it was Trudaine himself who saw to it that Jars was admitted to that school, on the recommendation of another Academician, Jean-Florent de Vallière, who had been highly impressed by Jars' zeal in learning about metallurgy in his father's mines.[18] The Ecole des Ponts et Chaussées taught Jars the theory of what other technologists had to learn largely by practice and on their own: the foundations of his science, in this instance, drawing, mathematics, and metallurgical chemistry.

EMPLOYMENT

The sharp division that prevailed in formal educational opportunities until the mid-eighteenth century between medical doctors and other scientists also prevailed in the occupational opportunities available to these two groups of Academicians. It was only from the 1760s on, and then only gradually, that positions of scientific instruction, with adequate salaries, full-time work, compensation for research, and increasing social recognition of the value of nonmedical sciences, improved by the direct action of the central government and the scientists themselves.[19] Hence, the overwhelming majority of nonmedical scientists eulogized before 1792 (except for astronomers) had to content themselves, before the mid-eighteenth century, with offices or sinecures that came their way and often had little to do with the specialty they had so laboriously mastered.

The situation was otherwise with the forty-odd physicians and surgeons, even before the midcentury mark. The practice of medicine had always attracted a large proportion of scientifically-minded young men eager to pursue research in the areas of botany, chemistry, or anatomy. It also attracted men with humanitarian impulses, eager to do good in ways that offended neither the state nor the church. The record of the *éloges*, however, also shows that this profession indubitably offered distinct financial and social rewards. Physicians were exempt from certain taxes and could hold municipal office. As is the case today, they earned a handsome salary and hence were able to provide for the costs of their sons' university training.

One of the greatest benefits to be derived from medical practice was the opportunity to purchase offices entitling their holders to the position of court physician of one kind or another. Sixteen physicians or surgeons had bought court offices permitting them to treat the health of the king, his near relatives, other noblemen and their families, or those in the army.[20] Whether out of economic necessity, social ambition, political opportunism, or humanitarian concern, few were the physicians (or surgeons) who could refuse offers from the state to fill positions, not only at court, but also in teaching or in administration. The most striking difference between the occupational status of physicians and surgeons and that of the other scientists is the extent to which the former group was addicted to multiple occupancy or pluralism (tables 4, 5, and 6). At least seventeen of the forty-one physicians and two of the four surgeons[21] occupied two or more simultaneous positions in institutions of learning, at court, or in leading Parisian hospitals.

Like first-rate physicians with medical degrees, first-rate surgeons without them were in demand in schools, the court, the army, and a number of important hospitals. Indeed, La Peyronie accumulated positions and sinecures to an extent unheard of even in the eighteenth century. His reputation as a brilliant surgeon and anatomist was first made when he attracted the best students to his public demonstrations at the University of Montpellier. It was enhanced and rewarded by his first two nonteaching positions as surgeon-major at the main hospital of the same city and surgeon-major and inspector in the army. It was further rewarded by the unbounded gratitude of the Duc de Chaulnes, a fellow Academician, whose fistula, believed to be inoperable, was removed by La Peyronie. The grateful Chaulnes bought no fewer than three offices for his medical savior: hence, by the end of 1715 La Peyronie held in his possession, not only the unsolicited position of démonstrateur at the Jardin des Plantes, but also the unsolicited offices of Surgeon-Major of the Royal Light Cavalry Guard, Surgeon at the Prévôté de l'Hôtel, and Surgeon-in-Chief of the Hopital de la Charité. His career was capped by his acquiring, in 1717, the office of First Royal Surgeon *en survivance*. Thus, in 1720, at the age of 42, La Peyronie held no fewer than five positions: one at the Jardin, one at court, and the three given to him by Chaulnes. Yet, the secretaries reporting on this or similar instances of industriousness saw nothing remarkable about it. It is only when an Academician appeared to fall short of the expected norm of industriousness that the secretary called attention to it. There is a curious remark by Fouchy to the effect that only by marrying one of his patients did the physician-anatomist Hérissant pay more attention to his practice.[22] Fouchy may have been struck by the bachelor Hérissant's apparent lack of financial ambition, so uncharacteristic of his profession. Hérissant was the anomaly, the pluralists, the obedient followers of a practice that was part and parcel of the ancien régime, were the norm.

Nonmedical scientists, however, had little opportunity throughout most of the eighteenth century to acquire a multiplicity of jobs to tempt their social ambition. The weight of a tradition that stifled progress in nonmedical education also held back the state's appreciation of the multiple uses of physics and mathematics. The one and partial exception to this delay in the recognition of the value of the physical sciences was astronomy, which had long since proven its worth in timekeeping, navigation, and geodesy. The state had financed astronomical expeditions as early as 1671; its Observatory near Paris had provided many an astronomer with a livelihood, and the court itself had in 1718 created the office of *Premier Géographe du Roi*. Aside from a few teaching positions, however, the only state jobs open to most mathematicians and all physical scientists and technologists before the 1750s were either sinecures, private tutoring, or ad hoc commissions: as tutor to courtiers or the

TABLE 4

POSITIONS HELD BY PHYSICIANS, BOTANISTS, CHEMISTS, AND SURGEONS

Type of position	M.D.-botanists	M.D.-chemists	Other M.D.'s	Chemists without an M.D.	Surgeons without an M.D.	Total
Teaching						
Prof. at Jardin des Plantes, Paris	4	5	6			15
Other positions at Jardin des Plantes	2			2	1	5
Prof. at Collège-Royal	1	2	2			5
At other Parisian institutions		2	2		2	6
At provincial universities		1	2		1	4
Subtotal	7	10	12	2	4	35
Court						
Premier médecin of royal family		2	10			12
Regular physican of royal family	1	2	6		1	10
Physician to noblemen	2	1	2			5
Military physician			8			8
Apothecary of royal family				2		2
Surgeons at court or with the army			1		6	7
Subtotal	3	5	27	2	7	44
Other						
Medical	1	1	7			9
Pharmaceutical				4		4
Surgical			3		4	7
Chemical		3		2		5
Nonscientific		2	3	2	1	8
Unspecified	3		1			4
Subtotal	4	6	14	8	5	37
Total	14	21	53	12	16	116

king's children or grandchildren, as hydraulic engineer for the fountains of Versailles, as a special diplomat for Louis XIV, or working for Louvois's Intelligence Bureau (see table 5). Hence, a number of mathematicians and physicists were compelled to find jobs wherever they could. Thus, Varignon and the abbés Molières and Gua de Malves[23] taught philosophy at the Collège Royal, Sauveur taught the elements of probability theory to gambling courtiers, Ozanam complemented his public lecturing with frequent bouts of gambling, and Lagny lectured on hydrography.

From the second quarter of the eighteenth century on, occupational opportunities improved somewhat for the nonmedical scientists. Various Academicians served as commissioners or inspectors at the bidding of

TABLE 5

POSITIONS HELD BY MATHEMATICIANS, ASTRONOMERS, AND GEOGRAPHERS

Positions	Mathematicians	Astronomers	Geographers	Total
Teaching				
Collège Royal, Paris	4	1		5
Other Parisian institutions	2	1		3
Provincial institutions	3	1		4
Private tutoring	6			6
Other		1		1
Subtotal	15	4	0	19
Government				
Paris Observatory		4		4
Premier Géographe du Roi			3	3
Examinateur of military schools	2			2
Military, diplomatic, and intelligence services	1	1		2
With *Chambre des Comptes*		3		3
Other	3	3		6
Subtotal	6	11	3	20
Other positions				
Clergymen	7	2		9
Military officers	1	2		3
Other	4	2		6
Unspecified	2			2
Subtotal	14	6	0	20
Total number of positions	35	21	3	59

ministers of state, some of whom held seats as *honoraires* on the basis of their patronage of applied science or their establishment and sponsorship of specialized schools. Specifically, they helped establish teaching institutions for army and navy officers and helped staff these schools with their colleagues in the Academy of Sciences. In the schools of Artillery, Naval Construction, and especially Military Engineering, "scientists, many from the Académie, were employed in teaching, whilst others were engaged in administering both entrance and graduation examinations and in composing suitable textbooks."[24] Thus, the position of *examinateur* was held by the mécanicien Camus at the schools of Artillery and Engineering and by the mathematician Bézout at the schools of Artillery and Navy. The experimental physicist Nollet held the position of professor of physics at the schools of Artillery and Engineering.

Far from all nonmedical scientists earned their livelihood from positions

TABLE 6

Positions Held by Experimental Physicists, Instrumentalists and Technologists, and "Universalists"

Positions	Experimental physicists	Instrumentalists and technologists	"Universalists"	Total
Teaching				
At court	2			2
Parisian institutions	2			2
Military schools	1	1		2
Other	2		1	3
Subtotal	7	1	1	9
Government				
High military	3	11		14
High civil servant	2	8	1	11
Intendant of the Jardin des Plantes, Paris			2	2
Other	2	3	1	6
Subtotal	7	22	4	33
Other				
Other military	1		2	3
Clergymen		1		1
Other		4	1	5
Unspecified		1		1
Subtotal	1	6	3	10
Total	15	29	8	52
Independent income			6	6

directly or remotely connected with the sciences; on the contrary, a sizeable number of them earned part or all of their incomes from service with the military or the Catholic church.[25] A few, like Mairan, Réaumur, Maupertuis, Duhamel du Monceau, La Condamine, and Buffon, found it unnecessary to earn a livelihood at all, since they managed very well with the large family incomes at their disposal.

Although Article XII of the Règlement of 1699 stated that no one could be nominated for the position of Academician, "if he were a member of a religious order, [or] attached to some religious order, unless it be to fill the seat of a Honorary Academician," a large number of Academicians belonged to the first or religious estate of the realm. However, the Carmelite Truchet took his place in the Academy among the Honoraires and Montmort, a canon of Notre-Dame of Paris, was exempt from the prohibition by virtue of his membership in the *secular* clergy. Yet seven regular Catholic clergymen were numbered among the working scientists. No illegality had been commited, however, as nearly all, if not all, were abbés *commendataires*. In distinction to those regular abbés who performed the duties expected of their vows and in return received certain remunerations, the abbés commendataires were frequently secular clergymen, and sometimes even laymen, who enjoyed the benefits of their monastic state without performing any of its duties.[26]

The presence in the Academy of seven abbés commendataires, who collected one-third of the revenues of their monasteries without performing any of the duties required of regular clergymen, is not surprising in light of the varied means by which Academicians earned their living. The seven may have taken holy orders because, like Carré, they thought of it as a bright but poor man's path to independence, or because, like La Caille and Gua de Malves, their family's fortunes were nil, or because, like Molières, they preferred a career that encouraged studiousness rather than worldly cares. In any case, all of them, except for Bragelongne and Chappe, had to supplement their ecclesiastical income with salaries earned as tutors or professors.

Were the financially disadvantaged among the Academicians treated more advantageously by the Academy of Sciences? They were not, since the amount of remuneration from that learned society varied according to seniority and, to a lesser extent, attendance. According to Roger Hahn, "Only the three most senior members of each class, called *pensionnaires*, received automatic compensations. Those lower in the academic ladder, the *associés*, were paid only when funds allocated for the administrative expenditure of the Académie permitted.[11]

Furthermore, as the 6,000 livres for each of the six classes of pensionnaires were distributed to all its members according to the ratio 5:3:2 on the basis of seniority, "only at a ripe old age could a scientist expect to earn a living directly and solely from being a member of the Académie." In addition, Academicians of any rank—pensionnaires, associés, or *adjoints*—could derive some income from attendance. When they attended any meeting of their institution, they were given *jetons* (i.e., tokens) as

> proof of attendance and [these were] later redeemable in currency. A specific amount was made available for each session and distributed in equal shares to those present. . . . In addition, the Académie had at its disposal funds earmarked for "experiments" and for the distribution of prizes, and the scientists could sometimes hope to be reimbursed for the immediate expenses involved in some particular work, or to be adjudged an occasional monetary reward for some of their efforts.[27]

Obviously, only the senior pensionnaires (for a total of six at any one time until 1785 and of eight after that date) could have lived solely on their pensions, jetons, and sundry research funds, since, as Roger Hahn has estimated, a modest living in eighteenth-century Paris could be had for a yearly sum of 5,000 livres.[28] It may have been a modest sum for a senior physician with teaching chairs and court positions to spare but it surely represented a lordly fortune to a young and penurious mathematician beginning his career.

Given the differing occupational opportunities, financial rewards, and types and amounts of Academic recognition, it is a wonder that intelligent men should have sacrificed a life of comfort and ease for one of discomfort and hardship. According to the *éloges*, however, these sacrifices had not been in vain. The very idée fixe that led these men to neglect worldly cares yielded an understanding of nature's operations, a certainty impervious to temporary fashions, and moral virtues extracted from the truth and beauty they had discovered in the universe. Indeed, the eulogies of Fontenelle, Mairan, Fouchy, and Condorcet abound in almost as many anecdotes testifying to the scientists' occupational determination as they do in perorations testifying to their moral virtues. In addition to serving as rhetorical devices that fuse the opening and closing sections of these testimonials, the peroration on character and the account of education and career merge to form a picture of men who, however differing in class background, educational opportunities, and occupational rewards, are as one in following the urgency of their calling and abiding by its moral imperatives.

·VI·
Science and Morality: Ancient and Modern Sources

O tempora! O mores!

— CICERO

If the *éloges* can be trusted as biographical accounts, two kinds of recognition awaited the scientists who had overcome the obstacles of paternal resistance, inadequate educational facilities, and unsuitable jobs. The first recognition, honored in the secular world, was a seat among the seventy-odd elect of the Paris Academy of Sciences. The second recognition, honored in the rhetorical world, was a lasting place in the annals of humanity. The wonder of it all, the secretaries continually remind us, is that these men had preserved their moral integrity amidst their struggles for recognition.

From the perspective of two centuries, the greater wonder is how most of these scientists, who had labored so hard to acquire their peers' and posterity's esteem, should have been endowed with reclusive qualities that implied their unfitness for worldly success. The paradox is compounded by the very intent of the *éloges* honoring them. If natural science was ever to acquire the kind of esteem (if not power) so ardently desired by Fontenelle and his successors, their eulogies perforce had to present the best possible image of the character of the scientists. Such a presentation could achieve maximum rhetorical effect, however, only if these men's quest for lasting fame were glossed over and the contradictions within their characters resolved. To some extent, these eulogists accomplished these results, but nowhere near as successfully as was subsequently done by Georges Cuvier in his *éloges* (1797—1832).[1]

According to Orinda Outram, Cuvier had to reconcile the two kinds of authority by which natural philosophers attempted to justify their endeavors. One authority was nature, which was increasingly being viewed not as a realm ruled by a beneficent Providence but as an arena of autonomous forces. Contact with nature, nevertheless, provided "clean" power, since it endowed the scientist with pastoral virtues that presumably established his "independence from the structures of dominance and dependence which organize human groups."[2]

Hence, the other authority justifying the natural philosopher's endeavors was the "ratification and consent of human groups." This was "dirty" power, primarily because mention of it might question the legitimacy of the scientist's newly-acquired power under a succession of unstable régimes. Besides, as Outram points out, in Cuvier's *éloges* the pastoral "description of the life of the ideal natural philosopher has to struggle with an explanation of the motivation of scientific activity in which the drive for power, fame, and recognition in the arena of public estimation is awarded a very large place."[3]

Cuvier resorted to various devices to ease this tension between "clean" and "dirty" power. First, he had at his disposal a stylized literary genre that permitted him "to contain the conflicts and uncertainties of the groups and individuals to whom it was addressed." The solemn occasion at which this panegyric was read helped "the living over the gap between their memory of the human imperfections of the departed, and the terrifying incomprehensibility of his departure."[4] Second, the idealized semipastoral language of the *éloges*, by extolling the natural philosopher as "a-political and a-social," implicitly condemned "dirty" power. Finally, Cuvier intentionally resorted to ambiguity to resolve apparent contradictions. Since the same man "might have to use both 'clean' and 'dirty' power in his life," Outram observes, "in many of Cuvier's *éloges* key words such as '*gloire*' and '*fortune*' have ambiguous, shifting connotations." In this manner he disguised the scientists' links with "dirty" power "by using changes of context within single sentences to imply changes of meaning."[5]

To what end did Cuvier resort to pastoral images and ambiguous language to resolve contradictory matter embodied in panegyrical form? To the end, as Outram convincingly shows, that science "be presented as neutral and therefore unchallengeable." The very ambiguity of the eulogy enabled him "simultaneously to call up and to paper over the very anxieties about the generation and use of power which lay behind the drive to establish the value-freeness of science." *Éloges*, therefore, should not be viewed as "proper" biographies but rather as devices "to facilitate the passage of the groups to whom they were addressed from doubt to resolution." Since these groups were still "small and interconnected" and employed a language whose reticences and omissions were understood by all, it was essential to avoid disrupting public discourse by a too explicit reference to difficulties and contradictions.[6]

Outram's penetrating analysis of the rhetoric of Cuvier's *éloges* illuminates our understanding of the contradictions within the eighteenth-century eulogies. Indeed, her discussion provides a partial explanation for the tension resulting from the clash between the authority of nature and human "ratification and consent." It is limited, however, because it addresses itself to one eulogist only and to a period in history (1797—1832) that offered unusual temptations to the politically ambitious scientist.

The contradictions in the *éloges* composed between 1699 and 1791 are of a somewhat different nature and result from three special circumstances. First, the four eulogists of the ancien régime differed in character, stylistic ability, and philosophical and scientific predilections. Second, Fontenelle, Mairan, and to a lesser extent Fouchy wrote eulogies with memories of Colbert's paternalism of science still fresh in their minds, while Condorcet witnessed the partial materialization of his liberal ideology in the opening years of the French Revolution. Finally, the sharp dichotomy that Outram draws between withdrawal and social action assumed in the eighteenth century nuances that derived not only from the distinct personalities of the secretaries but also from the differing panegyrical traditions from which they drew their moral exemplars.

THE SCIENTISTS AS PLUTARCHAN HEROES

To begin with, Outram's model of civic action assumed two distinct forms in the eighteenth-century *éloges*. The main form—the Plutarchan—appears mainly in the eulogies of Fontenelle, Mairan, and Fouchy.

The secretaries of the Paris Academy of Sciences were only two of the innumerable names in the early modern period on whom Plutarch's collective biography of fifty Lives had a lasting effect.[7] Martha Walling Howard has shown that at least thirty-nine references to him appear in Montesquieu's *Esprit des lois*, that Mably praised his historical method, and that Rousseau demanded that the contemporary teaching of history be replaced by "the presentation of the lives of the great men who by their genius, as well as by their human qualities, their virtues and their defects, fashioned the history of times past."[8]

Though the matter of the *éloges* is the new scientific revolution and its devoted practitioners, their end was nothing less than the depiction of the scientists as *partial* embodiments of the same moral values as were characteristic of ancient Greek and Roman heroes. Indeed, we need not consult M. W. Howard to discover that Plutarch's purpose in writing his *Lives* was ethical.[9] We have Plutarch's own words for it, in the opening passage of his Life of Timoleon:

> It was for the sake of others that I first commenced writing biographies; but I find myself proceeding and attaching myself to it for my own; the virtues of these great men serving me as a sort of looking-glass, in which I may see how to adjust and adorn my own life. . . . We . . . select from their actions all that is noblest and worthiest to know. "Ah, and what greater pleasure can one have?" or what more effective means to one's moral improvement?[10]

In description as in narration, the *Lives* and most of the *éloges* achieve their ethical intent by eliciting awe for the tasks achieved, sympathy for the efforts exerted, and pity for the occasional lapses from greatness—all told in a spirit of generosity that steers clear from either cynicism or indignation. Except for the ancients' more open expression of their thirst for fame and except for the savants' belligerent expression of contentiousness over the validity of their own point of view, the two possessed many of the same virtues, befitting them for heroism in their respective fields of endeavor. The qualities M. W. Howard ascribed to the Plutarchan hero might equally be applied to the new scientific hero. Like his ancient counterpart, the savant "was a man who made history," who possessed "fortitudo and sapienta," and who "lived and died . . . for the ideals in which he believed." In action, the ancient hero "was an extremist, although in theory he favored compromise." As depicted by their biographers, both groups of heroes were marked by "many divergent beliefs, but nobility and adherence to truth were common to all."[11]

A close reading of Plutarch's *Lives* bears out this thesis of conscious imitation. Like many of the scientists eulogized in the eighteenth century, many of the ancient heroes—Coriolanus, Marcus Cato, Sertorius, Phocion, Cato the Younger, Dion—were depicted as embodiments of Stoic fortitude. Like the scientists clinging to strict canons of scientific truth to the point of personal neglect and public ridicule, many of the Greeks and Romans—Numa Pompilius, Lycurgus, Solon, Pericles, Aristides, Marcus Cato, Nicias—possessed an overwhelming sense of duty to the tasks or offices devolved upon them. Numerous are the savants who, like Pompilius, Pericles, Fabius, Aristides, Marcus Cato, Sertorius, Agesilaus, Pompey, and Cleomenes, are honored for their temperance and equanimity. The savants also exhibit "that courage and resolution . . . not merely to resist armor and spears, but all the shocks of ill-fortune" that were the outstanding traits of Caius Marcus, Nicias, Sertorius, Cato the Younger, Tiberius and Caius Gracchus, and Dion.[12] And despite their uncontested humility in demeanor and speech, many of the scientists, like Lysander, Cicero, Alexander, Julius Caesar, and others, craved eternal fame.

Like the Plutarchan heroes, many of the scientists (e.g., Chazelles, Guglielmini, La Hire, Johann I Bernoulli, Bouguer, Belidor, La Caille, Baron, Chappe, Jars, Rouelle, Euler) did not shun government service when it devolved upon them. When the power they had not sought proved to be a disappointment, they bore their frustration stoically, without feigning the icy hauteur associated with some ancient Stoics.

Plutarch's *Lives* and the *éloges* initiated by Fontenelle—the juxtaposition between the heroes of antiquity and the scientists of the eighteenth century and between the praise of *virtu* and that of scientific morality—seems too paradoxical for credibility. No wonder that the parallels between the Greek biographer and his French counterpart have escaped the notice of nearly all scholars![13] They have either overvalued Fontenelle's modernity, excoriated his presumed want of grandeur, distinguished too sharply between "esoteric" science and other human activities, or, as with Suzanne Delorme, minutely analyzed the hagiography of his *éloges* without noting their kinship to that of his ancient predecessor.[14]

THE SCIENTISTS AS POLITICAL REFORMERS

In addition to the Plutarchan variety extolled by the first three secretaries, power in the *éloges* also assumed the reformist variety advocated by Condorcet. His civic-minded scientists (e.g., La Condamine, Haller, Mignot de Montigny, Duhamel du Monceau, Camper, Franklin, and Fourcroy de Ramecourt) craved to do good for humanity and hence, unlike the Plutarchan heroes, accepted with alacrity the power they hoped would enable them to display their benevolence.

To a much greater extent than his three predecessors, Condorcet would have concurred with the Renaissance Humanists' shift of wisdom from contemplation to action.[15] This shift had been especially pronounced in France. There Budé, Ronsard, and Charron (among others) had inveighed against the Platonic and Aristotelian equation of the highest wisdom with contemplation of the divine. Instead, according to Pierre Charron, the sage is one who "seeks the truth with perfect freedom, clean of prejudices, independent of all authority and the opinion of the vulgar. He examines everything, doubts every answer, weighs and balances every reason. He accepts—but only provisionally and never dogmatically—what seems most probable, honorable, and useful." Furthermore, he "has a natural obligation to be an *homme de bien*." In short, the moral ideal is to do good to others, cultivate friendship, and "conduct our personal lives, insofar as they impinge on others, with honesty, modesty, and self-control."[16] As this ideal portrait bears a close resemblance to that of Diderot's philosophe and the perorations of many of Condorcet's *éloges*, it comes as no surprise to learn that Charron was one of the favorite authors of the eighteenth-century Enlightenment.

Though neither Mairan nor Fouchy were philosophes in the manner of a Fontenelle or a Condorcet, they all pointed to the practical benefits to be derived from natural science. The first three secretaries, however, presented no specific program of action out of the substance and methodology of science except to applaud its capacity to eliminate or diminish superstition, credulity, ignorance, etc. They did describe their colleagues' participation in government commissions and their expertise in applied science, but they preferred to dwell on the contemplative and self-abnegating qualities that made them pastoral or Stoic models. It was Condorcet alone who seriously applied the Renaissance and Enlightenment dictum that to be wise was to be benevolent.

As noted in chapter 4, Condorcet envisioned a future ruled by a combination of natural science, enlightened politics, and an informed citizenry. Hence, he encouraged scientists to learn the intricacies of public administration and to accept, if not seek, public office. As early as 1773 he eulogized Frederick IV of Denmark for having been "above the prejudice common at court that savants were unfit to hold public office, as if the habit of seeking the truth could not take the place of the routine that is acquired in subordinate positions."[17] As the career of Benjamin Franklin amply demonstrated, scientific expertise in positions of public trust could at once rationalize and humanize society.

These sentiments had not been publicly expressed by Condorcet's predecessors. The prospect of scientists assuming political power (in distinction to serving as consultants) had been so remote before the 1770s that Fontenelle, Mairan, and Fouchy not so much as mentioned it in their *éloges*. They held that power was best vested in enlightened statesmen like Colbert who encouraged the scientific enterprise for the grandeur of the monarch or the welfare of the nation. These statesmen were especially enlightened if they were advised by the likes of Du Fay or Mignot de Montigny with easy access to the corridors of power. Fontenelle and Fouchy repeatedly decried the snares of courtly life, which they were at pains, however, to separate from the true seat of power.[18] The potential conflict between the search for truth and the quest for power was ever present in their minds but their warnings against that threat were unambiguous, even if at times indirect. Indeed, the sense gathered from the *éloges* written before the 1770s is that about half of the scientists had at one time or another served in some sort of consultative capacity, but that those who had suffered from it (like La Hire, Baron, and Rouelle) were in a small minority. On the whole, public clashes between the authority of nature and the authority of human power were avoided by the simple expedient of the government calling only for the services of men who were already noted for their worldliness. Those scientists who were ill at ease in society to begin with (e.g., Amontons, Blondin, Morin de Saint-Victor, Parent, Des Billettes, Littre, Claude-Joseph Geoffroy, Winslow, Baron, Deparcieux, Rouelle, Pitot) were rarely asked to give up their studious habits for consultative work.

Whether it was solicited or shunned, power at the governmental level apparently presented no difficulties that common sense or an abiding belief in progress could not dispose of. Power on a different, more individual level was a different matter altogether. Like Cuvier's *éloges*, those of his predecessors glossed over the scientists' "drive for power, fame, and recognition in the arena of public estimation."[19]

The one-hundred-odd accounts of the scientists' education and employment are almost monotonous in their depiction of the manner in which these young men had achieved scientific eminence. They had presumably not sought this eminence, it had been thrust upon them. The young scientists had written such excellent papers and the physicians had effected such marvelous cures that the Academy of Sciences had been bound to take notice of them. This notice was sufficient guarantee of the validity of the scientific or medical calling that had enabled these men to overcome all obstacles. It was not the eulogist's task to assert that the persistence these men had displayed had brought in its wake such human flaws as ambition, jealousy, rancor, and competitiveness. It is the alert reader who must infer, from the scattered evidence, that an even more blatant form of "dirty" power had most likely been wielded by these men. So many of them had studied with established members of the Paris Academy of Sciences (not a few of whom were related to them) that surely more than their own talent must have been responsible for their gaining admission into that same Academy.[20] With respect to these men's careers, therefore, Outram is correct in asserting that the secretaries' "papering over" had concealed a multitude of sins. If the *éloges* implied a necessary "relationship between the character of the scientist and the quality of his observation of the external world,"[21] then it was absolutely essential that the history of the scientists' education and employment display the same virtues of fortitude, want of ambition, and equanimity that were so freely scattered in the perorations.

THE SCIENTISTS AS ARCADIAN SHEPHERDS

The term "semi pastoral" that Outram applies to the allegedly asocial and apolitical careers of the eulogized scientists is somewhat misleading. In the *éloges* freedom from such social vices as ambition and greed assumes two forms, one voluntary and one involuntary. Properly speaking, pastoral retreat is involuntary in the sense that it is deemed to be innate to the members of precommercial civilizations, particularly shepherds. According to Gilbert Highet, their life as depicted in pastoral literature is characterized by, among other things, "purity of morals, simplicity of manners, healthy diet, plain clothing, and an unspoilt way of living, in contrast to the anxiety and corruption of existence in great cities and royal courts." The importance of the pastoral form, W. W. Greg points out, lies in the fact that it "is the expression of instincts and impulses deep-rooted in the nature of humanity."[22]

The contrast between the real and the ideal implicit in the dichotomy between urban and rural values serves a special purpose that in the *éloges* links pastoralism with Stoicism and the notion of progress. "Because the idyllic world is characterized by innocence, freedom, and harmony between nature and man and reflects on the fragmentation and uprootedness of urban man, it is translatable 'upward' as an image of perfection on a mythic level (the Golden Age, the Garden of Eden)." It is an image of perfection because in the metaphorical or mythical garden that is Arcadia or Eden humanity is presumed to have been undefiled, "virtues have preserved their wholeness, and feelings have retained their veracity and freshness."[23]

This image of perfection haunted Fontenelle all his life, as is evident in the large number of eclogues or pastoral poems with which he began his literary career in the 1670s, the *Traité sur la nature de l'Eglogue* (1688), and in the sixty-nine *éloges* he composed for the Academy of Sciences between 1699 and 1739. As the originator of these *éloges*, he also transmitted to his successors a convention of pastoral hagiography that lasted well into the nineteenth century.[24] The durability of that convention, however, is cause for wonder, since the virtues listed in the perorations often clash with the qualities described in the body of the eulogies and since the ideal of pastoral retreat was increasingly fused either with the Plutarchan ideal or with the late Enlightenment ideal of civic duty. Still, whether out of conviction or out of sheer panegyrical habit, Mairan, Fouchy, and to a lesser extent Condorcet endowed most of the scientists with one or more of the values of simplicity, humility, honesty, want of ambition, poverty, austerity, and frugality.

Despite the enormous number of scientific achievements reported in the *éloges* penned for over ninety years, nearly a third of the eulogized scientists went about their daily business with a simplicity and humility that would have done honor to Arcadian shepherds.[25] A superb example of a peroration that is one long variation on the semi-pastoral theme of simplicity was penned by Fontenelle in the *éloge* of Amontons:

> The qualities of his heart were even preferable to those of his mind, a rectitude so naive and unpremeditated that it made self-contradiction impossible, a simplicity, a frankness, and a candor that a few dealings with men might have preserved but had not bestowed, a total unfitness in self-advancement except by his works or in paying court except by his merit, and consequently a nearly total unfitness in making his fortune.[26]

The quasi-pastoral seclusion in which the scientists pursued their work also fostered the virtue of honesty or sincerity.[27] Indeed, the secretaries presented the love of truth, not only as the sine qua non of scientific pursuit, but also as a quality that, like so many others, had easily been transferred from the essence of the investigation to that of the investigator himself. These virtues were not simply personality traits, Leonard M. Marsak points out, but were "thought to derive from science." This view, he shows, can be inferred from the following excerpts from Fontenelle's *éloges* of Maraldi, Du Hamel, and Varignon, respectively:

> His character was that which the sciences form ordinarily in those who make it their sole occupation: seriousness, simplicity, righteousness.

> One easily saw that his humility was not a pose but a feeling founded on science itself.

> His character was as simple as his superiority of mind could require. I have already given this same praise to so many persons in this academy that one would believe the merit to pertain rather more to our sciences than to our savants.[28]

The humility bred by the limits of one's comprehension of Nature and the truthfulness engendered by the pursuit of that knowledge frequently combined to give rise to another virtue, namely, want of ambition. Many Academicians—e.g., Dodart, Rolle, Winslow, Van Swieten—possessed neither the desire nor the skill to advance themselves by the arts of intrigue, flattery, or courtliness.[29] And the same devotion that led many Academicians to sacrifice their ambition on the altar of science also led them to practice the vows of poverty, austerity, and frugality.[30]

Above all, the scientists were blessed with the virtue of tranquility or peace of mind. In Fontenelle's view, science deserved the highest commendation for its ability to diminish or even still the agitations that have perturbed humanity since the decline of pastoral cultures. He put the case for the causal connection among knowledge, tranquility, and moral virtue most strongly in his peroration on Homberg:

> A sound and peaceful philosophy predisposed him to withstand undisturbingly the various events of life and made him unsuited for those agitations that, for those willing to have them, derive from many causes. From this peace of mind there necessarily derive probity and rectitude; one is beyond the tumult of passions and whoever has the leisure to think sees nothing better to do than to be virtuous.[31]

In the *Traité sur la nature de l'Eglogue*, Fontenelle had insisted that "men desire happiness and would have it at little cost. Pleasure and tranquility are the common end of their passions and they are all ruled by a kind of sloth. Excessive restlessness is not precisely due to a love of action, but to the difficulty of being contented." How is the shepherd to avoid the extremes of sloth and restlessness? Through the power of love, a love that is "tender, simple, delicate, faithful, and . . . accompanied by hope."[32]

In the *éloges* science takes the place that love had held in the pastoral poems. The natural philosopher cannot be slothful since he is engaged in the activity of observing the universe. And he cannot be restless since science has endowed him with the soothing virtues of humility, frugality, and want of ambition. In other words, the purity of the scientific enterprise will automatically shield him from any moral corruption originating in advanced societies.

Alain Niderst draws the analogies between Fontenelle's pastorals and eulogies even further. The purity that haunted Fontenelle and that he had sung in his eclogues he had finally found in scientific life. "Shepherds are unaware of passions, savants are unaware of error," he observed. Inversely, all other social classes of his day are convicted by him of mendacity or greed. Niderst's conclusion is plain: the *éloges* are moral lessons: "The scientist is candid, disinterested, and above all happy . . . . By freeing ourselves from errors, we free ourselves from passions. The sole remedy against social corruption is seclusion—in nature, in books, and even within oneself, since indifference [*détachement*] is the best sanctuary."[33]

THE SCIENTISTS AS CONTENTIOUS BEINGS

If it be true, as Fontenelle alleged, that the extraction of truths from nature presupposed a pastoral state of innocence, he should not have been too surprised at the fury with which some of these Arcadian shepherds-cum-scientists greeted criticisms levelled against these truths in public. Nevertheless, he was surprised at the shock they experienced in being contradicted on truths they presumably had wrested from nature by "pure" apprehension. Though Fontenelle himself repeatedly challenged the truths of Newton's theory of attraction adopted by an increasingly larger number of his colleagues, he often deplored the contentiousness that made intercourse between scientists abrasive. Indeed, some debates—like the ad hominem recriminations between Ruysch and a certain Bidloo—were so acrimonious as to lead Fontenelle to question his own deeply-held belief in the scientific community towering above humanity in uprightness and enlightenment. "Will a simple dispute in wit or in learning," he sorrowfuly asked, "always be a reef for the virtue of men?"[34] Yet like his successors, Fontenelle included these lapses from decorum and equanimity in the same *éloges* whose perorations included pastoral and other virtues. Indeed, no fewer than twenty-seven of the 119 native "working" Academicians were unable to keep their wrangling within the bounds of courtesy set by Article XXVI of the 1699 Règlement of the Paris Academy of Sciences.[35]

Whereas Fontenelle had deplored disputation as unbecoming the pastoral character of scientists, Mairan justified argumentation for its dialectical ability to bring out the pure truth about nature. Learned disputes are not fruitless contestations, he asserted, but

genuine disputes engendered by the different aspects displayed by nature and upheld by the desire to see truth triumphant. This kind of warfare between savants, like that which fills the history of martial princes, can like them be just or unjust, well or ill justified, favorable or pernicious to those who stimulate or countenance them. The difference, however, is that real wars are at best advantageous to the victor, to a country or a nation, while learned wars almost always result in a common utility, a new light that illuminates the whole world. The discoveries of savants are the conquest of the human race.[36]

Mairan's assurance that the truth will emerge from debates between scientists points to one more explanation for the scientists' intense contentiousness. This explanation follows at once from a fundamental tenet of "classical" science and Fontenelle's special description of Arcadia. His shepherds, being in a prelapsarian state of innocence, are necessarily free from error. The scientists, being endowed with the right scientific method, must be in possession of the one and only truth about a particular set of phenomena.

Hence, assured of the perfect congruence between God's and their own rationality, they could not but attribute an adversary's differing truth "to pathological blindness or to bad faith."[37]

Nevertheless, Roger Hahn commends the Paris Academy of Sciences for permitting such disagreements to be aired in public:

> To decide by a majority vote which position was correct was absurd, for all the scientists firmly believed that truth was determined by nature and not by the will of men. In practice, the most that the company could assert as being true was that portion of evidence about which there was no disagreement. Generally it was the undigested observation of some phenomenon that was thereby considered as true "positively." For the rest, the greatest service the Academy could perform was to publish the opinion of each of its members, no matter how many contradictions might appear. . . .
>
> It is a remarkable sign of the Academy's sound judgment that it was able to recognize and distinguish fact from conjecture, to accept the former and sanction it, and to suspend corporate judgment on the latter. It is a sign of its wisdom and vitality that it felt sufficiently confident in the future of science and its own role in the progressive enterprise to vent members' personal disagreements about nature in public.[38]

Like the faithful of some religious sects, the adherents of a particular scientific interpretation claimed to be in possession of the exclusive truth. Unlike these faithful, however, the scientists were restrained from expanding this dogmatism into persecution by the very institution set up to encourage the search for truth. The irony of this situation probably escaped the eulogists who described it. It apparently took a learned company of an advanced civilization, ruled by fifty specific articles and many more unwritten rules, to maintain a semblance of the tranquility presumed to have been the sine qua non of the pastoral state. In Arcadia no impartial judge is appointed to settle differences of opinion, since the same truth is "instinctively" apprehended by all. In the republic of science, a modern-day counterpart of Arcadia, the truth revealed *in* nature by observation and experimentation is refracted by the prism of men's differing minds into contending interpretations.

THE SCIENTISTS AS STOIC SAGES

In his history of the Royal Society of London (1667) Thomas Sprat had presented a defense of disputation that in some ways anticipates the military simile to be drawn by Mairan some seventy years later. Argumentation, Sprat argued, is "a very good instrument, to sharpen mens wits, and to make them versatile, and wary defenders of the Principles, which they already know: . . . much contention, and strife of argument, will serve well to explain obscure things, and strengthen the weak, and give a good, sound masculine colour, to the whole masse of knowledge . . . ."[39] Whether Sprat acknowledged it or not, the contention, strife, and strengthening he speaks of suggest principles of action that he may well have borrowed from a Stoic morality dating from ancient Greece.

Whatever their disagreements on matters of detail and emphasis, such Greek and Roman Stoics as Zeno, Cleanthes, Chrysippus, Seneca, Epictetus, and Marcus Aurelius had agreed on certain essential points. To explain the conjunction between the realm revealed by the senses and that explained by the mind, they had "insisted that matter (or body), and nothing else, is capable alike of reception and origination of activity." This matter is suffused with a vitalizing force—logos or reason—that is the efficient cause of all events. Since logos permeates the universe, including man, he will, if he is wise, necessarily acquiesce in its ways. Hence "self-control, in the sense of self-sufficiency, became the ideal, to be attained through self-knowledge and self-denial." The sage will even become indifferent to "suffering, material disaster, and death itself."[40] In other words, the vicissitudes of the world, including "dirty" power, are discordant elements in a harmony presumed to exist between the true inner self and the universal logos. This discord is resolved into concord when the observation of the reason that governs the cosmos results in the moral integrity of the observer. In eighteenth-century terms, the natural laws within must agree with the natural laws without.

Many of the virtues that the Stoics had attributed to the sage appear to be the same that Fontenelle and other pastoral poets had attributed to the Arcadian shepherd. They do differ, however, not so much in their essence as in the manner in which they had been acquired. If the secretaries (especially Fontenelle and Fouchy) claim that such virtues as humility and honesty were reinforced rather than acquired by the cultivation of science, the provenance of these virtues is likely to be the pastoral tradition. In this case, the scientist, like the shepherd, lives in a state of inner concord. If, on the other hand, the eulogists dwell on the self-control the scientists exerted to sustain these virtues, then the provenance is probably the Stoic tradition. The Stoic, unlike the Arcadian hero, lives in a world whose *appearance* is corrupt. For him to obtain the state of mind that comes naturally to the shepherd, he must diminish his appetites, practice abstension, control his wrath, and dispel any and all fears. Life for him is not a meadow but a battlefield.[41] Whence the Stoic stress upon certain qualities that are wholly absent from the pastoral state, especially courage and fearlessness before death.

The recipients of the secretaries' commendations for deeds performed above and beyond the call of duty included G.-J. du Verney (for dying from a disease he had contracted from nightly observations of snails in the most humid spots of his garden), Chicoyneau (for risking his life in testing his belief that the bubonic plague is not communicated by contact), Chappe d'Auteroche (for losing his life from a tropical disease while on an expedition to observe a lunar eclipse in Baja California), and Bézout (for exposing himself to smallpox while testing naval candidates who had been struck down by the disease).[42] These acts of courage were deemed extraordinary because the men who performed them risked their lives in the pursuit of their scientific or medical inquiries. Although few of their colleagues were as intrepid in their fervor, many of them, when death came to take them, displayed a heroism that to the secretaries seemed almost as admirable. Hence, it was only fitting that *éloges* as exempla should conclude with a peroration on mortality. Sometimes the moral was embellished with an anecdote or a telling quotation. At other times the moral was conveyed in a lapidary fashion, as with the Duc d'Aiguillon, who was said to have confronted death ''with the most Christian resignation and the most Stoic firmness.''[43]

The juxtaposition of Christian and Stoic virtues was not fortuitous. Because of its affinities to the New Testament and the diffusion of the writings of Cicero, Vergil, Plutarch, Seneca, Epictetus, and Marcus Aurelius, Stoicism had become one of the most pervasive intellectual influences in Western civilization. Hence, as R. M. Wenley has pointed out, its impact has been so ubiquitous that it is no longer possible ''to tell what it owes to Greece, Rome, or the spirit of Christianity.''[44]

It is this Stoic theme, with differing interpretations attached to it by the four secretaries, that partly enabled them to resolve the tension resulting from the apparent clash between withdrawal and action, between pastoral and Plutarchan-humanitarian exempla. It is no matter that the secretaries' inability to keep their own predilections out of their allegedly unbiased biographies invalidated their conviction of the unassailability of natural laws, or that the scientists exhibited flaws that tainted their reputations as pastoral, civic, or Plutarchan heroes. Nor does it matter that the scientists' tranquility was frequently disturbed by contentious colleagues out to disprove their claim to the monopoly of particular truths. Their confidence in the congruence between natural truths and moral integrity remained unshaken. A time-honored tradition dictated that the panegyric speak to the issue of moral authority and the muted natural theology of the Enlightenment dictated that the new sciences find their raison d'être in humanistic and Christian values bequeathed by antiquity and the Renaissance. To men educated in a blend of Christian orthodoxy and Classical Humanism, science and epideictic literature had fused to exhibit the new natural philosophers as modern-day counterparts (with variations) of Stoic philosophers.

Conclusion
The Moral Philosophers of Nature

All discord, harmony not understood,
All partial evil, universal good
    —ALEXANDER POPE, *An Essay on Man*, 1733

L'amour des Sciences est une passion qui exige ordinairement de
ceux qu'elle possède, le sacrifice de tous les autres.
    —FOUCHY, *Eloge de M. Geoffroy*, 1752

Science is his forte and omniscience his foible.
    —SYDNEY SMITH, 1837

Whatever its provenance—whether pastoralism, Stoicism, Humanism, Enlightenment humanitarianism, or Plutarchan biography—the message conveyed in all the *éloges* publicly delivered at the Paris Academy of Sciences between 1699 and 1791 is incontrovertible. It is that science is not so much a natural as a moral philosophy, less a lesson in the acquisition of right knowledge than a lesson in right conduct. The deaths of over one hundred natural philosophers served as sublime occasions with which to preach secular sermons to bereaved colleagues and to future men ambitious to join their ranks. These men had not died in vain: their immortality was assured by the *éloges'* homage to their lasting contributions and to their exemplary lives. Near the half-century mark Fouchy expressed the sentiments of all the secretaries in his apology for not doing full justice to the "immense collection" of works that Johann I Bernoulli had left behind him. Even the enumeration of these works, he said,

> would have exceeded the limits prescribed to us, it would have compelled us to suppress the history of his life, which is, however, more useful and more in conformance with the goal the Academy has set itself in the honor it grants to those of its members removed by death. In fact, the history of the works of a great man can arouse the emulation of only a small number of men who follow the same career; that of his life is a model for those who mean to rise to equal fame, though by different paths.[1]

The modern scientific temper dictates that entries in biographical dictionaries and encyclopedias be exclusively devoted to the bare events of a scientist's life and a listing and brief analysis of his more significant achievements. Since most of the subjects of the *éloges* were natural scientists, one would have expected these eulogies to address themselves almost entirely to scientific matters. Such is far from being the case, however. Although Bacon and d'Alembert, among others, had placed the natural sciences into the category of positive knowledge, the classical, humanistic, and historical traditions had subsumed them into the category of lettres or literature. Hence, the writers of the *éloges* were compelled, by both precedent and preference, to give an account of the scientist's character as well as of his achievements, of the exemplary lesson his conduct might teach as well as of the knowledge his discoveries might contribute to. It is because of this ethical intent that the secretaries of the Paris Academy of Sciences exhibited the natural philosophers not only as discoverers of natural worlds but also as philosophers imbued with the finest moral qualities ever vouchsafed to mortal men.

The Neoclassical Weltanschauung in which Fontenelle, Mairan, and Fouchy had been raised confirmed their belief in the immutability of human character and of those virtues that conferred lasting immortality. Whence the widespread view, dating from the Renaissance, that "ancient life was a museum of striking examples." The part played by rhetoric in making that museum accessible to future generations and in encouraging Fontenelle to set up his own museum of striking examples is made manifest by the term "exemplum." As E. R. Curtius tells us, that word "is a technical term of ancient rhetoric from Aristotle onwards and means 'an interpolated anecdote serving as an example.' " Subsequently rhetoric added the " 'exemplary figure' (*eikon, imago*), i.e., 'the incarnation of a quality.' . . ."[2]

This exemplary figure, as O. B. Hardison explains, blends with historical narrative to form a *pictura*. They are so joined "because *pictura* has the two epideictic functions of imitating an individual and creating a pattern that will arouse emulation or abhorrence." However, since these two functions are not fully compatible, the didactic biographer and the epideictic orator have at their disposal two methods of reconciling truth and morality. They can, as Cinthio advised, draw an ideal personage, "a composite of perfect parts," or more commonly, employ "the epideictic technique of heightening." In order to make these examples attractive, the speaker or writer must heighten certain virtues presumed to be in his subject's possession.[3]

Like the ancient orators, the eulogists of the Paris Academy of Sciences made extensive use of exempla and picturae. They extracted virtues out of various mimetic sources, especially Stoicism, transformed them into the qualities traditionally and popularly associated with the terms "philosopher" and "philosophical," and attributed them to their scientific colleagues.

Stoicism, indeed, permeated all the sources from which the secretaries drew their exemplars of natural philosophy. Like pastoralism, it appealed to nature (however differently interpreted) for standards of right conduct and stressed such unworldly virtues as frugality, temperance, simplicity, and tranquility. Moreover, many Plutarchan heroes exhibited Stoic virtues in their forbearance of popular fickleness, their resignation before misfortune, and their courage before death. Finally, Condorcet's heroes of civic and humanitarian action, like the philosophes of the Enlightenment in general, embodied the Stoic quest for "the total possession of the world by the mind of man. Behind the *will* of the sage is asserted the sovereignty of a *reason* that informs the whole."[4]

For Condorcet as for the other secretaries, and indeed for a goodly number of their educated contemporaries, Stoicism in combination with natural science provided the equation formulated in the *éloges* between scientific inquiry and the moral rectitude of the inquirer. These *éloges*, like the biographies of Georges Cuvier and the eulogies of natural philosophers he himself wrote between 1797 and 1832, implied a necessary "relationship between the character of the scientist and the quality of his observation of the external world."[5] It is true that the panegyrical tradition dictated that such virtues as modesty and simplicity be attributed to men whose eminence in any field of learning, whether scientific or not, had earned them a seat in an academy. Since, however, most of these learned men were not natural philosophers, the *éloges* they received called attention to the congruence between certain facets of their character and the object of their pursuit. Thus, the deceased members of the Académie des Inscriptions et Belles-Lettres were lauded not only for the above pastoral-Stoic virtues but also for such "erudite" faculties as a sharp critical sense, vast learning, a prodigious memory, and regularity of study habits.[6]

The moral bond presumed to link the eminent nonscientist to his field of endeavor connected even more tightly the scientist to his. As the repository of the latest and most assured form of knowledge, natural philosophy was deemed to have inherited, and increased, the Stoic legacy of moral and intellectual submission to the logos or reason that informs the universe. As Chrysippus had argued, and as countless Stoics had repeated after him, the end of man is to live by the principles of nature and to participate in its divinity. And once we live in conformance with universal reason, Epictetus had added, we are instinctively able to distinguish good from evil.[7]

To elevate the common soul towards the heights reached by Stoic sages, Seneca had recommended the lives of famous personages for moral inspiration. These exemplars included not only demigods and kings who had triumphed over adversity but also a number of philosophers, especially Diogenes the Cynic and Socrates, "who in life and in death was equally a model as a man and as a citizen."[8] He was a model to the Stoics and to the Renaissance Humanists because his public and private lives both exhibited all the virtues that were to characterize him as the ideal philosopher.[9]

Yet the moral perfection of the philosopher as exhibited in the *Apology*, *Crito*, and *Phaedo* represents only one side of the equation between scientific inquiry and the moral rectitude of the inquirer. After all, the Renaissance Humanists, by freeing themselves from the metaphysical-theological-scientific curriculum of Scholasticism, had hailed Socrates for his shift of philosophy from the study of nature (natural philosophy) to the study of man (ethics). Such a total shift undoubtedly proved embarrassing to the men who had acquired enormous self-confidence from the stupendous scientific achievements performed in the seventeenth century. The revival of Stoicism at the beginning of that century enabled the apologists for the new science to retain the model of the perfect philosopher Socrates had embodied and without ever alluding to him by name to combine that moral exemplar with scientific truth. Specifically, the eulogists of the Paris Academy of Sciences blended Socrates' search for a morality "independent of all temporal changes [and] governing the realm of local prescriptions, and national institutions" with the Stoic quest for the law that embodied the reason or logos of the universe.[10] Whence the other side of the equation proves to be the right reason discovered by the new science.

As we have seen, the secretaries lavished a multitude of virtues on at least one hundred scientists in the perorations of their *éloges*. Whether these virtues had characterized these men since their early youths, had been fostered by their cultivation of the natural sciences, or were attributed to them out of a spirit of generosity is impossible to gather from the eulogies themselves. What is certain is that the innate virtuous character, the moral pursuit of science, and the ethical intentions of the biographers are so tightly intertwined as to yield a veritable catalogue of saintly attributes.

It is not likely that the virtues extolled in the Plutarchan heroes sufficed for modern scientists, since the former, however honest, austere, or equanimous, were rarely exhibited as paragons of humility, want of ambition, or charitableness. And though virtues like humility, honesty, piety, frugality, etc. suspiciously read like the attributes of the ideal Christian, the name "Christian" was employed by the secretaries to designate only the qualities of charity, piety, and resignation before death. The perorations make it abundantly clear that the scientists were viewed not only as reincarnations of Plutarchan heroes or as latter-day Christian saints but primarily as a transfigured species of moral philosophers. Consider the following examples:

> He was not a philosopher by his uncommon knowledge and a common man by his passions and his weaknesses; genuine philosophy had dug deeply into his heart and established therein that delightful tranquility, which is the highest and the least sought-after good.

> He was always of a cheerful temper and lacking this, of what use is it to be a philosopher?

> He forgave easily, as a philosopher who blushes of his weaknesses and excuses

those of others and as a Christian who knows that the forgiveness he expects from the Supreme Being is proportionate to that he himself grants to his equals.

He was as much a philosopher in his deeds as in his writings: he lived so temperately that he had even foregone the use of wine.[11]

It is in the peroration to the abbé Terrasson that the words philosophie and philosophe take on all the meanings these terms had accrued for centuries: probity, want of ambition, public zeal, generosity, and, simultaneously, absentmindedness and oddity.

His philosophy never permitted him to force himself upon others. The curtailment of useless wants had the same effect on him as did a brilliant fortune; perfectly content with his condition he did not aspire to any other; he loved the public weal with passion and the polity that guided his designs had been drawn from the same foundation as his morality, that is, the rectitude of his heart. He was generous and never failed any occasion to be of service to others; in addition, he was singular in his manners, extremely absent-minded, and all with the best will in the world and without self-consciousness. He told stories in an ingenious and droll manner. In short, he had everything capable of making a philosopher lead a happy and peaceful existence, without a moment of his long career being exposed to any of the disorders brought about by violent desires in those who instead of seeking to master them become their willing slaves.[12]

Condorcet, while not denying the uses that Fontenelle and Fouchy had attached to the word "philosophe," laid greater stress upon zeal for public welfare, as in the opening paragraph of the extended peroration to his patron Trudaine de Montigny. Frenchmen and foreigners alike, he declared, "depicted him [de Montigny] as an enlightened and incorruptible magistrate, as a citizen friend of the people, as a philosopher occupied with the happiness of all men, loving his fatherland without being the enemy of [all] nations. . . ."[13]

When Fontenelle, Fouchy, and Condorcet lauded their colleagues by the term "philosophe" or by its moral attributes, they selected only a few of the contemporary connotations of that term. As Ira Wade has pointed out, "not only was there diversity of opinion" about the meaning of that word "among the various groups, there was diversity of opinion among individuals more or less closely united into one group."[14] This diversity reflected not only semantic differences but the intensity of contending ideologies, as is best exhibited by the following definitions given in the Encyclopédie edited by Diderot and the Dictionnaire de Trévoux edited by the Jesuit order:

the philosophe is an honnête homme who acts according to reason in all matters and who joins sociable manners and qualities to a reflective and precise mind.

Society also dignifies by the name of philosophes those so-called free thinkers [esprits forts] who more out of display and a kind of mental libertinism than out of moral corruption place themselves above the duties and obligations of civil and Christian life and who, liberated from everything they call the prejudices of education in religious matters, scoff at human beings who are sufficiently weak to respect the established laws and sufficiently idiotic not to dare to shake off the yoke of a very old superstition. [15]

Yet, though Fontenelle and Condorcet themselves would easily rank among the esprits forts condemned by the Jesuits, their *éloges*, no more than those of the devout Mairan and Fouchy, equate philosophie with criticism of the throne and altar. Like Pierre Bayle, Fontenelle did define the term "philosophe" as a critic of "superstition, prejudice, metaphysical speculation, and dogmatism," but unlike some of the members of the *parti encyclopédique* of the second half of the eighteenth century, he "used in his portrait of the philosopher almost exclusively ideas from the humanistic tradition." [16] And although Fontenelle, like the other writers of the *éloges*, attributed to some of their subjects oddities like absentmindedness, none of them used the word "philosophe" in any of its multiple pejorative senses: visionary (for which they substituted the term *"homme à projects"*), misogynist, libertine, or subversive. Nor did they *exclusively* reserve that word for an "author of a system of ideas or the creator of a comprehensive interpretation of the world." When the *éloges* describe the members of the Paris Academy of Sciences as philosophes or as possessing philosophic qualities, they mean to imply any or all of the following connotations found in contemporary usage:

[One who practices a] morality [founded on] the two principles of indifference to wealth as well as to honors. [17]

A retired gentleman, who seeks to do good to his small community.

A practical man who, in the face of adversity, displays a courage and a fortitude worthy of the ancient philosophers. [18]

[One who] seeks to understand things by their first causes or principles [and] leads a calm, secluded, modest life, practicing the virtues of moderation and serenity.

A mind resolute and eminent above others, who is cured of popular preoccupations and errors and disabused of the vanities of this world; who loves honest pleasures; who prefers a private existence to the commotions of this world; a faithful friend, hardly a dangerous enemy; serviceable when put to work and content when not; attentive to the present, little concerned about the future, and caring less for the judgments of the common people; who views with a steady and peaceful gaze the inconstancy of earthly matters and who, without lacking sensibility, is not struck down by misfortunes and sorrows. [19]

The secretaries of the Paris Academy of Sciences applied the term philosophe or the qualities assumed to be affixed to it to the mathematician-esprit fort d'Alembert, the devout mathematician Euler, the Deist-scientist-statesman-revolutionary Franklin, the police *intendant* Marc-René de Voyer d'Argenson, the astronomer Bradley, the engineer Deparcieux, the physiologist Haller, the botanist Bernard de Jussieu, the surgeon Chirac, and the science amateur Chaulnes, as well as to the metaphysicians Leibniz and Wolff. What all these men had in common was evidently not religious preference, political commitment, scientific interest, or metaphysical inclination. However varied their ideologies and interests, they shared certain moral qualities, moral qualities derived from the Stoic tradition and now associated with either the pursuit or the patronage of natural science. By a verbal transformation implied in the *éloges*, most of them were not so much natural philosophers as moral philosophers whose philosophy was enhanced by their investigation of nature.

These men are not yet described as either savants or *scientifiques*, though the criteria for admission to the Academy of Sciences shifts over the century from erudition or *savoir* in the broadest sense of the term to aptitude and originality in using "reason, observation, experimentation and objectivity to uncover progressively natural reality."[20] For the French substantive savant to possess the connotation of scientist almost to the exclusion of that of scholar—as it had by the end of the nineteenth century—the definition of the Latin word *scientia* gradually had to be narrowed from "knowledge" or "learning" to "systematic investigation of nature." The eighteenth-century devotees of natural philosophy were not as confident as their nineteenth-century successors, nor were they so liberated from their Latin or classical heritage as to reserve for themselves the appellation of savant. Hence, it was some time before the Academy of Sciences, as the ambiguous meaning of "Sciences" implies, both defied and redefined common usage by closing its doors to learned men in areas other than natural philosophy.[21]

For want of the French equivalent of the English term "natural philosopher" as well as of a specific designation to distinguish the scientist from the "savant" or learned man, the secretaries resorted either to such professional names as "*mathématicien*," "*chimiste*," and the like, or to the generic yet ambiguous word "philosophe." No such ambiguity was intended, however, as the *éloges* repeatedly called attention to the "philosophical" qualities informing their subjects' characters and pointedly associated those qualities with outstanding philosophers or noble men of the past and with the new natural sciences in which they were presently laboring.

The natural philosophers were like past philosophers in the moral sense in that they embodied such qualities as fortitude, humility, and honesty, and they were like past philosophers in the technical sense in that they were imbued with the burning desire to seek the truth. They were different from all those philosophers, however, in that they sought the truth not in metaphysical principles, not in entelechies, not in scholastic categories, but in the direct observation of the operations of nature. It is the eulogists' implicit contention that the natural philosophers inherited the moral legacy of the Plutarchan heroes, Christian saints, and especially the Stoics and transmuted that legacy into an investment whose dividends increased exponentially with each new discovery in the natural sciences.

Indeed, the moral qualities and the scientific activities are so entwined in the *éloges* as to lead to a veritable symbiosis. Natural science made men free if they knew the truth that it gradually disclosed and it made men philosophical if they engaged heart and soul in the pursuit of that truth. And in the process of elucidating that truth—by following such principles as noncontradiction, efficient causality, and identity; by employing such devices as Occam's Razor, mathematization, precise observation, and arduous experimentation; and by discarding all forms of untested beliefs—they sacrificed wealth and position.

Yet the heroes of the scientific revolution are presumed to have cheerfully accepted their sacrifices in the name of a transcendent cause. They were allegedly sustained in their selfless pursuit of the truth by past examples of philosophical abnegation, the expectation of secular immortality, the certitude of the validity of the scientific enterprise, and for some the privilege of obtaining a glimpse into the mechanism of God's handiwork. Their labors purified the grosser aspects of their being and elevated their souls to the sublimity heretofore accorded only to Christian saints and Stoic philosophers. As Joseph Priestley (1733-1804), premier chemist, historian of electricity, Unitarian minister, and subsequently martyr to the cause of Enlightenment liberalism,[22] most eloquently expressed it,

> A Philosopher ought to be something greater, and better than another man. The contemplation of the works of God should give a sublimity to his virtue, should expand his benevolence, extinguish every thing mean, base, and selfish in nature, give a dignity to all his sentiments, and teach him to aspire to the moral perfections of the great author of all things. What great and exalted beings would philosophers be, would they but let the objects about which they are conversant have their proper moral effect upon their minds! A life spent in the contemplation of the productions of divine power, wisdom, and goodness, would be a life of devotion. The more we see of the wonderful structure of the world, and of the laws of nature, the more clearly do we comprehend their admirable uses, to make all the percipient creation happy: a sentiment, which cannot but fill the heart with unbounded love, gratitude, and joy.[23]

Stripped of its Deistic argument, the creed expressed by Priestley and expounded in countless *éloges* (including Cuvier's) became the profession of faith, however badly observed, of the scientific culture, until at least World War II. As Outram put it most forcefully:

> The image of science and the scientist which has dominated the history of science until very recently has emphasized a picture of science as an objective, self-

contained, value-free, emotionless, progressive kind of knowledge and has fashioned the image of the ideal man of science in corresponding terms. Clearly, however, this ideology rules out of serious discussion problems such as the impact of individual personality and of extra-scientific activity on the development of science.[24]

Like Priestly's natural philosopher, the scientist was (and sometimes still is) expected to "expand his benevolence" to all, to "extinguish every thing mean, base, and selfish" in his pursuit of that ideal, to "give a dignity to all his sentiments," and to "let the objects about which they are conversant have their proper moral effects upon their minds" and characters. The layman, for his part, was expected to view the new scientific hero as the embodiment of objectivity in and out of the laboratory, of abnegation of all earthly pleasures and profits, of humanitarian zeal, of homage to material and mental progress, and, in short, of selfless and honest dedication to the only cause worthy of credence and capable of utility. The Galileos, Newtons, Faradays, Darwins, Pasteurs, Curies, and Einsteins of both scientific and lay hagiography have endowed the word "science" with "a highly authoritative quality whose unmistakable halo effect is borrowed by many different self-serving groups. The appropriation of the word by all manner of charlatans emphasizes its popular association with all things that are good, true, and beneficial."[25] Fashions in taste come and go and political and religious creeds are subject to contending interpretations, but the results of the scientists' labor, so it is believed inside and outside the scientific community,[26] withstand the storms that shake and topple styles, ideologies, and professions of faith. In short, an "abstraction named 'the scientist' has been given form in people's minds as a new figure of authority, corresponding to the priest or witch-doctor of a more primitive culture, whose 'scientific' statements can be accepted with child-like reliance."[27]

The unquestioned authority of the scientists and of their works, of course, has come under increasing attacks since World War II. The better scientists have come to recognize the provisional nature of their most fundamental assumptions, the historians of science have elucidated the interaction between cultural values and scientists' methodological approaches and selected subjects of inquiry, and laymen, in the wake of nuclear, genetic, and ecological developments, have become increasingly skeptical of, if not hostile to, the value of the whole scientific enterprise. Still, the reception accorded to James D. Watson's *The Double Helix* (1968) is evidence of the tenacious durability of scientific hagiography. At least two book reviewers welcomed Watson's demythologization of science, one congratulating him for having depicted scientists "as fallible humans with their peccadillos sharply etched" and the other, for the Nobel Prize winner having "told all in a frank, untechnical memoir that will destroy some laymen's illusions about the austerity of science and will also enrage some biologists."[28] The book certainly enraged John Lear, whose review of *The Double Helix* in *Saturday Review* lambasted Watson for his undistinguished style, shallowness, and fragmentary account of the search for DNA structure. More pertinently, Lear figuratively cast Watson out of the scientific community for having revealed the whole secret about the human frailties of his peers. The book, Lear sorrowfully exclaimed,

> is a bleak recitation of bickering and personal ambition too intense to leave room for caring about the larger concerns of Pepys's modern counterparts [some review-ers had rashly compared this book to Pepys's Diary]. . . . What worries me about *The Double Helix* is the effect it may have on immature minds. . . . The more idealistic they are, the more they [the larger concerns] are needed in science, and the more negatively they [the immature minds] will react to Watson's story.[29]

In this reverential assessment of the scientific enterprise and its practitioners, John Lear, like most of us, is but the beneficiary of the testament bequeathed to us by the *éloges* and other writings (especially textbooks) of the early modern period. Science as the only "philosophy" capable of fathoming the mysteries of the universe, laboratories as the gardens of uncounted blessings for humanity, and the savants as the incarnations of truth and goodness—all are the clauses of that testament to which so many men and women of the nineteenth and twentieth centuries have subscribed.

Of course, the *éloges* are much more than documented testimonials to the greatness of the natural philosophers and their labors. Shorn of their moralistic and didactic intent, these eulogies would still remain an exhaustive account of scientific activity in eighteenth-century France, a fragmentary sociology of the distinguished scientists of that period, and an exhibition of the partialities of the four men who composed them. From this limited view, the *éloges* are collectively a vast storehouse of historical and biographical information. Yet to view them solely as documents stored for the use of historians and biographers is to gravely miss the very intent so carefully and repeatedly expounded by Fontenelle, Mairan, Fouchy, and Condorcet. These eulogists also intended to sing the praises of a new breed of philosopher, deserving to take their place alongside, if not above, the political, military, and religious heroes memorialized since the beginning of time. Like the heroes of old, these natural philosophers were fortunate in having their deeds recorded in a subgenre fashioned by Fontenelle and his successors. As the English historian Herbert Butterfield has so brilliantly argued in an account that meets Fontenelle's high literary standards, the *éloges* of Fontenelle comprise the epic of the heroic age of science.[30]

Collectively the *éloges* are the epic of the scientific revolution because they discourse on a great and serious subject, are often narrated in an elevated style, and are centered on heroic figures whose deeds allegedly embody the highest aspirations of the community at large. Striking a mean between narrative and encomium, the eulogies of the Paris Academy of Sciences describe the rise of modern science, omit details that would unduly debase the protagonists in the public esteem, and dwell on the new breed of natural philosophers on whose character and investigations presumably hang the fate of humanity.

Appendix A
"Public" *Éloges* in the Chronological Order of their Publication

COMPOSED BY FONTENELLE

Dates and pages of volumes of histoires of the Paris Academy of Sciences in which the *éloges* were published	Names of members	Dates of death of members	Dates of public readings of the *éloges*[a]
1699, 151–152.	Bourdelin, Claude (1er)	Oct. 14, 1699	1699[b]
1701, 161–162.	Tauvry, Daniel	Feb. 7, 1701	April 6, 1701
1702, 139.	Tuillier, Adrien	June 2, 1702	1702[b]
1703, 137–148.	Viviani, Vincenzio	Sept. 22, 1703	April 2, 1704
1704, 125–135.	L'Hospital, Guillaume-François-Antoine de	Feb. 2, 1704	April 2, 1704
1705, 139–150.	Bernoulli, Jakob	Aug. 16, 1705	Nov. 14, 1705
1705, 150–154.	Amontons, Guillaume	Oct. 11, 1705	Nov. 14, 1705
1706, 142–152.	Du Hamel, Jean-Baptiste	Aug. 6, 1706	Nov. 13, 1706
1707, 157–165.	Régis, Pierre-Sylvain	Jan. 11, 1707	May 4, 1707

[a]Unless noted otherwise, the dates for the readings of the *éloges* are as given in the *procès-verbaux* of the Paris Academy of Sciences and printed in the *Index biographique des membres et correspondants de l'Académie des Sciences* (Paris, 1968). Other dates given in this column were found in various documents as specified below.

[b]A thorough search in the Spring of 1974 through the procès-verbaux and plumitifs of the Archives of the Paris Academy of Sciences as well as through contemporary periodicals has not yielded any specific dates for the reading of these eight *éloges*.

APPENDIX A *(Continued)*

1707, 165–175.	Vauban, Sébastien Le Prestre, seigneur de	March 30, 1707	May 4, 1707
1707, 176–181.	Gallois, Jean	April 19, 1707	May 4, 1707
1707, 182–192.	Dodart, Denis	Nov. 5, 1707	April 18, 1708
1708, 143–154.	Tournefort, Joseph Pitton de	Dec. 28, 1708	April 10, 1709
1709, 114–124.	Tschirnhaus, Ehrenfried Walther	Oct. 11, 1708	Nov. 13, 1709
1709, 125–128.	Poupart, François	Oct. 31, 1709	Nov. 13, 1709
1710, 143–151.	Chazelles, Jean-Mathieu de	Jan. 16, 1710	April 30, 1710
1710, 152–166.	Guglielmini, Domenico	July 11, 1710	April 22, 1711
1711, 102–107.	Carré, Louis	April 11, 1711	Nov. 14, 1711
1711, 108–111.	Bourdelin, Claude (II)	April 20, 1711	Nov. 14, 1711
1712, 81–82.	Berger, Claude	May 22, 1712	Nov. 12, 1712
1712, 83–104.	Cassini, Jean-Dominique (Ier)	Sept. 14, 1712	Nov. 12, 1712
1713, 78–80.	Blondin, Pierre	April 15, 1713	Nov. 15, 1713
1714, 129–134.	Poli, Martino	July 29, 1714	Nov. 14, 1714
1715, 68–72.	Morin de Saint-Victor, Louis	March 1, 1715	May 4, 1715
1715, 73–82.	Lémery, Nicolas	June 19, 1715	Nov. 13, 1715
1715, 82–93.	Homberg, Wilhelm *alias* Guillaume	Sept. 24, 1715	Nov. 13, 1715
1715, 93–114.	Malebranche, Nicolas	Oct. 13, 1715	April 22, 1716
1716, 79–87.	Sauveur, Joseph	July 9, 1716	Nov. 14, 1716
1716, 88–93.	Parent, Antoine	Sept. 26, 1716	Nov. 14, 1716
1716, 94–128.	Leibniz, Gottfried Wilhelm	Nov. 14, 1716	Nov. 13, 1717
1717, 86–92.	Ozanam, Jacques	April 17, 1717	April 27, 1718
1718, 76–89.	La Hire, Philippe de	April 21, 1718	Nov. 12, 1718
1718, 90–93.	La Faye, Jean-Elie Leriget de	April 20, 1718	Nov. 12, 1718
1718, 94–100.	Fagon, Guy-Crescent	March 11, 1718	Nov. 12, 1718
1718, 101–104.	Louvois, Camille Le Tellier, abbé de	Nov. 5, 1718	Nov. 15, 1719

APPENDIX A *(Continued)*

1719, 83–93.	Montmort, Pierre Rémond de	Oct. 7, 1719	April 10, 1720[c]
1719, 94–100.	Rolle, Michel	Nov. 8, 1719	April 10, 1720
1719, 101–120.	Renau d'Elissagaray, Bernard	Sept. 30, 1719	Nov. 13, 1720
1720, 115–121.	Dangeau, Philippe de Courcillon, marquis de	Sept. 9, 1720	April 23, 1721[d]
1720, 122–124.	Des Billettes, Gilles Filleau	Aug. 15, 1720	April 23, 1721[d]
1721, 99–108.	Argenson, Marc-René de Voyer	May 8, 1721	Nov. 14, 1722
1722, 124–128.	Couplet, Claude-Antoine	July 25, 1722	April 7, 1723
1722, 129–135.	Mery, Jean	Nov. 3, 1722	April 7, 1723
1722, 136–146.	Varignon, Pierre	Dec. 22–23, 1722	April 7, 1723
1725, 105–128.	Czar Peter I of Russia	Jan. 28/Feb. 8, 1725[e]	Nov. 14, 1725
1725, 129–136.	Littre, Alexis	Feb. 3, 1725	April 11, 1725
1725, 137–153.	Hartsoeker, Nicolas	Dec. 10, 1725	May 4, 1726
1726, 73–84.	Delisle, Guillaume	Jan. 25, 1726	Nov. 13, 1726
1727, 145–151.	Malézieu, Nicolas de	March 4, 1727	Nov. 12, 1727
1727, 151–172.	Newton, Isaac	March 20/31, 1727[e]	Nov. 12, 1727
1728, 112–116.	Reyneau, Charles-René	Feb. 4, 1728	April 7, 1728
1728, 117–120.	Tallard, Camille	March 29, 1728	Nov. 13, 1728
1729, 93–101.	Truchet, Jean, known as *le père* Sébastien	Feb. 5, 1729	April 25, 1729
1729, 102–115.	Bianchini, Francesco	March 2, 1729	Nov. 15, 1730
1729, 116–120.	Maraldi, Giacomo Filippo	Dec. 1, 1729	Nov. 15, 1730
1730, 117–122.	Valincourt, Jean-Baptiste-Henry du Trousset de	Jan. 4, 1730	April 19, 1730

[c]Procès-verbaux of the Paris Academy of Sciences, 39:115
[d]Procès verbaux, 1721.
[e]The first date is in the old style, the second in the new.

APPENDIX A *(Continued)*

1730, 123–131.	Du Verney, Guichard-Joseph	Sept. 10, 1730	Nov. 14, 1731
1730, 132–143.	Marsigli, Luigi-Fernando	Nov, 1, 1730	Nov. 14, 1731
1731, 93–100.	Geoffroy, Etienne-François	Jan. 6, 1731	April 4, 1731
1731, 100–109.	Ruysch, Frédéric	Feb. 22, 1731	Nov. 12, 1732[f]
1731, 109–111.	Maisons, Jean-René de Longueil de	Sept. 13, 1731	April 23, 1732
1732, 120–130.	Chirac, Pierre	March 1, 1732	Nov. 12, 1732[f]
1732, 131–136.	Louville, Jacques Eugène d'Allonville, chevalier de	Sept. 10, 1732	April 15, 1733
1734, 107–114.	Lagny, Thomas Fantet de	April 12, 1734	Nov. 13, 1734
1735, 105–108.	Ressons, Jean-Baptiste Deschiens de	Jan. 31, 1735	April 20, 1735
1737, 110–120.	Saurin, Joseph	Dec. 29, 1737	April 16, 1738
1738, 105–116.	Boerhaave, Hermann	Sept. 23, 1738	April 8, 1739
1739, 59–72.	Manfredi, Eustachio	Feb. 15, 1739	Nov. 14, 1739
1739, 73–83.	Du Fay, Charles-Francois de Cisternay	July 16, 1739	Nov. 14, 1739

COMPOSED BY MAIRAN

1741, 169–179.	Petit, François Pourfour du	June 18, 1741	Nov. 15, 1741
1741, 180–200.	Polignac, Melchior de	Nov. 20, 1741	April 4, 1742
1742, 167–171.	Boulduc, Jean-Francois	Jan. 15, 1742	Nov. 14, 1742
1742, 172–188.	Halley, Edmond	Jan. 25, 1742	Nov. 14, 1742
1742, 189–194.	Brémond, François de	March 21, 1742	April 24, 1743
1742, 195–205.	Molières, Joseph Privat de	May 12, 1742	April 24, 1743
1742, 206–212.	Hunauld, François Joseph	Dec. 15, 1742	April 24, 1743
1743, 175–184.	Fleury, André Hercule de	Jan. 29, 1743	Nov. 13, 1743

[f]*Mercure* (November 1732), 2447–2448.

APPENDIX A *(Continued)*

1743, 185—194.	Bignon, Jean-Paul	March 14, 1743	Nov. 13, 1743
1743, 195—208.	Lémery, Louis	June 9, 1743	Nov. 13, 1743

COMPOSED BY FOUCHY

1744, 65—70.	Bragelongne, Christophe-Bernard de	Feb. 20, 1744	April 15, 1744
1746, 123—132.	Torcy, Jean-Baptiste Colbert, marquis de	Sept. 2, 1746	Nov. 12, 1746
1747, 130—144.	La Peyronnie, François Gigot de	April 24, 1747	Nov. 15, 1747
1748, 124—132.	Bernoulli, Johann (I)	Jan. 1, 1748	Nov. 13, 1748[g]
1749, 188—192.	Amelot, Jean-Jacques	May 7, 1749	Nov. 12, 1749
1750, 173—178.	Aiguillon, Armand-Louis Duplessis de Richelieu, duc d'	Feb. 4, 1750	April 8, 1750
1750, 179—190.	Crousaz, Jean-Pierre de	March 22, 1750	Nov. 14, 1750
1750, 191—202.	Petit, Jean-Louis	April 17, 1750	April 21, 1751
1750, 203—207.	Terrasson, Jean-Baptiste	Sept. 15, 1750	April 21, 1751
1751, 178—194.	Aguesseau, Henri François d'	Feb. 9, 1751	Nov. 13, 1751
1751, 195—202.	Albert, Charles	Feb. 10, 1751	Nov. 15, 1752
1752, 153—164.	Geoffroy, Claude-Joseph	March 9, 1752	April 12, 1752
1752, 164—172.	Chicoyneau, François	April 13, 1752	May 2, 1753
1753, 305—320.	Sloane, Hans	Jan. 11, 1753	Nov. 14, 1753
1754, 143—154.	Onsenbray, Louis-Léon Pajot, comte d'	Feb. 22, 1754	Nov. 13, 1754
1754, 155—167.	Wolff, Christian	April 9, 1754	April 9, 1755
1754, 168—174.	Folkes, Martin	June 28, 1754	April 28, 1756
1754, 175—184.	Moivre, Abraham de	Nov. 27, 1754	April 28, 1756
1755, 148—160.	Lowendal, Ulric Frederic Woldemar, comte d'	May 27, 1755	Nov. 12, 1755

[g]Procès-verbaux, 67:447.

APPENDIX A *(Continued)*

1755, 161–169.	Helvétius, Jean-Claude-Adrien	July 17, 1755	Nov. 12, 1755
1755, 170–175.	Boyer, Jean-François, bishop of Mirepoix[h]	Aug. 20, 1755	Nov. 13, 1756
1756, 134–146.	Cassini, Jacques (II)	April 15, 1756	Nov. 13, 1756
1756, 147–156.	La Galissonnière, Roland-Michel Barrin, marquis de	Oct. 26, 1756	April 20, 1757
1757, 185–200.	Fontenelle, Bernard Le Bovier de	Jan. 9, 1757	April 20, 1757
1757, 201–216.	Réaumur, René-Antoine Ferchault de	Oct. 17, 1757	April 5, 1758
1758, 107–114.	Nicole, François	Jan. 10, 1758	April 5, 1758
1758, 115–126.	Jussieu, Antoine de	April 22, 1758	Nov. 15, 1758
1758, 127–136.	Bouguer, Pierre	Aug. 15, 1758	Nov. 15, 1758
1759, 249–258.	Vallière, Jean-Florent de	Jan 6, 1759	Nov. 14, 1759
1759, 259–276.	Maupertuis, Pierre-Louis Moreau de	July 27, 1759	April 16, 1760
1760, 165–180.	Winslow, Jacques Bénigne	April 3, 1760	Nov. 12, 1760
1760, 181–194.	Godin, Louis	Sept. 11, 1760	April 1, 1761
1760, 195–212.	Séchelles, Jean Moreau de	Dec. 31, 1760	Nov. 14, 1761
1761, 167–181.	Belidor, Bernard Forest de	Sept. 8, 1761	April 21, 1762
1761, 182–188.	Rouillié, Antoine-Louis, comte de Jouy	Sept. 20, 1761	April 21, 1762
1762, 197–212.	La Caille, Nicolas-Louis de	March 21, 1762	Nov. 13, 1762
1762, 213–230.	Hales, Stephen	Jan. 1, 1761	Nov. 12, 1763
1762, 231–242.	Bradley, James	July 13, 1762	May 2, 1764
1763, 151–163.	Poleni, Giovanni	Nov. 15, 1761	April 17, 1765
1764, 187–197.	Argenson, Marc-Pierre de Voyer de Paulmy	Aug. 26, 1764	Nov. 14, 1764
1764, 198–206.	Montmirail, Charles-François Le Tellier, marquis de	Dec. 13, 1764	April 17, 1765

[h]The heading of his *éloge* is under the name of "Mirepoix."

APPENDIX A *(Continued)*

1765, 144–159. Clairaut, Alexis-   May 17, 1765   Nov. 13, 1765
                Claude
1766, 167–179. Hellot, Jean   Feb. 13, 1766   April 9, 1766
1768, 134–143. Baron, Hyacinthe-   March 10, 1768   Nov. 12, 1768
                Théodore
1768, 144–154. Camus, Charles-   May 4, 1768   Nov. 12, 1768
                Etienne-Louis
1768, 155–166. Deparcieux, Antoine   Sept. 2, 1768   April 5, 1769
1768, 167–183. Delisle, Joseph-   Sept. 12, 1768   Nov. 15, 1769
                Nicolas
1769, 135–150. Trudaine, Daniel-   Jan. 19, 1769   April 5, 1769
                Charles
1769, 151–162. Ferrein, Antoine   Feb. 28, 1769   Nov. 15, 1769
1769, 163–172. Chappe d'Auteroche,   Aug. 1, 1769   Nov. 14, 1770
                Jean-Baptiste
1769, 173–179. Jars, Antoine-   Aug. 23, 1769   April 25, 1770
                Gabriel
1769, 180–188. Chaulnes, Michel-   Sept. 23, 1769   April 25, 1770
                Ferdinand d'Albert
                d'Ailly, duc de
1770, 121–136. Nollet, Jean-Antoine   April 24, 1770   Nov. 4, 1770
1770, 137–149. Rouelle, Guillaume-   Aug. 3, 1770   April 10, 1771
                François
1770, 149–152. Douglas, James,   Oct. 12, 1768   Nov. 13, 1771
                Lord Aberdour, 14th
                Count of Morton[i]
1771, 89–104.   Mairan, Jean-   Feb. 20, 1771   Nov. 13, 1771
                Jacques Dortous de

COMPOSED BY CONDORCET

1771, 105–130. Fontaine, Alexis   Aug. 21, 1771   Nov. 13, 1773

COMPOSED BY FOUCHY

1771, 131–142. Morgagni, Giovanni   Dec. 5, 1771   April 29, 1772
                Battista
1771, 143–157. Pitot, Henri   Dec. 27, 1771   Nov. 14, 1772
1772:1,   Van Swieten, Gerard   June 18, 1772   April 21, 1773
   114–128.

[i]The heading of his *éloge* is under the name of "Morton."

APPENDIX A *(Continued)*

1772:2, 135–150.	Buache, Philippe	Jan. 27, 1773	Nov. 13, 1773
1773, 99–117.	Morand, Sauveur-François	July 24, 1773	April 13, 1774
1773, 118–134.	Hérissant, François-David	Aug. 21, 1773	Nov. 12, 1774

COMPOSED BY CONDORCET

| 1774, 85–121. | La Condamine, Charles-Marie de | Feb. 4, 1774 | April 13, 1774 |

COMPOSED BY FOUCHY

| 1774, 122–138. | Quesnay, François | Dec. 16, 1774 | April 26, 1775 |
| 1776, 53–64. | Vallière, Joseph-Florent de | Jan. 10, 1776 | April 17, 1776 |

COMPOSED BY CONDORCET

1777, 70–93.	Trudaine de Montigny, Jean-Charles-Philibert	Aug. 5, 1777	April 29, 1778
1777, 94–117.	Jussieu, Bernard de	Nov. 6, 1777	April 29, 1778
1777, 118–126.	Bourdelin, Louis-Claude	Sept. 13, 1777	April 29, 1778
1777, 127–154.	Haller, Albrecht von	Dec. 12, 1777	Nov. 14, 1778
1778, 57–65.	Malouin, Paul-Jacques	Jan. 3, 1778	Nov. 14, 1778
1778, 66–84.	Linnaeus, Carl von	Jan. 10, 1778	April 14, 1779
1779, 44–53.	Jussieu, Joseph de	April 11, 1779	April 5, 1780
1779, 54–70.	Arcy, Patrick d'	Oct. 18, 1779	April 5, 1780
1780, 46–59.	Lieutaud, Joseph	Dec. 6, 1780	1780[b]
1780, 60–76.	Bucquet, Jean-Baptiste-Michel	Jan. 24, 1780	Nov. 15, 1780
1781, 53–70.	Bertin, Exupère-Joseph	Feb. 25, 1781	Nov. 14, 1781
1781, 71–78.	Courtanvaux, François-César Le Tellier, marquis de	July 7, 1781	April 10, 1782[j]

[j]Bibliothèque de l'Institut, Ms. 1385, p. 17.

APPENDIX A *(Continued)*

1781, 79–102.	Maurepas, Jean-Frédéric Phélypeaux de Pontchartrain, comte de	Nov. 21, 1781	April 10, 1782[j]
1781, 103–114.	Tronchin, Théodore	Nov. 30, 1781	Nov. 13, 1782
1782, 57–68.	Pringle, John	Jan. 18, 1782	1782[b]
1782, 69–77.	Anville, Jean-Baptiste Bourguignon, d'	Jan. 28, 1782	Nov. 13, 1782
1782, 78–81.	Bordenave, Toussaint	March 12, 1782	1782[b]
1782, 82–107.	Bernoulli, Daniel	March 17, 1782	April 30, 1782[k]
1782, 108–121.	Montigny, Etienne Mignot de	May 6, 1782	Nov. 13, 1782
1782, 122–130.	Margraaf, Andreas Sigismund	Aug. 7, 1782	1782[b]
1782, 131–155.	Duhamel du Monceau, Henri-Louis	Aug. 22, 1782	April 30, 1783
1782, 156–168.	Vaucanson, Jacques de	Nov. 21, 1782	1782[b]
1783, 29–36.	Hunter, William	March 30, 1783	April 21, 1784
1783, 37–68.	Euler, Leonhard	Sept. 7/18, 1783[e]	1783[b]
1783, 69–75.	Bézout, Etienne	Sept. 27, 1783	Nov. 13, 1784
1783, 76–120.	Alembert, Jean Le Rond d'	Oct. 29, 1783	April 22, 1784[l]
1783, 121–127.	Tressan, Louis-Elisabeth de la Vergne, comte de	Oct. 31, 1783	Nov. 13, 1784
1783, 128–132.	Wargentin, Pehr Wilhelm	Dec. 13, 1783	Nov. 12, 1785
1784, 20–30.	Macquer, Pierre-Joseph	Feb. 15, 1784	Nov. 13, 1784
1784, 31–47.	Bergman, Torbern Olof	July 8, 1784	April 26, 1786
1784, 48–53.	Morand, Jean-François Clément	Aug. 13, 1784	Nov. 13, 1784
1784, 54–63.	Cassini de Thury, César-François (III)	Sept. 4, 1784	Nov. 12, 1785

[k]Archives of the Paris Academy of Sciences, Plumitifs of 1783.
[l]Bibliothèque Nationale, catalogue, 31:504.

APPENDIX A *(Continued)*

1784, 64–69.	Milly, Nicolas-Christian de Thy, comte de	Sept. 17, 1784	Nov. 12, 1785
1785, 130–136.	Courtivron, Gaspard le Compasseur de Créqui-Montford, marquis de	Oct. 4, 1785	April 26, 1786
1785, 137–155.	Praslin, César-Gabriel, duc de	Nov. 15, 1785	April 26, 1786
1786, 47–62.	Guettard, Jean-Etienne	Jan. 6, 1786	April 18, 1787
1786, 63–76.	Gua de Malves, Jean-Paul de	June 2, 1786	Nov. 15, 1786
1787, 49–60.	Paulmy d'Argenson, Marc-Antoine-René de Voyer, marquis de	Aug. 13, 1786	April 2, 1788
1787, 61–76.	Bouvard, Michel-Philippe	Jan. 19, 1787	Nov. 14, 1787
1788, 23–32.	Lassone, Joseph-Marie-François de	Dec. 8, 1788	April 14, 1790
1788, 33–36.	Luynes, Paul d'Albert, cardinal de	Jan. 22, 1788	April 14, 1790
1788, 37–49.	Fouchy, Jean-Paul Grandjean de	April 15, 1788	Nov. 14, 1789
1788, 50–84.	Buffon, Georges-Louis Leclerc, comte de	April 16, 1788	Nov. 12, 1788
1789, 31–38.	Turgot, Etienne-François	Dec. 26, 1788	April 22, 1789
1789, 39–44.	Fougeroux de Bondaroy, Auguste-Denis	Dec. 28, 1789	Nov. 12, 1791
1789, 45–52.	Camper, Petrus	April 7, 1789	April 14, 1790
_____m	Franklin, Benjamin	April 17, 1790	Nov. 13, 1790
_____m	Fourcroy de Ramecourt, Charles-René de	Jan. 12, 1791	May 4, 1791

mThese two *éloges* were not published in the last *Histoires* of the Paris Academy of Sciences but can be found in *Oeuvres complètes de Condorcet* (Paris, Heinrichs 1804), ed. A. A. Barbier, P.-J.-G. Cabanis, and D.-J. Garat, II:91–165, 190–208, respectively.

Appendix B
Condorcet's "Written" *Éloges* and Notices in the Alphabetical Order of Their Subjects[a]

Page numbers in the 1773 edition	Names of members	Year of admission to the Academy of Sciences	Year of death
	ÉLOGES		
77–82	Blondel, Nicolas-François	1669	1686
134–141	Charas, Moÿse	1692	1698
66–77	Duclos, Samuel Cottereau-	1666	1685
30–35	Frénicle de Bessy, Bernard	1666	1675
104–134	Huyghens, Christiaan	1666	1695
11–17	La Chambre, Marin Cureau de	1666	1669
49–66	Mariotte, Edme	1666	1684
83–103	Perrault, Claude	1666	1688
36–48	Picard, Jean	1666	1682
17–29	Roberval, Gilles Personne de	1666	1675
141–152	Roemer, Olaüs	1672	1710
	NOTICES		
153–155	Auzout, Adrien	1666	1691
155	Bessé, Henri de	1683	1694
155–157	Borel, Pierre[b]	1674	1689

[a]All these eulogies and notices were published by Condorcet as *Eloges des Académiciens de l' Académie Royale des Sciences, Morts depuis 1666, jusqu'en 1699* (Paris: Hôtel de Thou, 1773). Eleven members received full *éloges* while twenty received notices ranging from a few words to three pages. All these biographical entries should be supplemented with Condorcet's marginal notes, which were printed in the 1804 edition of *Oeuvres complètes de Condorcet*, vol. 1.

[b]Condorcet mistakenly gave the name of another scientist, Pierre Borel, to the Academician Jacques Borel or Borelly.

APPENDIX B *(Continued)*

157	Buot, Jacques	1666	c. 1677
157–158	Carcavi, Pierre de	1666	1684
158	Coudraye, ? de La	1693	?
158	Cusset, ?	1685	?
158–161	Fèbvre, Jean le	1682	1706[c]
161	Gayant, Louis	1666	1673
161	Lannion, Pierre de	1679	?[d]
161–162	Marchant, Nicolas	1666	1678
162	Mignot, ? La Voye-	1666	1684
162	Morin de Toulon, ?	1693	1707
162–163	Niquet, ?	1666	?
163–164	Pecquet, Jean	1666	1674
165	Pivet, ?	1666	?
165	Pothenot, Laurent	1682	1732[e]
165–167	Richer, Jean	1666	1696
167	Sédileau, ?	1681	1693
168	Thévenot, Melchisedech	1685	1692

[c]Following a quarrel with Philippe and Gabriel-Philippe de La Hire, Le Fèbvre was expelled from the Academy on January 18, 1702 on the official grounds of prolonged absence.
[d]Lannion was expelled from the Academy on February 23, 1686.
[e]Sometime before 1699 Pothenot was expelled for reasons of absence.

Appendix C
"Public" *Éloges* in the Alphabetical Order of Their Subjects, by Class, with Their Dates of Publication

119 "WORKING" NATIVE SCIENTISTS

d'Albert 1751
d'Alembert 1783
Amontons 1705
d'Anville 1782
d'Arcy 1779

Baron 1768
Belidor 1761
Berger 1712
Bertin 1781
Bézout 1783
Blondin 1713
Bordenave 1782
Bouguer 1758
Boulduc 1742
Bourdelin, Claude (Ier) 1699
Bourdelin, Claude (II) 1711
Bourdelin,
    Louis-Claude 1777
Bouvard 1787
Bragelongne 1744
Brémond 1742
Buache 1772:2
Bucquet 1780
Buffon 1788

Camus 1768
Carré 1711

Cassini (I) 1712
Cassini (II) 1756
Cassini de Thury 1784
Chappe d'Auteroche 1769
Chazelles 1710
Chicoyneau 1752
Chirac 1732
Clairaut 1765
Couplet 1722
Courtivron 1785

Delisle, G. 1726
Delisle, J.-N. 1768
Deparcieux 1768
Des Billettes 1720
Dodart 1707
Du Fay 1739
Du Hamel, J. B. 1706
Duhamel du Monceau 1782
Du Verney 1730

Ferrein 1769
Fontaine 1771
Fontenelle 1757
Fouchy 1788
Fougeroux de
    Bondaroy 1789
Fourcroy de
    Ramecourt . . . . .1804[a]

[a]In *Oeuvres complètes de Condorcet* (Paris: Heinrichs, 1804), II:190−208.

39 FOREIGN ASSOCIATES

Bergman 1784
Bernoulli, Daniel 1782
Bernoulli, Jakob 1705
Bernoulli, Johann (I) 1748
Bianchini 1729
Boerhaave 1738
Bradley 1762

Camper 1789
Crousaz 1750

Douglas ("Morton") 1770

Euler 1783

Folkes 1754
Franklin ....1804[b]

Guglielmini 1710

Hales 1762
Haller...................1777
Halley 1742
Hartsoeker 1725
Hunter 1783

Leibniz..................1716

Linnaeus 1778

Manfredi 1739
Margraaf 1782
Marsigli 1730
de Moivre 1754
Morgagni 1771

Newton 1727

Peter I of Russia 1725
Poleni...................1763
Poli 1714
Pringle 1782

Ruysch..................1731

Sloane 1753

Tronchin 1781
Tschirnhaus 1709

Van Swieten ....1772:1[c]
Viviani..................1703

Wargentin 1783
Wolff 1754

35 HONORARY MEMBERS

d'Aguesseau 1751
d'Aiguillon 1750
Amelot..................1749
d'Argenson, M.-P. 1764
d'Argenson, M.-R. 1721

Bignon 1743

Boyer ("Mirepoix").........1755

Chaulnes 1769
Courtanvaux 1781

Dangeau.................1720

[b]In *Oeuvres complètes de Condorcet* (Paris: Heinrichs, 1804), II:91–165.
[c]This is the only year in which two volumes were published.

Fagon	1718	Polignac	1741
Fleury	1743	Praslin	1785
L'Hospital[d]	1704	Renau	1719
Louvois	1718	Rouillié	1761
Lowendal	1755		
Luynes	1788	Séchelles	1760
Maisons	1731	Tallard	1728
Malebranche	1715	Torcy	1746
Malézieu	1727	Truchet	1729
Maurepas	1781	Trudaine, D. C.	1769
Montmirail	1764	Trudaine de Montigny	1777
d'Onsenbray	1754	Valincourt	1730
Paulmy d'Argenson	1787	Vauban	1707

[d]Admitted to the Academy in 1693 but made honoraire under the règlement of 1699.

Appendix D
Members of the Paris Academy
of Sciences Not Eulogized
Between 1699 and 1791

One hundred ninety-three *éloges* were publicly delivered between the Renouvellement of the Paris Academy of Sciences in 1699 and its annulment in 1793. Of these, sixty-nine were composed by Fontenelle, ten by Mairan, sixty-four by Fouchy, and fifty by Condorcet. This list of those eulogized includes thirty-five académiciens honoraires,[1] thirty-nine foreign associates,[2] and 119 "working" Academicians[3] resident in France (see appendix C). The 193 Academicians who were honored with *éloges*, however, did not comprise the entire roster of members who had died between 1699 and November 1791. Seventy of them were not honored, some for reasons that are explicitly stated in the procès-verbaux of that institution, some for reasons that are implicit from the available information, and some for reasons that can only be guessed at.

A few of these unhonored members were no longer Academicians at the times of their death, since they had been expelled from the Academy for failing to attend regularly the biweekly sessions.[4] Filippo Maria Monti and Pierre Magnol resigned from the Academy in 1702 and 1710, respectively, both within a few years after their admission. John Law was expelled by a royal edict based on public opinion: the notorious Scottish financier had left France following the debacle of his Louisiana scheme, which provided Louis XV and his ministers with the pretext of annulling the election of the former Comptroller-General on the grounds that his letters of naturalization had not been registered. To this roster of delinquents should be added the name of Du Torar (date of death unknown), who had been admitted as mathematical *élève* in 1699, excluded in February 1714 for repeated absences, then readmitted by a special edict of March 24 of the same year.

A glance at the above dates of expulsion reveals that they all occurred within the first twenty-five years of the "renewed" Academy. This peculiar chronology suggests that either the expelled members had not taken seriously the 19th Article of the Règlement requiring assiduous attendance or that the institution before 1724 had been patient or lax with repeated absentees. And attendance, according to Articles IV through VI of the same *Règlement*, implied residence in Paris (and Versailles, if broadly interpreted) for all "working" members. Yet "native" Academicians who had taken positions abroad were not, by virtue of this absence alone, expelled from the Academy; the penalty meted out to them appears to have been the denial of a public eulogy.[5]

The above members were deprived of their share of posthumous fame on the evidence provided by the registers of attendance or by inference from their habitual residence abroad. But neither the minutes of meetings nor the extant plumitifs kept by Réaumur and others inform us as to the reasons for the neglect of the other members. Since the composition and public reading of the *éloges* had been dictated by the precedent set by Fontenelle in 1699 and not by any specific provision in the Règlement, nothing compelled Fontenelle nor any of his three successors to honor each and every Academician with a eulogy. An honoraire had to be deserving of an *éloge* by virtue of his lofty position in the state; outstanding political, ecclesiastical, or military accomplishments; unusual erudition; administrative originality; or beneficial services rendered to science, the government, or the nation. If he was a foreign associate or a "working" native, he would find merit in the secretary's eyes primarily by the originality, breadth, or depth of his scientific or technological contributions.

Most of the Academicians who were honored with *éloges* met one or more of these exacting standards; the few who did not meet them yet who were eulogized had been noted for an eminent medical or surgical practice, scholarship in natural philosophy, an unusually eventful life, or moral conduct verging on the saintly. The last point is worth stressing, for two members were unquestionably excluded from posthumous homage on moral grounds. Cardinal Dubois, a chief minister under the Regency (1720–1723), led a life unbecoming a primate of the Church, a minister of state, and an Academician, even in an age not particularly noted for strict bourgeois morals: his conduct was an affront to the image that the Academicians had of themselves or that Fontenelle had drawn for them. The other Academician excluded from praise on moral grounds was the Duc de Lavrillière, minister of the Maison du Roi and notorious for the ease with which he issued the dreaded lettre de cachet. In a private letter Condorcet revealed the reasons for his refusal to honor him: "Would you prefer that I be persecuted for some foolish rather than for a just and moral deed? Think about it: I will be more easily forgiven for my silence than for my words, for I am wholly resolved never to betray the truth."[6]

The majority of unhonored members, however, appear not to have failed tests of attendance, residence, morality, or political practice, but rather the test of achievement. It was not for conduct unbecoming an honnête homme but for performance unbecoming a member of the Academy of Sciences that they deserved to be unremembered by posterity. As Fouchy, the least inclined of the four secretaries to pass judgment on his fellow men, put it: the purpose of these *éloges* was less to honor the glory of the dead ''than to arouse the emulation of those who are sufficiently daring to attempt to imitate them.''[7] And imitation, of course, implies something to imitate. Unfortunately, the scientific record of too many Academicians was not worthy of emulation. These men rarely climbed the Academic ladder of scientific success from the rank of élève or adjoint through that of associé to that of pensionnaire. By the time of their death most of them had not risen above the lowest rank or, what was more damning, had been put out to pasture by being reassigned to the class of *vétérans*, or more humiliatingly yet, *associés vétérans*. For that category of membership had been created ''to allow younger and more active academicians to reach the position of pensionnaire.''[8] Nine working members who failed to receive *éloges* never rose above the lowest rank, although Deslandes and Christophe du Verney had sat in the Academy for nearly half a century;[9] seven others had been given the rank of vétéran, presumably to give way to younger and more productive members.[10]

Promotional stagnation was one sure sign of unproductivity since, if a candidate was worthy of advancement yet found his way to the top blocked by filled quotas in his own class of specialization, he was both promoted and transferred into whichever class had a vacancy.[11] But even promotion itself was not necessarily an indication of achievement under certain conditions. Five scientists did reach the middle rank of associé in their class[12] but died within less than seven years after their admission to the Academy, probably too short a time to have bequeathed to posterity any lasting memorial of their work. Time also seemed to have operated against five scientists who became Academicians at the age of fifty or older[13] and who presumably were guilty of having waited too long to show their promise. Although these Academicians all lived past 78, the secretaries, as if to atone for the mistake the Academy had made in selecting these men in the first place, chose to ignore them in their semiyearly commemorations to the dead.

The last category of working scientists who did not receive posthumous homage for reasons that seem plausible are the less distinguished members of families that made up a sizeable part of the Academy's membership, such as the Bourdelins, the Cassinis, the Du Verneys, the Jussieus, and the La Hires. They probably had been admitted into this select company, especially during the first half of the eighteenth century, either because of family connections, a belief in the inheritance of talent, or actual instances of multiple achievements by two brothers, father and son, or uncle and nephew. Familial influence may have enabled some members to join the ranks of the elect but it could not guarantee achievement of any consequence to natural philosophy.[14]

Finally, the list of unhonored members is rounded out by twenty-one additional names: six honoraires, six foreign associates, and nine working *régnicoles*.[15] The reasons for their exclusion from the honor roll are purely conjectural. They may have been defective in character, achievement, or status, or if none of these, they may not have been worth considering for a eulogy by the secretary at times of excessive work, illness, imminent retirement, or revolutionary ferment.

Appendix E
Sources of the *Éloges*

As Ernest Maindron, a nineteenth-century historian of the Paris Academy of Sciences, has stated, there are no extant manuscripts of the drafts of the *éloges* Fontenelle, Mairan, and Fouchy wrote (as we have for some of Condorcet's) nor of material supplied by heirs of the deceased or other interested parties (save again for Condorcet's).[16] Still, circumstantial evidence testifying to the greater part of the sources that the four secretaries drew upon is easily available. The material on which the working members' scientific activity was based was easily accessible to the secretaries in the yearly Mémoires of the Academy which they themselves had collected as well as in their précis of this material in the Histoires of the Academy, which they or their predecessor had drafted. As for the activities of the honoraires and occasional working members who were not scientists (like Galloys and Régis), their public record had been reported in various journals and their treatises were easily accessible. For the portraits or character sketches with which they invariably closed their *éloges*, the secretaries obviously drew upon a long acquaintance with all but foreign associates, not to speak of intimate friendships such as those between Fontenelle and Varignon, Fouchy and La Caille, and Condorcet and d'Alembert. As for the complete record of foreign associates as well as accounts of the lives of members before they joined the Academy, they undoubtedly made use of notarial documents, reminiscences, and sources collected by their assistants or the Academicians' heirs. (This last is a moot point, but papers found in the dossiers of Fouchy and Condorcet at the Archives of the Academy of Sciences make this conjecture more than hypothetical.)

Fortunately, two kinds of sources for the *éloges* have survived the ravages of time and vagaries of privacy. One of these sources refers solely to Condorcet's eulogies. Because of the impending dissolution of the Academy, the tumultuous events of the early 1790s, and his own flight from certain death, he did not have the time or the desire to take with him pertinent dossiers, as his three predecessors appear to have done. Thus, we are fortunate that the Archives of the Academy contain the manuscript Fouchy's son gave to Condorcet for the eulogy of his father as well as the lives of

Bernard and Joseph de Jussieu provided by their nephew Antoine-Laurent de Jussieu. Condorcet also left behind him drafts of his eulogies of Fouchy, Haller, Linnaeus, Luynes, and Trudaine de Montigny, which can be compared to the final versions for critical study.[17]

The other kind of information available on the exact sources of some of the *éloges* are not documents, but simply acknowledgments made by all the four secretaries in these same eulogies. Fontenelle acknowledged his indebtedness to Eckard for his memoirs on Leibniz; to Saurin for an account of his own unjust imprisonment; and to A. Schultens, from whom he obtained information on Boerhaave's final three weeks.[18] For the greatest part of his *éloge* of Halley, Mairan thanked Martin Folkes, Halley's successor at the Academy of Sciences, and for his account of Cardinal de Fleury's courageous defense of the capital of his bishopric, he acknowledged two witnesses in a footnote.[19]

As is to be expected, a secretary would have been most grateful for any information anyone could provide him on foreigners who had been members of the Academy but who naturally lived all or nearly all of their lives outside France. This gratitude Fouchy expressed to three correspondants who had provided him with sources on de Moivre, Lowendal, and Wolff. Much more unusual are the two other acknowledgments he made. In the first, Fouchy thanked "*des personnes extrêmement respectables*" for the anecdote that Bragelongne spent his free time away from school with the famous philosopher and mathematician Malebranche. The second acknowledgment is truly exceptional: Fouchy stated in a note that the *éloge* he composed of D. C. Trudaine had been composed almost in its entirety by the latter's son, the Academician Trudaine de Montigny. The draft that the son had composed, Fouchy stated, "seemed to him to be of such excellence and the portrait drawn therein of that worthy magistrate so well delineated that he thought it best to give them almost without alteration and he declares having had no part in them than that of having approved them." The statement preceding this acknowledgment says that in order to write Trudaine's *éloge*, Fouchy had addressed himself to his son, an indication that this manner of obtaining sources may have been widespread.[20]

Interesting as these acknowledgments are, most of Condorcet's are even more so. Two of these are conventional: Montigny's *éloge* was partly based on memoirs sent to Condorcet by the family of the deceased while an anecdote about Bouvard's extremely generous help to a banker was obtained from a eulogy of Bouvard composed for the Faculté de Medecine of Paris. Somewhat less conventional sources are the account of Bertin's paranoiac bout obtained from his letters and from his physician and best friend, the description of d'Alembert's philosophy from Condorcet's conversations with him over a period of twenty years, and an account of La Condamine's childhood and youth from a memoir the latter had written in his old age for the edification of his young wife. The last two acknowledgments, however, are remarkable in that they speak superbly well of the high esteem eulogies had acquired by the last quarter of the eighteenth century as vehicles for immortalizing accomplished citizens. Condorcet incorporated wholesale a peroration of her husband written by Mme. de Courtivron and Linnaeus had sent the secretary a brief notice of his life to be used in the *éloge* of him.[21]

Appendix F
Three Sample "*Éloges*"

The three *éloges* reproduced below have been appended to this volume to illustrate some of the major themes discussed here and to exhibit the variety of treatment accorded to their subjects by Fontenelle, Fouchy, and Condorcet. Mairan is not represented here because the ten Academicians he eulogized did not give him sufficient scope to display the range of his abilities. Yet, however dissimilar in treatment, approach, and style, these *éloges* are similar in their special blend of biographical accuracy (though not completeness) and hagiographic intent.

Except for one sentence (duly acknowledged in note 38 below), the translation of these eulogies is entirely my own, as is its inadequacy to convey the full flavor of the original. I have tried to adhere as closely as possible to the French diction and syntax except where extraordinarily long sentences replete with colons and semi-colons necessitated their division into shorter sentences. The names of the eulogists, missing in the Histoires of the Paris Academy of Sciences, have been added in this translation.

ÉLOGE OF M. LEMERY
by
Fontenelle[22]

Fontenelle wrote finer *éloges* than that of Nicolas Lémery (e.g., of Vauban, Guglielmini, Cassini I, La Hire, Varignon, Peter the Great, Newton, Saurin), but none that exhibits so compactly his most salient characteristics as a eulogist. As a "Cartesian" chemist, fashionable lecturer, and victim of anti-Protestant persecution, Lémery offered Fontenelle the perfect subject for a variety of themes expressed in a variety of styles. Here Fontenelle strikes a mean between understated irony at the expense of the older chemistry and barely-contained indignation at the sufferings experienced by Lémery. Finally, this *éloge historique* is also one long variation on the theme explicitly stated in its conclusion, namely, the intimate connection between the moral character of science and that of its practitioners.

Nicolas Lémery was born in Rouen on November 17, 1645 to Julien Lémery, attorney [*Procureur*] at the *Parlement* of Normandy and of the so-called Reformed faith. He completed his formal studies in his native town, after which his natural aptitude led him to study pharmacy from one of his relatives, an apothecary of Rouen. He soon discovered that what then passed for chemistry, which he had known only by reputation, had to be more extensive than the science familiar to his teacher and his colleagues and therefore in 1666 he went to Paris in search of that chemistry.

He addressed himself to M. Glazer, then Démonstrateur[23] of chemistry at the Jardin du Roi, and he took out lodgings at his house so as to be at the best possible source of experiments and analyses. Unfortunately it so happened that M. Glazer was a true chemist: full of obscure notions, avaricious about those very notions, and very unsociable. M. Lémery therefore departed from him after two months and resolved to travel through France, successively to observe experts and to fashion a science out of the varying knowledge he would acquire from them. It is in this manner that travel had provided the main source of instruction before civilized nations entered into communication with one another through books. Chemistry was then in such an imperfect and uncultivated state that the only assurance of making some progress in it was to renew this ancient method of instruction.

For three years he boarded at Montpellier with M. Verchant, Master Apothecary, whose quarters provided him with the comforts of study and, more importantly, with the benefit of being able to give lessons to a number of his host's students. He was bound to draw much profit from his own lessons and in no time at all these attracted all the professors of the Faculty of Medicine as well as inquisitive persons of Montpellier, for he had already collected some exotic matter for the more skillful of them. Though he did not hold a medical degree, he practiced medicine in the city where it has been practiced so well from time immemorial, his reputation serving as his degree.[24]

At the completion of his journeys through the length and breadth of France, he returned to Paris in 1672. In those days lectures were still being given at the homes of various individuals; those with an inclination for the true sciences gathered in little groups, almost like rebels conspiring against ignorance and the dominant prejudices. Such were the gatherings held at the homes of M. the abbé Bourdelot, physician to M. le Prince the *Grand* Condé, and of M. Justel.[25] M. Lémery appeared at all of them and everywhere made a striking impression. He became intimate with M. Martin, apothecary to the Prince, and taking advantage of his friend's laboratory at the Hôtel de Condé, gave there a course in chemistry, which soon earned him the acquaintance and esteem of the prince, at whose residence he was working. He was frequently summoned to Chantilly, where the hero, like some idle Ceasar, had surrounded himself with wits and savants.[26]

M. Lémery meant to have a laboratory of his own and paid out of his own funds. He likewise desired to be licensed either Doctor of Medicine or Master Apothecary. Chemistry made him opt for the second choice and soon thereafter he opened public courses in chemistry in the rue Galande where he was lodging. His laboratory was not so much a room as a cellar and almost a magic den, illuminated entirely by the furnaces. Yet the throng of onlookers was so large as to leave hardly any space for his experiments. Among the auditors were some famous names like Rohault, Bernier, Auzout, Régis, and Tournefort.[27] Even ladies, carried away by the fashion, were bold enough to show themselves at such learned gatherings. Concurrently M. du Verney was giving anatomical lessons with equal brilliance and all the European nations supplied them with students.[28] It has been reckoned that in one year alone forty Scotsmen had come to Paris solely for the purpose of hearing these two teachers and who left France at the completion of their courses. As M. Lémery took in lodgers, his house was scarcely large enough for all who wished to reside there and the rooms of the neighborhood were filled with daytime pensioners eager to share at least dinner with him. His reputation also brought him great material benefits: as the prescriptions he himself prepared were in great demand, he sold a stupendous quantity of them in Paris and the provinces. The prescription of bismuth alone sufficed to cover all his household expenses, yet it is not a remedy, since it is properly speaking only *Blanc d'Espagne*. At that time he was the only one in Paris in possession of this treasure.

Until that time chemistry had been a science in which, to borrow its own terms, a bit of truth had been so dissolved in a large quantity of error as to become almost invisible and both, nearly inseparable. To the few known natural properties of mixtures there had been added at will many imaginary and more glittering ones: metals that were in sympathy with the planets and the main parts of the human body, an alkahest that no one had ever seen dissolve anything. The greatest absurdities were revered under cover of a mysterious obscurity, which enveloped them and sheltered them from reason. The chemists prided themselves in speaking exclusively in a barbarous tongue, similar to the sacred language of ancient Egyptian theology, understood by the priests alone and apparently rather devoid of sense. Chemical operations were described in books in such an enigmatic manner and often intentionally encumbered with so many impossible or useless details as to make it obvious that their authors only meant to secure for themselves the glory of understanding them and to make others despair of ever succeeding. At that, it was frequently the case that these very authors did not understand them that well or had not done as much as they wished others to believe. M. Lémery was the first to dissipate the natural or affected obscurity of chemistry, to reduce it to clearer and simpler terms, and to abolish the useless barbarism of its language. He, for his part, promised only what it was, and knew to be, capable of executing, whence its great success. More than mental integrity is involved in stripping of false dignity a science that one professes; there is also a kind of greatness of soul.

The wish to broaden the appeal of his science led him to publish his *Cours de Chimie* in 1675. Learned books normally do not acquire the fame of best-sellers but this one was an exception: it sold like a romance or a satire. Editions followed one another almost yearly, not counting a large number of pirated editions, which do the author both honor and harm. It was an entirely new science that appeared in the open and that aroused everybody's curiosity.

This book was translated into Latin, German, English, and Spanish. We said in the *éloge* of M. Tschirnhaus[29] that it was he who out of love for the sciences had had it translated into German at his own expense. The English translator, a former student of M. Lémery in Paris and who in his preface expresses the wish he were still studying with him, treats chemistry as a science that is almost entirely the creation of his master. The Spaniard, founder and president of the Royal Society of

Medicine in Seville, says that "in matters of chemistry the authority of the great Lémery is unique rather than recommendable."

Even though the book divulged the secrets of chemistry, he had reserved some for himself. Among these were a very mild emetic that is more effective than the one commonly used and a mesenteric opiate with which, it is said, he made surprising cures and whose secret not one of those who worked under him has ever been able to discover. He even simplified several experiments, without revealing the highest degree of simplification he was capable of, and he was confident that he could keep for his own use a portion of the vast wealth he had freely scattered to the public.

From 1681 on, the tranquility of his life was gravely disturbed on account of his religious faith. He was ordered to relinquish his position within a specified period: the Elector of Brandenburg, taking advantage of this occasion, offered him via M. Spanheim, his envoy in France, a position of chemist that he would especially create for him in Berlin.[30] Love of his country, the trouble of transporting his family to a distant land, the hope—very uncertain—of receiving some sort of honor, all held him back. Even after the period of grace had expired, he continued giving several lessons in chemistry to a large number of students, who made haste to profit from them. Finally, however, the tolerance which he had hitherto been favored with was succeeded by a strict interpretation of the law and he proceeded to England in 1683. He had the honor of paying his respects to King Charles II and of presenting him with the fifth edition of his book. This prince, though sovereign of a learned nation and habituated to savants, gave him marks of special esteem and led him to hope for more, but he sensed that these hopes would materialize from afar, if at all. The troubles that were then brewing in England presaged an existence as agitated as that he had suffered in France and he resolved to return home, without, however, having made any firm decision on the matter.

He hoped to lead to quieter existence in the shelter of a doctorate of medicine. At the end of 1683 the medical degree was conferred upon him by the University of Caen, which rewarded him with great honors for the preference he had shown it. Very shortly after he returned to Paris he found numerous patients but not the tranquility he had sought. Religious matters worsened from day to day: with the revocation of the Edict of Nantes in 1685[31] the practice of medicine was denied to members of the so-called Reformed Church. He was left without a position and utterly ruined, his house entirely stripped out of an unfortunate precaution, his effects dispersed almost randomly and concealed wherever possible, his mediocre fortune, still in its beginning, overthrown rather than disturbed, his mind incessantly preoccupied with the sorrows of the present and with anxieties about the future, which was nearly as terrifying as one's imagination would lead one to believe.

Nevertheless, M. Lémery still gave courses in chemistry, but under powerful protection: one to the younger brothers of M. le Marquis de Seignelay, *Sécrétaire d'Etat*, and the other to Milord Salisbury, who thought it impossible to obtain the same quality of education in England.[32]

Amidst the misfortunes and unhappiness he experienced, M. Lémery had reason to fear a yet greater evil, one of suffering for a wrong cause and to no purpose. He applied himself more diligently to studying the evidence of Catholicism and soon thereafter, at the beginning of 1686, joined the Church with his entire family.

With the full support of the law he took up anew the practice of medicine, but because he was no longer an apothecary, he had need of royal patent letters for his courses in chemistry and the sale of his remedies or prescriptions. He obtained the letters with ease, but when he tried to have them registered by the *Parlement* of Paris, the Lieutenant General of the Police M. de La Reynie, the Faculty of Medicine, and the Masters and Guards of the apothecary guilds, all expressed their opposition to it.[33] Apparently it was more out of a wish to keep these applications rare and difficult than out of a genuine desire to thwart him, since even his least disinterested opponents withdrew their objections almost immediately and yielded with good grace both to the merit of M. Lémery's character and to the merit he had acquired by his conversion. The peaceful days returned, and with them students, patients, the widespread sale of his chemical preparations, the whole greatly augmented by the interruption.

Beginning with Hippocrates, the physicians of antiquity had been physicians, apothecaries, and surgeons all in one. Subsequently, however, the physician had been divided into three, not that an ancient equals three moderns, but because of the vast increase in the functions and the knowledge associated with them. Yet M. Lémery combined all three, for he was also a surgeon, and in his youth had very successfully applied himself to surgery, especially blood-letting. At least he was the double of an ordinary physician, by his vast erudition in pharmacy and his actual practice of that art. He proved it by two big volumes that appeared in 1697, the first entitled *Pharmacopée universelle* and the other, *Traité universel des Drogues simples*. For both of them he requested a privilege of fifteen years but M. the Chancellor deemed it too short a time and had it extended to twenty.[34]

The *Pharmacopée universelle* is a compendium of all the chemical compositions of remedies that are described in all the pharmaceutical books of all the European nations. Hence, these different nations can find in this book, as in a large apothecary shop, the remedies that are particular to themselves alone, either because of differences in climates and temperaments or because of immemorial usage. In it can even be found the secrets that so many physicians are accused of feigning to ignore and that are the more admired the more ignorant the people who distribute them. This compendium, however, has been expurgated of all the erroneous chemical compositions that have been reported by authors too misinformed on the very matters they discuss and too slavish copyists of previous authors. On all the remedies that M. Lémery has retained and whose number is still stupendous, he wrote comments that explain their virtues, gave an account of their preparations, and more often than not either simplified them or eliminated whatever useless ingredients they contain. For instance, he removed twelve out of the sixty-four elements of the famous Theriac of Andromachus, and that number is possibly too small, but things rooted in custom can only be extirpated in degrees.

The *Traité universel des Drogues simples* is the foundation of the *Pharmacopée universelle*. It is an alphabetical compendium of all the mineral, vegetable, and animal matters that enter into accepted remedies; and as very few of them do not enter therein, this compendium comprises a good part of natural history. It includes a description of medical matters, their virtues, their method of selection, their history, or at least with respect to foreign matters whatever is known of their history until the present, for there are several that though widely used are nonetheless insufficiently understood. The common belief that genuine opium is a drop has been proved false and it is only recently too that it has been disproved that coffee is a bean.

The immense collection of remedies, whether simple or compound, contained in either the *Pharmacopée* or the *Traité des Drogues* seems to offer the promise of immortality, or at least of an assured cure for each illness. Yet as with society, where many offers of service are proferred but few are actually given, there are very few friends in this crowd of remedies. M. Leméry, who knew them intimately, trusted but a small number of them. It is only with great circumspection that he resorted to chemical remedies, though he might naturally have been predisposed in their favor by the same self-interest that is the common lot of men. It is only for the curiosity of physicians that he divulged almost all the analyses. He held that in comparison with medicine, chemistry, by dint of reducing chemical mixtures to their elements, often reduced them to nothing, and that one day chemistry would take an inverse route and from being an analysis it would change to a synthesis, that is, it would fashion new and better remedies out of the blend of different compounds. The people most skillful in an art are not the ones who are most vainglorious about it but the ones who are above it.

When the Academy was renewed in 1699, his reputation alone sufficed for him to be solicited and to obtain the seat of Associate Chemist, which by the death of M. Bourdelin at the end of the year[35] became that of Pensionnary. He then began to work on a large book that he read in segments at the Academy until he had it published in 1707. This is the *Traité de l'Antimoine*. This very useful mineral is exhibited there in al! its facets by dissolutions, sublimations, distillations, calcinations; it assumes all the forms that art can fashion and blends with whatever was believed capable of augmenting or modifying its virtues. It is considered from both a medical and a physical point of view; unfortunately, however, physical curiosity has a far greater scope than does medical utility. One could learn from this instance that the study of a single compound is almost limitless and that each by itself might need its own chemist.

Once the book was printed, M. Lémery began to feel heavily the infirmities of old age. He had several attacks of apoplexy, followed by the paralysis of one of his sides, which, however, did not prevent him from leaving his house. He always took his place at the sessions of the Academy, for which he had acquired the love that it never fails to inspire, and there he fulfilled his duties beyond what his health seemed to permit him. He was finally compelled to renounce attending these sessions and to shut himself up in his own house. He resigned from his position of Pensionnary, which was given to the oldest of the two sons belonging to this company.[36] He was struck by a last attack of apoplexy, which lasted six or seven days, and died on June 19, 1715.

Almost all of Europe has learned its chemistry from him and most of the great chemists, French or foreign, have acknowledged the debt their great learning owes him. He was a man of unremitting labor, being acquainted solely with his patients' room, his study, his laboratory, and the Academy, and he assuredly attests to the fact that he who does not waste time has a great quantity of it at his disposal. He was a good friend, he always lived with M. Régis[37] on very intimate terms that never underwent any alteration. The same probity and simplicity of manners united them. We are almost weary of extolling this virtue in the men we are obliged to talk about. This praise pertains rather generally to this small, private group of men that the business of science separates from the majority of mankind.[38]

ÉLOGE OF MR. BRADLEY
by
Fouchy[39]

No secretary in the eighteenth century surpassed Fouchy in rendering a precise technical account of any and all scientific achievements. And, as in the case of Bradley, when these achievements were in his own specialty of astronomy, Fouchy could be trusted to make them palpable to his mixed audience by clear expositions and felicitous analogies. What he cannot be asked to do is to describe these contributions in memorable prose, to probe beneath their surface, or to comment on their extrascientific significance. In this *éloge* variety is lamely achieved by frequent allusions to friends in high places, listings of titles held, and by monotonous assertions of Bradley's tireless assiduity. Typical of Fouchy, too, is the elaborate peroration testifying to the scientist's pastoral or Stoic virtues.

James Bradley, Astronomer Royal, Doctor of Divinity of the University of Oxford, Savilian Professor of Astronomy, Reader in astronomy and physics at the museum of the same university, astronomer and director of the Royal Observatory at Greenwich, and member of the royal academies of France, Great Britain, St. Petersburg, and of the Institute of Bologna, was born in Sherbourne in the county of Gloucestershire in 1692,[40] the third son of William and Jane Bradley.

He was educated at Northleach Grammar School by Messrs. Eggles and Brice, who warmly encouraged the auspicious talents they early discovered in their pupil. Having completed his course of humanities, he was sent to Oxford, the famous English university, and it is there that he became receptive to the advanced sciences in which he has since made such rapid progress and where he received his degrees.[41]

Mr. Bradley had been destined by his family for a clerical vocation. Perhaps he too believed himself to have been called for it; in any event, he applied himself in good faith to the studies requisite for that position and it was not long before he reaped its rewards. As soon as he was able to officiate in a vicarship, the bishop of Hereford, who had conceived a high esteem for him, appointed him to that of Bridstow,[42] and shortly thereafter provided him with the benefice of Wellfry in the county of Pembrokeshire. Yet despite the auspicious beginnings that seemed to promise the highest positions in the calling he had embraced, he soon abandoned it to give himself up entirely to the inclination he began to feel for mathematics in general and astronomy in particular. Nature is often imperious and, when not sufficiently consulted, is likely to overturn the best laid-out plans with one blow.

Mr. Bradley was the nephew of Mr. Pound, who is known in the Republic of Letters for several observations[43] and who could have published many more had not the journals of his voyages been lost in the conflagration of Palo-Condon associated with the general massacre that the natives of that island inflicted on the English residents. It is with this relative that Mr. Bradley spent the few months left over from his clerical duties and perhaps even some moments stolen from his ministry without his being too cognizant of it. He had by then acquired enough knowledge of mathematics to be able to profit from his conversation. We say "acquired," for it is not known whether anyone had facilitated his debut in the sciences; he probably had no other teacher than his own genius nor any other assistance than his own diligence.

One can well imagine that the example and conversation of Mr. Pound did not lighten the burden of Mr. Bradley's ministry. He professed it as assiduously as possible, however, but often let his gaze wander towards the heavens and by his observations he began to lay the foundations of the beautiful discoveries that were to earn him a place among the greatest astronomers of the century.

Though these observations were made, so to speak, in secrecy, the name of Mr. Bradley had become sufficiently known to reach the ears of the most famous men in England. They earned him the esteem and friendship of the Chancellor of England, Lord Macclesfield, Mr. Newton, Mr. Halley,[44] and several other famous members of the Royal Society. It is from the testimony of such good judges of these matters that the talents and progress of Mr. Bradley became known to this famous company, which decided to make him a Fellow.

At this time there died the famous John Keill,[45] who had filled with distinction the chair founded by Sir [Henry] Savil at the University of Oxford;[46] it probably would have been very troublesome to find a subject as qualified as Mr. Bradley to occupy it, both for ability and for love of astronomy. It is difficult to speak dispassionately of the object of one's affection and no one is more qualified to teach a science than he who loves it dearly. Hence, the approbation in his favor was universal and he was appointed to that chair on October 31, 1721. At the age of twenty-nine he thus found himself by this appointment a colleague of the famous Halley, who occupied in the same university the chair of geometry created by the same Sir [Henry] Savil.

As soon as he was appointed to that chair, he resigned from his vicarship of Bridstow and even gave up his benefice. His truly honest soul had for some time been divided between his duties and his interests and he took this opportunity with alacrity so as to free himself from this constraint.

Free at last to yield entirely to his love of astronomy, nothing further interrupted the course of his observations and from 1727 on he was in a position to convey its results to astronomers and publish them in the form of the theory of the aberration of the stars—a theory worthy to be ranked among the most beautiful, the most useful, and the most ingenious discoveries of modern astronomy.

For a long time observations had disclosed that the positions of the stars were subjected to certain deviations that did not correspond to the apparent displacement of a degree in seventy-two years caused by the precession of the equinoxes. The late abbé Picard had since 1671 noticed these deviations in the pole-star but he had made no attempt either to reduce them to a general rule or to find their cause;[47] the constantly repeated observations of Mr. Bradley not only revealed the deviations noted by M. Picard but also many others that had not even been suspected. He discovered stars that appeared, in the space of a year, to have been displaced in longitude without in any manner changing their latitudinal position, others that deviated in latitude without changing in longitude, and others still—the largest in number—that seemed, in the space of a year, to describe in the heavens a small but more or less elongated ellipse.

The period of one year taken by all these motions that otherwise were so different from each other plainly showed that it had some connection with the motion of the earth, but the difficulty was to determine the nature of that connection. At first Mr. Bradley's attempts to find the solution came to nothing; finally, his reiterated efforts solved this difficulty and led him to find the cause of these apparent anomalies in the successive and combined motions of light and of the earth around the sun.

It had long been believed that the velocity of light was physically infinite. The late M. Rømer of this Academy[48] was the first to dare disprove this belief and even to determine the time it took for light to traverse the sixty-six million leagues of the diameter of the annual orbit. This exact and industrious observer had noticed that the first satellite of Jupiter emerged the more slowly as Jupiter moved away from the opposition and that this delay lasted as long as eleven minutes in the eclipses closest to the conjunction. He held that eleven minutes were precisely what was required for the first ray of the satellite emerging from the shadow to traverse the distance between the two positions of the earth closest to the opposition and to the conjunction and therefore that the velocity of light was not only finite but measurable as well.

However well founded in nature, this explanation seemed too daring at the time and it was long after the death of M. Rømer that it was adopted and that physicists universally agreed on the successive motion of light. It is from this successive motion that Mr. Bradley derived his explanation of the irregular deviations he had observed in the stars and which he named "Stellar aberration." We will attempt to give an explanation of it.

Let us imagine rows of small bodies moving in a parallel direction to one another, as for example, rain on a windless day falling perpendicularly to the horizon. Let us place in the same vertical position a fixed and straight tube and expose it to the rain. Should this tube be moved in a direction parallel to itself, it will necessarily follow that despite its position always remaining parallel to the direction of the raindrops, the motion of the tube will cause them to come into contact with one of its walls, and the earlier as the motion of the drops will be slower relative to that of the tube. And it can be easily demonstrated that when the two motions are equal, the raindrop falling into the center of the upper orifice of the tube will reach the interior wall after having traversed only a length equal to the radius of the tube and that its direction will consequently form an angle of 45 degrees with the axis of the tube. Whence, to prevent the waterdrops, despite their motion, from touching the tube, it is necessary to incline it at an angle of 45 degrees in the direction of the drops' motion and that if it described the circumference of a circle, the tube will describe around the vertical line passing through the center of its base a cone with a 90-degree angle.

It is evident that the change of inclination required to prevent the interior walls of a moving tube from coming into contact with raindrops absolutely depends on the ratio between the velocity of that motion and that of the raindrops and that the greater the latter with respect to the former, the less inclination to be applied to the tube. Hence, if the motion of the raindrops were infinite with respect to that of the tube, there would be no need to alter the position of the tube, since the drops will just as soon reach the bottom as the top and since the tube, in this amount of time, can only advance over an infinitely small distance.

The application of this theory to stellar aberration should make it evident that the rows of raindrops are the rays emanating from the stars, that the tube we supposed to be first at rest then in motion is that of the telescope that determines the position of the stars and is always swept along by the motion of the earth around the sun, and that, finally, if the velocity of the motion of light has a finite ratio to that of terrestrial motion, the tube should change its inclination with the change of direction of its motion, whence each star should follow a sequence of different positions or, what amounts to the same, an apparent motion in the sky that causes it with each change of position to describe in the space of one year more or less elongated ellipses.

This is the beautiful theory of aberration that Mr. Bradley published in 1727 and that was received by the scientific world with the praise it justly deserved. M. Clairaut of this Academy[49] has since then made it the subject of an excellent mémoire, published in 1737, in which he thoroughly examines the theory of aberration and gives the rules on how to apply it to practice. It follows from Clairaut's calculations that the velocity of light necessarily imparted to it by the observed aberrations of the stars is exactly equal to that given by M. Rømer to the retardment of the eclipses of the first satellite of Jupiter—a new proof of this hypothesis, if one were ever needed.

Three years after this very glorious period in Mr. Bradley's life, he was given the vacated place of Reader in astronomy and physics at the Museum of Oxford. No one certainly was better qualified than he to occupy this double position.

The more honors and benefits that astronomy bestowed upon Mr. Bradley, the more did his love of that science and his assiduity in observing the heavens increase. These repeated observations soon led him to discover that the inclination of the terrestrial axis on the plane of the ecliptic was not constant but experienced a nodding [balancement] of several seconds every nine years. What satisfactory reasons could apparently be offered for it and what did a period of nine years have in common with the yearly motion of the earth? The increased investigations and efforts of Mr. Bradley nevertheless led him to find the cause of that phenomenon, and in the Newtonian theory of attraction.

It is a well-known fact that the first principle of that theory is the mutual attraction of all bodies in direct proportion of their masses and in inverse proportion of the squares of the distances between them. It is from this attraction combined with motion in a straight line that Mr. Newton deduced the form assumed by planetary orbits, especially that of the earth. If this orbit were a circle and the terrestrial globe a perfect sphere, the attraction of the sun would simply maintain the earth in its orbit and never perturb the position of its axis; since neither of these suppositions is true, the earth is appreciably inflated at the equator and its orbit is an ellipse with one focus occupied by the sun. When the position of the earth is such that its equatorial plane passes through the center of the sun, this star can attract our globe only in a line parallel to itself and without perturbing the position of its axis—an action that affects the two equinoxes. The farther the earth moves from these two points, the farther does the sun deviate from the equatorial plane and approach one of the two tropics. Since the radiuses of the earth exposed to the sun are then no longer equal, the equator is more powerfully attracted than is the remainder of the globe, thus leading to some change in its position and in its inclination on the plane of the ecliptic. And as the part of the orbit lying between the autumnal and vernal equinoxes is smaller than the one lying between the latter and the former, it follows that the perturbation caused by the sun as it traverses the winter solstice is not wholly compensated by the one it causes as it traverses the summer solstice, and it follows too that the parallelism of the terrestrial axis with its inclination toward the ecliptic remains somewhat altered. Up to now, however, nothing has been said that bears any relation to the nine years of the [nodding] period. We shall forthwith see the causes of it.

To the effect of the solar attraction on the earth should be added that of the lunar attraction, an effect that is the greater the farther it moves away from the equator. Now, during the time it takes for its nodes to align themselves with the equinoctial points, its greatest latitude is added to the greatest obliquity of the ecliptic; this therefore is the time of its strongest capacity to perturb the position of the terrestrial axis. And the revolution of the lunar nodes being eighteen years in duration, it is evident that in this amount of time the nodes will have appeared twice in the equinoctial points, and consequently twice in a period of eighteen years. In other words, every nine years the terrestrial axis will experience its greatest perturbation, or, what amounts to the same, it will have a nodding whose period, as Mr. Bradley has observed, will be nine years long: it is this nodding that he named the nutation of the terrestrial axis. He announced it to the public in 1737, so that he made in less than ten years two of the most beautiful discoveries of astronomy, which will forever mark an era in the history of that science.

Mr. Bradley had always enjoyed the esteem and friendship of Mr. Halley. The latter, burdened with the weight of years and his labors, thought that the best service he could henceforth render to astronomy was to do his utmost to obtain for Mr. Bradley the position of Astronomer and Director of the Royal Observatory of Greenwich that he himself had occupied so deservingly and for so long. With this aim in mind, he wrote several letters, subsequently found in Mr. Bradley's papers, in which he entreated him to accept his position on reversion and he even offered to resign, should it be necessary to do so. Mr. Halley's wishes, however, were not fulfilled, at least in his lifetime, and his death prevented its execution. Since then Mr. Bradley has obtained this position through the protection and influence of Milord Macclesfield, later President of the Royal Society and a member of this Academy, the loss of whom was lamented by both companies. We are reporting these facts about Mr. Halley solely to show the great esteem that this Nestor of astronomy held for Mr. Bradley. It is essential that his *éloge* make mention of the esteem and friendship of such a great man.

As soon as the appointment of Mr. Bradley was made public, the University of Oxford, which until then had only had the honor of numbering him among its students, meant to attach him more closely to itself, by admitting him into its corporation; without prompting it gave him the degree of doctor of theology.

The position of astronomer at Greenwich put Mr. Bradley in his true element: he devoted himself to observation with indefatigable assiduity and henceforth his history becomes, so to speak, part of celestial history.

However large the collection of instruments in the possession of the Greenwich Observatory, it was almost impossible for an astronomer of such fervor as Mr. Bradley not to desire many more, as much for the greatest possible precision in observation as for the pursuit of individual research. In 1747 he took advantage of the yearly visit that the Royal Society paid to the Greenwich Observatory to verify the inventory of instruments and to request from the other astronomers a copy of the observations of that year. So vividly did he depict the necessity for repairing the old instruments and for constructing new ones that the Society was bound to inform the king, who, because of these remonstrances, donated for this important purpose a sum of one thousand pound sterling or the equivalent of about twenty-two thousand fifty livres. One can well imagine, from all that has been said about Mr. Bradley's love of astronomy, what use he made of that money: he availed himself of the talents and knowledge of Messrs. Graham and Bird of the Royal Society to carry out his plans,[50] with the result that the Observatory was furnished with the most complete collection of excellent instruments that could have been desired by an astronomer most anxious to secure perfect observations. Provided with this assistance, Mr. Bradley redoubled the assiduity of his observations; an almost incredible quantity of them were found posthumously and we cannot announce early enough to the public that they were entrusted to the care of the Royal Society. One can be certain that this precious depository will be used in a manner befitting the Royal Society and Mr. Bradley's memory.

We mentioned above that he had given up his vicarship of Bridstow and his benefice as soon as he had been appointed to one of the chairs of astronomy at the University of Oxford. The vicarship of Greenwich having become vacant, it was held that it would be the finest gift he could receive, but though he was obliged to reside in Greenwich, the same delicacy that had led him to resign from his curate at Bridstow led him to turn down the latter, in spite of its rich benefice. He feared that the duties of an astronomer conflicted with those of a minister and, not wishing to incur any reproaches on this matter, felt no compunction in declining this benefice. The king of England [George II] was so taken by the merit of this noble gesture that to reward Mr. Bradley for his deed gave him, by a patent letter dated February 15, 1752, an annuity of two hundred and fifty pound sterling or the equivalent of five to six thousand livres. This letter specifically stated that it was given in consideration of his great skill in and deep knowledge of astronomy and other branches of mathematics, which have been of such great utility to the commerce and navigation of England. Motifs of this kind do Mr. Bradley too much honor for us to omit them. This same annuity was renewed by the present king of England [George III], who did himself credit, at the time of his accession to the throne, by having declared himself the protector of letters, sciences, and the useful arts.

It was during this period that Mr. Bradley was admitted into the Council of the Royal Society.[51] He had been appointed in 1747 member of the Royal Academy of Sciences and Letters of Berlin and the following year obtained in this company that of Foreign Associate that had become vacant upon the death of Mr. Cervi, first physician to his Catholic Majesty,[52] in 1754 that of the Imperial Academy of St. Petersburg, and in 1757 that of the Institute of Bologna. His reputation was so secure and so widespread that none of the learned societies of Europe neglected to include him among its members.

All these unequivocal tokens of public esteem only inflamed Mr. Bradley's ardor and induced him to redouble his efforts to make this esteem even more deserving. Relentlessly advancing age did not abate his assiduity, which, however, became disproportionate to his strength; he finally succumbed to it and in the year 1760 found himself overwhelmed with extreme fatigue. He had no fear of death, but only of the risk of ceasing to be of utility and of surviving the faculties of his soul; they were nevertheless respected by the illness and for two years he had no other affliction than this kind of exhaustion. Toward the end of June 1762, however, he was attacked by a retention of urine caused by a kidney inflammation, from which he died the following July 13 in the seventieth year of his life. He was buried in Michenhampton in the county of Gloucestershire, in the same spot that already held the bodies of his mother and his wife. We say "his wife" because in 1744 he had married Susannah Peach, daughter of a gentleman from the same county, from whose marriage one daughter survived him.

The essence of his character was a most perfect modesty and a gentleness uncommon in a man of a temperament ardent and strong enough to endure the longest vigils and the greatest diligence. To these two qualities he joined the most perfect equanimity and the greatest generosity for those who were in need; the vanity that is so natural to men and that is so frequently leveled against men of learning had almost no hold on him. Though he was fluent in speech and endowed with the precious art of enunciating his ideas with all the clarity they were susceptible of, never was there a man more infatuated with silence: he never spoke unless obliged to do so, but he was not sparing in speech if he thought it could be of some utility. He even roused his students to ask him questions by the precise manner in which he answered them and by the care he took always to put himself within reach of those he was conversing with. He no more attempted to display himself by his writings than by his speech, hence he has not much published. The extreme mistrust he had of himself was the cause of his never being satisfied with his works and induced him to suppress a great many that would undoubtedly have deserved to come out into the open; it was only the requirement imposed on the astronomer of Greenwich to communicate his observations to the Royal Society that disclosed his modesty and has preserved for us the immense collection of those he had made. He acquired his fame almost in spite of himself; at least we can attest that his reputation was solely due to his merit and not at all to vanity. Yet despite his extreme simplicity and the reluctance he felt to be communicative, he was very well known and consequently very esteemed by the highest personages of England: all men of learning, whether English or foreign, hastened to show him marks of respect. Above all, there was no famous astronomer in Europe who did not feel honored to be directly or indirectly in communication with him. In short, it can be said that no one has ever cultivated great talents more successfully and has deserved to be placed by unanimous consent among the greatest astronomers of this century.

The seat of Foreign Associate that had been occupied by Mr. Bradley in this Academy has been taken by M. Linnaeus, Knight of the Royal and Military Order of the Pole-Star, Doctor of Medecine and Professor of Botany at Uppsala, member of the academies of Uppsala, Stockholm, St. Petersburg, Berlin, and the *Collegium Naturae Curiosorum*,[53] and of the royal societies of London, Montpellier, Toulouse, and Florence.

ÉLOGE OF M. DE FOUCHY
by
Condorcet[54]

The unsubstantial record of astronomical achievement that Fouchy, in contrast to Bradley, had accumulated in his lifetime must have presented his eulogist Condorcet with both a vexing dilemma and a golden opportunity. If the secretary was to limit himself to telling the bare truth about his predecessor, seven pages would have sufficed to cover his life and achievements (pp. 37−39, 40−42, 45, 47−49). Since such a short eulogy would have given the appearance of demeaning the office of the secretariat, he seized this opportunity to describing the ideal secretary and to drawing a favorable comparison between Fouchy and the almost perfect Fontenelle (pp. 42−45). Condorcet devoted three more pages to a summary of the history of science during the thirty-two years of Fouchy's tenure of office (1744−76) and of the causal connection between science and enlightenment (pp. 45−47). Yet even in the biographical passages Condorcet typically could not resist converting plain descriptions into elaborate professions of secular faith.

Jean-Paul Grandjean de Fouchy, auditor of the Chambre des Comptes and ordinary secretary to M. the duc d'Orléans,[55] honorary perpetual secretary of the Academy of Sciences,[56] and member of the Royal Society of London, etc., was born in Paris on March 1707, of Philippe Grandjean de Fouchy and Marie-Magdelaine Hynault.

His father, descended from a noble family of Maconnais, had been destined by his parents for an ecclesiastical career, by nature for an occupation in the arts, and by chance for the improvement of the art of printing. Once led by curiosity into a print shop, he was struck by the imperfection of the letters used by the French presses of the day. That very evening he attempted to draw several capital letters and to endow them with an elegance, clarity, and beautiful proportion whose absence had shocked his taste. These attempts having been confided undesignedly to one of his friends, they were brought by him to the attention of the Chancellor M. de Pontchartrain and soon thereafter shown to Louis XIV, who, with the eagerness of a prince infatuated with all kinds of glory, seized this opportunity to give French editions the advantage over the Dutch ones and to bring to an end this inferiority with respect to an enemy nation that seemed the more humiliating because of the large number of elegant writers and men of genius that France took pride in.

The young Grandjean was assigned the task of drawing and casting new letters and by a stroke of luck that vindicated the minister's choice he combined within himself the capacity of tasteful drawing, the talent for and love of the arts, and diligence and patience in work.

The discovery of printing has opened to all of humanity the road to happiness as well as that to liberty. It alone has rendered truths everlasting, it alone has made them the common patrimony of all men, and it alone has removed all barriers to either the progress of the human mind or the perfectibility of social institutions.

Gratitude, therefore, should suffice to justify the luxury of beautiful editions, but it is fair to observe that even the most refined perfection in the useful arts should not be considered an extravagant fantasy. Without the superb editions that have been designed for the sole gratification of some wealthy amateurs, the reading of common editions would not have been facilitated. In order for the majority to enjoy progress in an art, it is almost always necessary that this same progress should first have given exclusive pleasures to the minority. Even the strictest moralists should not censure connoisseurs of art objects that join genuine and newly-found utility to splendor and rarity and it is only right that the wealthy should be forgiven for whims that one day may open new sources of enjoyment to all men.

Filled with enthusiasm for his art, M. de Fouchy *père* had destined his son to succeed him and had reserved for him the honor of completing the alphabets of Oriental languages that were still lacking. Hence, after receiving an education of a quality that would have met the standards of a father he had lost in childhood, M. de Fouchy occupied himself with the task of drawing Hebrew letters and of having them engraved. Circumstances, however, were changing. Louis XIV had attached such a high value to the exclusive perfection of the French editions that he refused a set of matrices of the Imprimerie Royale, engraved by Fouchy père, to the same Philip V, his grandson, for whom he had squandered the blood and treasure of France.[57] M. de Fouchy, however, soon perceived that only the protection of Louis XIV had prevented the subordinate officials from confusing simple workers with artisans who, by improving a practical art, serve the glory of the nation, its trade, and even the diffusion of knowledge, since improvement of printing results in the ability to read longer without enduring fatigue and to read more in an equal time.[58]

M. de Fouchy was therefore compelled to renounce the career that had been pursued by his father and, determined by a natural inclination that his education had fostered, devoted himself entirely to the study of the sciences. A society had been formed in Paris, composed of savants and artisans, with the intent of applying to the arts the scientific principles and theories capable of directing, assuring, and improving their practice. This society, which numbered among its members Messrs. Clairaut, [the abbé] de Gua, La Condamine, the abbé Nollet, Rameau, Sully, and Julien Le Roy and his sons, could be equally useful to the sciences and the arts.[59]

To seek to bring the sciences and practice into too close an alliance, to prohibit them from engaging in pure speculations on the pretext of their present uselessness, is to lay oneself open to the charge of having retarded their progress. Such an action would deprive genius of his freedom, confine his soaring to a narrow compass, and even impede his movement, since the succession of truths that follow from one another and that are discovered successively by new methods has no relation whatever with the succession of truths which also yield successively practical applications. It is precisely because difficult investigations, discoveries that broaden the sphere of the human mind, can for a long while remain impractical to common life that it is right for learned companies to preserve the inclination for them, gather together the men engaged in their pursuit, reward them, and encourage them by attracting the attention and securing the esteem of those who are incapable of judging them. Should these companies ever show any preference for practical achievements, for those which already assure greater popularity and join greater facility with the hope of greater benefits, the sciences would be threatened with a debility that would soon extend to the very arts to which they had been imprudently sacrificed. On the other hand, the fortunate conjunction of artisans and savants resulted in the latter becoming, so to speak, useful intermediaries between savants unfamiliar with the arts and artisans insufficiently grounded in the sciences. Now discussing with the savants the principles fit to serve as guides to the arts, now enlightened by the artisans on the difficulties besetting these applications, in turn instructing the former on the insights that the practice of the arts can offer for the progress of the sciences and the latter on the utility to be desired by this same progress, they would have obtained for both the sciences and the arts all the mutual benefits that may have arisen out of such a combined gathering. Prejudices and petty jealousies led to the downfall of this useful institution, whose disappearance cannot be but cause for regret.

M. de Fouchy was removed from the Society by the Academy, which gave him the seat of astronomer in 1731.[60] His numerous Mémoires include ingenious and easy methods of observation; skillful, ready, and inexpensive means of dispensing with instruments that are difficult to obtain or to transport without threatening the precision of the observations; and they prove that a happy blend of simplicity and nicety formed the special character of his talent. We shall cite only two instances of this.

The immersions and emersions of the Jovian satellites displayed in their periodicity irregularities that astronomers had not yet been able to account for. M. de Fouchy imagined a way to seek their cause in the laws of optics. It is well known that objects become visible only when their apparent diameter is of a certain length, as it is for all bodies that are uniformly illuminated; thus a satellite that is more distant from the earth [than is another satellite] and whose apparent diameter is therefore smaller should, with equal illumination, disappear earlier and reappear later. At the same time a body with a smaller apparent diameter but with greater illumination is visible to the same degree; hence a satellite should disappear the later and reappear the earlier as the amount of light it radiates is the greater. M. de Fouchy showed that these two causes provide the explanation for the observed irregularities; but only computed explanations are admitted in astronomy. Another optical principle presented him with the means to offer such an explanation: all other things being equal, the light of objects viewed through a lens varies in proportion to the size of its aperture. It was therefore a matter of comparing the moment of emersion or immersion of a satellite by observing it with lenses equal in size except for their apertures; from which it followed that the effect exerted on their disappearance could be estimated by the lesser or greater amount of light and that it was possible to compute the law by which this cause affected the phenomenon.

This ingenious idea of M. de Fouchy, which he subsequently abandoned, was pursued and successfully improved by one of our colleagues who, since then summoned by the free choice of his compatriots to fill honorable and important positions, has by his example refuted the prejudice that excluded from public office those whose reason has been strengthened, whose soul has been elevated, and whose character has been ennobled by the study of literature, science, or philosophy.[61]

It is difficult to construct a telescope with fixed parts that are perfectly parallel. This difficulty vanishes if only an ordinary level is used, but it would then be necessary for both tubes of the level, placed within the telescope, to be seen distinctly. M. de Fouchy accomplished this feat by means of a telescope with four lenses: one of its tubes is viewed in direct position and the other in reversed position, with the result that the bearing of the level can be observed with greater precision.

In 1743 M. de Fouchy was nominated perpetual secretary of the Academy. This meant that he was succeeding M. de Fontenelle, whose place M. de Mairan had agreed to occupy for a few years only[62] so as to leave enough time for a proper selection to be made, a selection made the more difficult by the talents and fame of Corneille's nephew.[63] In order to be worthy of this replacement, it was essential that his successor make no attempt to resemble him and also be capable of accommodating himself to the changing times and beliefs. A contemporary of Arnauld and Voltaire, of Bossuet and Montesquieu,[64] a witness to the last days of the old physics, of the reign and fall of Cartesianism, which thanks to the discoveries of Newton and Locke has been replaced by a truer philosophy, M. de Fontenelle had observed these great revolutions, of which he himself had been one of the most useful instruments; he had seen truths, which in his youth had been buried in the consciousness of several sages, become towards the end of his life the fashionable beliefs of men of the world. Concealing the insights of a profound philosophy within unadorned forms, endowed with the double gift of popularizing truths he deemed expedient for diffusion and of disguising those he thought proper for dissemination only among a small number of minds, he possessed the ability of choosing his expressions so as to awaken different ideas in different classes of readers and of leading each person to understand what he was capable of understanding, what he was permitted to learn, all the while leading everyone to believe that they had understood him equally. Either as a result of his temperament or by free will, Fontenelle's philosophy was best suited to an age when the natural progress of knowledge had marked for the European nations the passage from the yoke of prejudices to the rule of reason, that is, to an era when truth, timorous and ignored, could no longer be concealed yet could only be displayed with great caution, when it was necessary to disguise her with a veil so as not to injure eyes too long accustomed to darkness and that nevertheless could be easily removed by men hidden in the crowd and worthy of contemplating her.

But these ingenious forms, this talent for disclosing truth only in halves so as to augment the pleasure of grasping it, for concealing under common expressions the force or daring of ideas, would have been in M. de Fontenelle's successors only the mannerisms of a writer and not the art of a philosopher, unwilling to compromise with reason; the moment had arrived when it could be exhibited with less finery.

At a time when the sciences were not so widely diffused, M. de Fontenelle was bound to connect their principles, progress, and methods to the notions of general metaphysics. At a time when they had become more universal, M. de Fouchy was bound to apply himself to showing the essence of the principles and methods particular to each science. The aim of the one had to be the presentation of an accurate notion of all the sciences to those who had studied none, of the other, the initiation of those who had cultivated one science to the principles of all the others. One had to disentangle the facts or the results of hypothetical explanations that everywhere intermingled with them and almost involuntarily, the other to link, to systematically arrange isolated facts that were often presented without the connections that alone could impress their importance [on the public]. The former had to recall to people's minds the general utility of the sciences, the beauty of the spectacle they offered to the human mind, the noble exercise they afforded to its activity; the latter, addressing himself to men already infatuated with them, had to restrict himself to impressing upon them the utility of each task for the progress of the science in which it was pursued. The history of M. de Fontenelle was more philosophical, that of M. de Fouchy more technical [*savante*], and it is evident from reading the latter that its author, faithful to this principle, was able to endow it with the rigorous precision and the clarity that imply a blend of extreme mental accuracy with a facility in diversifying and expanding his learning without confounding one part with another.

In his *éloges* M. de Fouchy was less ingenious than Fontenelle, but he almost always deserves credit for not attempting to be so. Simplicity, truth, and exactness comprise the principal qualities of his portraits. He inspires confidence because he apparently avoids embellishment. If subtle thoughts or happy images offer themselves to him, it is evident that he is inspired by the subject and has not labored to adorn it. His ever-unpretentious style, however, is almost always noble and pure: a virtue rare at a time when the desire to make an impression through utterance and to compensate for mental nullity by verbal singularity confounds all styles and genres and converts defects of measure and taste into one of the secrets in the art of acquiring evanescent fame and thus escaping by a prompt oblivion the redoubtable judgment of posterity.

M. de Fontenelle had transmitted to his successors other models that M. de Fouchy was able to imitate.

The secretary of a learned company is the unavoidable confidant of all the petty passions that are prompted among its members by the love of fame or of esteem, by differences in opinion, and even by rivalry between dissimilar sciences. He is a witness to the secret weaknesses of vanity that are not always cured by knowledge, talent, or even celebrity. His indiscretion could frequently have caused the seeds of discord to blossom into quarrels had not silence stifled these seeds forever.

Constrained into silence without being obliged to conceal his beliefs, to maintain an even hand without renouncing his personal attachments, to avoid to the point of scrupulousness the suspicion of desiring power for which the perpetuity of his office offers so many possibilities, it would be impossible for him to fulfill his duties if they had not been lightened by the moderation of his soul, the complaisance and serenity of his character, and even a mind superior to the petty and dangerous honor of appearing to dominate those who have appointed him their spokesman.

M. de Fouchy fulfilled them all, and their sweet and just reward has been the confidence and friendship of his colleagues.

After having occupied his position for thirty years with a punctuality that never flagged and a zeal that nothing could dampen or weary, M. de Fouchy thought that his infirmities and his [advanced] age entitled him to seek not rest but freedom; he was good enough to cast his eyes on me to assist him in his functions and to destine me to succeed him. Zeal for the sciences, a deep-seated conviction of their utility, a life devoted uniquely to their cultivation, all had determined him to show me this very honorable mark of his esteem. As modest about his successor as he had been about himself, he considered the love of truth a quality that should determine his selection, since it was the only one that he ever permitted himself to take pride in. Three years later he ceased to exercise the functions of secretary.[65]

The period during which he fulfilled his duties was noted for a successful revolution in the sciences.

Cosmology [le système du monde], the most impressive monument to the might and grandeur of the human mind, erected by Newton on unshakable foundations, had risen through the genius of his successors to a height that one would hardly have thought possible from the labors of several centuries. The reciprocal actions of the celestial bodies, the motion of their axes, the revolutions of their orbital planes had all been subjected to computations, their masses established, their forms determined.

The very comets have been unable to escape this action in the immense spaces where, after appearing for a few moments, they disappear for several centuries. New methods of analysis, new principles of mechanics have changed the state of these sciences and demonstrated that there is nothing that genius, given time, cannot expect to attain.

Chemistry, which for so long had strayed into obscure chimeras that flatter the two most violent passions of common souls—that of seeking wealth and that of subsisting—and had been carried to the point of superstition and delirium, had found itself blocked in its early progress by its delight in mechanical principles. Finally, however, it had extricated itself from these bonds. At the very moment when it already had offered a stock of precise and interconnected facts, the discovery of new substances which heretofore had escaped our instruments has led to the disappearance of one of the degrees that separate the principles of bodies we can apprehend from those simple and unalterable elements, which are the latest limits of our efforts and our hopes.

While new methods improved the nomenclature of natural history, this science, after having for so long restricted itself to testing the memory by lists and the imagination by systems, has finally become what it ought to be, namely, the description and history of natural creatures, the examination of their relationships, and the study of their properties.

Physics has acquired a new division; the wonders of electricity have been analyzed and subjected to laws and an illustrious physicist has at once discovered the nature of lightning and the means to prevent its ravages.[66]

While the general system of the sciences thrived on new methods of computation, new instruments, and facts hitherto unknown, they all simultaneously acquired a better method and greater precision, all obtained greater utility from repeated applications. A more intimate union was formed between them, not as in the past by ingenious and unnatural applications, but because all the sciences, having simultaneously expanded, had reached the point where they could assist one another and begin to intermingle.

This rapid progress in the sciences presaged a general intellectual revolution: men acquired a greater sense of justice, reason advanced with greater certainty, and the sophistries of prejudice could no longer be upheld when in such close proximity to the logic of the sciences. In observing all the great things that the human mind has created in the sciences, one could hardly maintain any longer that only errors would result from their application to other matters and, without a ridiculous imposition of tyranny, one could no longer forbid the human mind from examining issues important for its happiness at the very time when, to its glory, it was making such a fortunate use of this examination.

M. de Fouchy witnessed the noble efforts that have finally liberated human reason from its ancient fetters. He followed its progress and must have foreseen the even more useful revolution that was bound to ensue, the one that should at last restore men to their genuine rights, which had not so much been usurped by force as disregarded out of ignorance or betrayed out of misapprehension; for the dominion of force lasts but a moment except where prejudices foment disunion or deception among its victims. As long as they are misled by their interests, their passions, and their very love of freedom, men will only be exchanging one form of enslavement for another; enlightenment alone can assure a lasting and peaceful freedom and it can be said of political liberty as of national independence what a famous philosopher said about moral freedom, that the more enlightened a man is, the freer he is.[67]

In laying down the functions of his office, M. de Fouchy had no desire to renounce either the sciences or the Academy, being assiduous more out of zeal and friendship for his colleagues than out of habit; he resumed the tasks that his position had led him to neglect for over thirty years and completed several of them. He even had the courage to form new projects, such as that of collecting within a small compass the most interesting facts of the history of the Academy, to form a catalogue of all it had done for common utility and the progress of the sciences. In this manner he offered at once an instructive and lively reading to those who cultivate or love them and to those who take delight in following the developments of the human mind, and he presented to the Academy, for which he had spent almost his entire life, a last token of his loyal and pure devotion.

Several years after his retirement M. de Fouchy met with a peculiar accident. Having had a fall during a fit of dizziness, and having the next day regained full consciousness and the use of his faculties, he noticed that though his vocal organs, which for some time had been obstructed, had become almost entirely free, they had ceased to obey to his will; that whenever he meant to enunciate a word, his mouth uttered another, so that his words became incoherent while his ideas remained distinct. He himself gave an account of this accident in our *Mémoires*,[68] minutely related all the symptoms, all the details of this phenomenon with a simplicity, a serenity, even an indifference worthy of the heroes of ancient Stoicism; and it is evident from these details that in the very midst of the very frightening symptoms that threatened him with a painful and humiliating existence for the remainder of his life, he was more occupied in observing his ailments than in grieving over them. After a long succession of infirmities that he endured with philosophical patience and Christian resignation, M. de Fouchy succumbed to them on April 15, 1788.

Born with a peaceable and moderate character, he had all the inclinations of gentle souls. He cultivated poetry, but in the privacy of friendship, composing solely society poems, and knowing the extent to which their value is depreciated when propagated among the public where they lose whatever charm they possess, and the virtues of suitability, spontaneity, and personal convenience, without which qualities they cannot be appreciated with justice. Yet these were ingenious and flowing verses, and by sentencing them to oblivion he has displayed even greater modesty than prudence.

He loved music and played several instruments. He never ceased to cultivate the talents that are acquired in one's youth only to be neglected soon thereafter, when ceasing to be a means of achieving worldly success they remain but a means of securing one's happiness. Almost every Sunday he played on the organ in a church of his neighborhood at the request of the organist eager to have him take his place. In this manner he satisfied at once his taste for music, his piety, and his eagerness to be of assistance, and he rendered this service with such simplicity and good nature that he may possibly have been the only man to display in public talents foreign to his position and occupations without ever incurring the suspicion of even the slightest display of vanity.

He had been married twice: the first to Mlle. de Boitissandeau, whose brother built an arithmetical machine that was approved by the Academy, and the second to Mlle. Desportes-Pardaillan. From his first marriage he had only one daughter, married to M. Petau, grandnephew of the Jesuit father Petau and also, by his mother, grandnephew of Père Malebranche. From the second marriage he had two sons, one an officer in the colonial troops and the other an officer in the Orléans regiment of dragoons, and a daughter, today the widow of M. le marquis de Gerins.

Abbreviations

Baker, *Social Mathematics*

Keith Michael Baker, *Condorcet, From Natural Philosophy to Social Mathematics* (Chicago: University of Chicago Press, 1975)

Condorcet, *Morts depuis 1666*

Condorcet, *Eloges des Académiciens de l'Académie Royale des Sciences Morts depuis 1666, jusqu'en 1699* (Paris: Hotel de Thou, 1773)

Hahn, *Anatomy*

Roger Hahn, *The Anatomy of a Scientific Institution: The Paris Academy of Sciences, 1666–1803* (Berkeley: University of California Press, 1971)

HARS

Histoire et Mémoires de l'Académie Royale des Sciences: Histoire

MARS

Histoire et Mémoires de l'Académie Royale des Sciences: Mémoires

Niderst

Alain Niderst, *Fontenelle à la recherche de lui-même (1657–1702)* (Paris: A. G. Nizet, 1972)

Notes

INTRODUCTION: SCIENCE AND EULOGY

1. Preserved Smith, *The Enlightenment*, vol. 2 of *A History of Modern Culture* (New York: Crowell-Collier, 1962), p. 118.

2. Hélène Metzger, "La Littérature scientifique française au XVIIIe siècle," *Archeion* 16 (1934): 15.

3. Ibid., pp. 3—6.

4. Ibid., p. 11.

5. Louis Basso, "Le Problème de la vulgarisation scientifique," *Revue philosophique de la France et de l'étranger* 97 (1924): 109—11.

6. Ibid., p. 108.

7. Voltaire, "Conseils à un journaliste, etc. [1737]," *Oeuvres complètes de Voltaire*, 52 vols., ed. L. E. D. Morand and G. Bengesco (Paris: Garnier, 1877—85), 22:242—43, 264—65.

8. Emile Saigey, *Les Sciences au XVIIIe siècle*, pt. 1, *La Physique de Voltaire* (Paris: Germer Baillière, 1873), pp. 66—71.

9. "Reglement ordonné par le Roi pour l'Académie Royale des Sciences," Articles 16, 24, and 40, in Fontenelle, *Histoire du Renouvellement de l'Académie Royale des Sciences en M.DC.XCLX*, bound with Fontenelle, *Eloges des Académiciens, avec l'histoire de l'Académie Royale des Sciences*, 2 vols. (The Hague: Vander Kloot, 1740; Brussels, Culture et Civilisation, 1960), 1: 8, 10, 14.

10. Ibid., Articles 18, 34, and 35, pp. 8, 13.

11. Hahn, *Anatomy*, p. 73 (for this and other abbreviated citations, see List of Abbreviations); L.-F. Alfred Maury, *L'Ancienne Académie des Sciences* (Paris: Didier, 1864), p. 172.

12. Niderst, p. 597.

13. Ernst Robert Curtius, *European Literature and the Latin Middle Ages*, trans. Willard R. Trask (New York: Pantheon Books, 1953), pp. 64—65; O. B. Hardison, *The Enduring Monument* (Chapel Hill: University of North Carolina Press, 1962), pp. 19—20; Theodore C. Burgess, *Epideictic Literature* (Chicago: University of Chicago Press, 1902), pp. 102—3.

14. Curtius, op. cit., pp. 64—66, 436—38; Burgess, op. cit., pp. 91—92, 115; James D. Garrison, *Dryden and the Tradition of the Panegyric* (Berkeley, Los Angeles, London: University of California Press, 1975), pp. 40—41; François de Caussade, *Notions de rhétorique et étude des genres littéraires* (Paris: Masson, [1906]), p. 7.

15. Curtius, op. cit., p. 69; Garrison, op. cit., pp. 6—9; Hardison, op. cit., pp. 30—31; Burgess, op. cit., pp. 137—38, 146—48.

16. Curtius, op. cit., p. 179.

17. Ibid., pp. 176–78.

18. Ibid., p. 70.

19. Ibid., pp. 83–87, 159–60.

20. Ibid., pp. 162–66.

21. Paul Oskar Kristeller, *The Classics and Renaissance Thought*, vol. 15 of the *Martin Classical Lectures* (Cambridge: Harvard University Press, 1955), pp. 10–13.

22. Ibid.

23. Ibid., pp. 20–25; Burgess, op. cit., pp. 139–41.

24. Hardison, op. cit., pp. 37–40.

25. R. Munteano, *Constantes dialectiques en littérature et en histoire* (Paris: Didier, 1967), pp. 175–81; François de Dainville, "L'Evolution de l'enseignement de la rhétorique au XVIIe siècle," *Dix-septième siècle* 80–81 (April 1968): 19–21.

26. Peter France, *Rhetoric and Truth in France: Descartes to Diderot* (Oxford: Clarendon Press, 1972), p. 5.

27. Dainville, op. cit., pp. 39–40. André Schimberg lists the more distinguished students of the collèges run by the Jesuit order, which controlled more than half of France's secondary schools until 1762. Among these students should be mentioned, in addition to the four given in the text, Peiresc, Guez de Balzac, Corneille, Molière, Colbert, the historian Mézeray, Bourdaloue, Louvois, Montesquieu, the poet J. B. Rousseau, the two Crébillon, Le Sage, Voltaire, Helvétius, Malesherbes, Diderot, the scientists Tournefort, Varignon, Chazelles, Réaumur, Buffon, La Condamine, Lalande, and Lamarck, and the secretaries Fontenelle and Condorcet. (*L'Education morale dans les collèges de la Compagnie de Jésus en France sous l'Ancien Régime* [Paris: Honoré Champion, 1913], p. 433.)

28. Orest Ranum, *Paris in the Age of Absolutism* (New York: John Wiley, 1968), pp. 188–89.

29. A. L. Thomas, *Essai sur les éloges*, 2 vols. (Paris: Auguste Delalain, 1829), 1: 294–95, 317, 322, 366–70.

30. Jean Le Rond d'Alembert, "Eloges Académiques," *Encyclopédie ou Dictionnaire raisonné des sciences, des arts et des métiers*, 17 vols. (Paris: Le Breton, Briasson, Durand, David, 1751–72), 12: 149–51.

31. Ibid., p. 149; Thomas, op. cit., 1: 457–58.

32. Hardison, op. cit., pp. 30–32.

33. D'Alembert, op. cit., 12: 149.

34. Thomas, op. cit., 1: 457.

35. Ibid., 1: 409–17.

36. See chap. 1.

1: FORM AND STYLE

1. Quintilian, *The Institutio Oratorio*, trans. H. E. Butler, 4 vols. (London: William Heinemann, 1933), 1: 483 and 2: 9, 25.

2. In the *Histoires* of the Paris Academy of Sciences, though not in the collections of *éloges* that were printed by sundry publishers, the first twenty and the thirty-seventh *éloges* of Fontenelle as well as many written by his successors carry as

their last paragraph the name of the person who took the seat of the deceased in the Academy.

3. Paul Janet, ed., *Choix d'Eloges* (Paris: Ch. Delagrave, 1888); Louis Maigron, *Fontenelle. L'homme, l'oeuvre, l'influence* (Paris: Plon, 1906), pp. 337–69; A. L. Thomas, *Essai sur les éloges*, 2 vols. (Paris: Auguste Delalain, 1829, but written between 1758 and 1785), vol. 1, chap. 34; A.-F. Villemain, *Cours de littérature francaise* (Paris: Perrin, 1891), 1: 305–29; and especially two articles by Suzanne Delorme: "Des Eloges de Fontenelle et de la psychologie des savants," *Mélanges Georges Jamati* (Paris: Centre National de la Recherche Scientifique, 1956), pp. 95–100, and "La Vie scientifique à l'époque de Fontenelle d'après les éloges des savants," *Archeion* 19 (1957): 217–35.

4. On Peter I see *HARS* (1725), pp. 107–12 and on d'Argenson (1721), pp. 102–5. On stylistic, oratorical or pedagogical talents, see J. B. Duhamel (1706), pp. 145–47, Régis (1707), pp. 157–58, Carré (1711), pp. 103–4, N. Lémery (1715), pp. 74–75, Malebranche (1715), pp. 95–96, and Boerhaave (1738), pp. 109–10; on the importance of instruments, Amontons (1705), p. 151; on astronomy, Cassini I (1712), p. 83; on the crafts, Homberg (1715), pp. 86–87; on algebra, Rolle (1719), pp. 95–96; on geography, G. Delisle (1726), pp. 75–81; on Descartes and Newton (1727), p. 160; on popular credulity, Louville (1732), p. 133; and on Cartesian vortices, Saurin (1737), pp. 116–17.

5. *HARS* (1705), pp. 139–50.

6. Francois de Caussade, *Notions de rhétorique et étude des genres littéraires* (Paris: Masson, [1906]), pp. 23–26.

7. Cf. *HARS* (1706), p. 143, (1715), p. 98, (1719), pp. 86–87, (1722), p. 141, and (1738), p. 111.

8. Ibid., *éloges* of Montmort (1719), p. 92 and Ressons (1735), pp. 105–6.

9. Quintilian, op. cit., 2: 447–49; *HARS* (1722), p. 139.

10. *HARS, éloges* of Duhamel (1706), p. 147; Sauveur (1716), p. 83; Vauban (1707), p. 166; Cassini I (1712), p. 91; and Carré (1711), p. 104.

11. Leonard M. Marsak, "Bernard de Fontenelle: In Defense of Science," *The Rise of Science in Relation to Society*, ed. L. M. Marsak (New York: Macmillan, 1964), pp. 75–76.

12. *HARS, éloges* of Polignac (1741), pp. 180–83 and Fleury (1743), pp. 175–77.

13. Condorcet's *éloge* of Fouchy (in translation) has been reproduced in Appendix F.

14. E.g., a tribute to Fontenelle as the ideal sécrétaire, *HARS* (1757), pp. 191–92; a description of the functions of an *Intendant* and of the minister of war (1760), pp. 198–200 and (1764), pp. 189–92; asides on mathematical specialization and mechanical talent (1758), p. 108 and (1768), pp. 144–54 passim.; a comparison of La Caille's and Bradley's astronomical observations (1768), pp. 178–79; and a fairly long exposition on the complexity of astronomy and on the 1726 Aurora Borealis (1760), pp. 183–84.

15. In the *éloge* of Réaumur (*HARS*, 1757, pp. 201–16) the following numbered paragraphs are devoted to his work in mathematics (6–7), natural history in general (9–11), applied science (12–13), marine biology (14–15), various applied sciences and miscellaneous researches (17–20), metallurgy (21–25, 27), pottery (28), thermometry (29–30), ornithology (31–33; 38–39), and entomology (34–37). The entire *éloge* contains only 42 paragraphs.

16. *HARS, éloges* of Helvétius (1755), pp. 163−64; Maupertuis (1759), pp. 263−64; Chappe (1769), pp. 165−69; Hales (1762), pp. 216−22; and La Caille (1762), pp. 197−212.

17. In his bid for the position of sécrétaire of the Paris Academy of Sciences, Condorcet in 1773 published a collection of *éloges* and notices of members of the Academy who had either died between its founding in 1666 and Fontenelle's composition of his first *éloge* in 1699 or who had left or been expelled from that company between those two dates. As far as is known, these eulogies were never read in public and hence have been designated in this book as "written" *éloges*, in distinction to the "public" *éloges* he delivered between 1773 and 1791. The volume in which he published these encomiums (*Eloges des Académiciens de l'Académie Royale des Sciences, Morts depuis 1666, jusqu'en 1699* [Paris, Hôtel de Thou, 1773]) lists thirty-one Academicians (see appendix B above). Twenty of these received either notices of a few words (name, date of admission to the Academy and sometimes their scientific specialization and a few vital statistics) or fuller descriptions, including their major achievements, but not exceeding 350 words (the equivalent of one page in the *Histoires* of the Academy). The other eleven Academicians received regular *éloges*, ranging from 800 to 4500 words.

18.

Approximate number of words	Number of *éloges* composed by			
	Fontenelle	Mairan	Fouchy	Condorcet[*]
Fewer than 1,000	8			
1,000- 1,999	12	1	4	6
2,000- 2,999	16	2	8	7
3,000- 3,999	20	4	13	9
4,000- 4,999	3	1	15	6
5,000- 5,999	4		16	6
6,000- 6,999	1	1	8	4
7,000- 7,999	3	1		1
8,000- 8,999	1			3
9,000- 9,999				2
10,000-10,999				1
11,000-11,999				1
12,000-12,999	1			
13,000-13,999				3
14,000-16,999				
17,000-17,999				1
Total	69	10	64	50
Mean	3,152	3,900	4,359	5,520
Median	2,500	3,500	4,500	4,500

[*]The numbers for Condorcet's *éloges* refer only to his "Public" *éloges*, those he delivered at the public sessions of the Paris Academy of Sciences, and not those he composed in 1773 in his bid for the position of sécrétaire of that Academy.

19. Condorcet, "Elogue de Franklin" in *Oeuvres complètes de Condorcet*, ed. A. A. Barbier, P.-J.-G. Cabanis, and D.-J. Garat (Paris: Heinrichs, 1804), 2: 91–165.

20. *HARS* (1781), pp. 53–70, and (1779), pp. 44–53.

21. "To weep," "misfortune," "martyr," "tenderness," "sensibility," "touching kindness," and "gratitude."

22. Baker, *Social Mathematics*, p. 24.

23. *HARS* (1777), p. 78 and (1783), pp. 101–2.

24. *Ibid.* (1782), pp. 109–10.

2: ATTRACTION AND AFFINITY: FONTENELLE AND MAIRAN

1. This hagiography will be discussed in chap. 6 and in the Conclusion.

2. Pierre Brunet, *L'Introduction des théories de Newton en France au XVIIIe siècle* (Paris: Albert Blanchard, 1931), p. 202; Stephen F. Mason, *Main Currents of Scientific Thought* (New York: Abelard-Schuman, 1956), pp. 161–62.

3. Mason, op. cit., p. 134.

4. In *Oeuvres de M. Fontenelle* . . . , new ed. (Paris: Chez les libraires associés, 1766), 9: 304–5, cited in Niderst, p. 576.

5. *HARS* (1737), pp. 115–19.

6. Ibid. (1719), p. 91.

7. "The two great men, who found themselves in such sharp opposition, had many great affinities with one another. Both were geniuses of the first order, born to dominate other minds and to found empires. Both excellent mathematicians, they saw the necessity of attaching mathematics to physics. Both founded their physics on a mathematics that they all but invented themselves. But one, soaring boldly, meant to place himself at the source of everything, to master the first principles by means of some clear and fundamental ideas so that he might simply descend to the phenomena of nature as so many necessary consequences. The other, more timid or possibly more modest, commenced his journey by leaning on phenomena in order to ascend to unknown principles, and resolved to admit them, whatever the chain of consequences might lead to. One commenced with what he understood clearly in quest of the cause of his observation. The other commenced with his observation in quest of its cause, be it clear or obscure. The evident principles of the first did not always direct him to the phenomena such as they are; the phenomena did not always direct the second to principles that are sufficiently evident. The limits that in their contrary routes halted two men of this kind are not the limits of their minds but those of the human mind." (*HARS*, 1727, p. 160.)

8. Ibid., pp. 154–63 passim.

9. Henry Guerlac, "An Augustan Monument: The *Opticks* of Isaac Newton," in *Essays and Papers in the History of Science* (Baltimore: Johns Hopkins University Press, 1977), p. 159.

10. *HARS* (1727), p. 164.

11. Ibid., pp. 160–62, and Fontenelle, "Eloge de M. Hartsoeker," *HARS* (1725), pp. 142–43.

12. Ibid. (1768), pp. 136–37.

13. Fontenelle, "Eloge de M. Geoffroy," *HARS* (1731), pp. 99–100; J. R.

Partington, *A Short History of Chemistry* (3d ed.; New York: Harper Torchbooks, 1957), pp. 322–23.

14. See G. A. Lindeboom, *Herman Boerhaave: The Man and His Work* (London: Methuen, 1968), pp. 202–5, on contemporary confirmations of Fontenelle's admiring words.

15. *HARS* (1738), pp. 110–11.

16. Hélène Metzger, *Newton, Stahl, Boerhaave et la doctrine chimique* (Paris: Félix Alcan, 1930), pp. 36–37, 40–41, 48, 88–89, and *Les Doctrines chimiques en France du début du XVIIe à la fin du XVIIIe siècle* (Paris: Presses universitaires de France, 1923), pp. 196–99.

17. *HARS*, Condorcet, *éloge* of Bergman (1784), pp. 40–42.

18. Ibid. (1716), p. 107–8.

19. Mairan, "Eloge de M. l'Abbé de Molières," *HARS* (1742), pp. 198–200.

20. Henry Guerlac, "The Newtonianism of Dortous de Mairan," in *Essays and Papers in the History of Science* (Baltimore: Johns Hopkins University Press, 1977), p. 487, summarizing Mairan's *Traité physique et historique de l'aurore boréale* (Paris: n.p., 1733), p. 88; 2d ed., 1754, p. 96.

21. Ibid., p. 486.

22. Ibid., pp. 483–86.

23. Mairan, "Troisième partie des Recherches Physico-Mathématiques sur la Réflexion des Corps," *MARS* (1738), p. 7. In the *éloge* of Molières Mairan put his own support of eclecticism in the mouth of that last-ditch defender of the vortex theory. Molières, he says, decided "to follow constantly Descartes in anything relating to method and the clarity of principles, but he had no hesitation in leaving him whenever he seemed to be straying from Nature. Nor did he scruple to work up the calculations and discoveries of Newton, being likewise resolved to abandon or to combat him on several of his tenets [*dogmes*], above all on the inherent attraction of matter . . ." (*HARS*, 1742, p. 202).

24. Mairan, "Troisième partie . . . ," pp. 13–26.

25. Cited in P. Barrière, *L'Académie de Bordeaux: Centre de culture internationale au XVIIIe siècle (1712–1792)* (Bordeaux, Paris: Bière, n.d.), p. 158.

26. Ibid.

27. Ralph N. Blake, "The Role of Experience in Descartes' Theory of Method," in Edward H. Madden, ed., *Theories of Scientific Method: The Renaissance through the Nineteenth Century* (Seattle: University of Washington Press, 1960), pp. 84–85.

28. Francisque Bouillier, *Histoire de la philosophie cartésienne*, 3d ed., 2 vols. (Paris: Delagrave, 1868), 2: 557–75; Brunet, op. cit., passim.; Ernst Cassirer, *The Philosophy of the Enlightenment*, trans. F. C. A. Koelln and J. P. Pettegrove (Boston: Beacon Press, 1955), pp. 50–80.

29. Denis Diderot, "Pensées sur l'interprétation de la nature," *Oeuvres complètes de Diderot*, ed. J. Assézat, 20 vols. (Paris: Garnier, 1875), 2: 38–39.

30. Mairan, *Dissertation sur la Glace, ou Explication physique de la formation de la Glace, et de ses divers phénomènes* (Paris: L'Imprimerie royale, 1749), pp. iv–v.

31. Ibid., pp. vi–viii.

32. *HARS* (1742), p. 203.

33. Ibid., *éloges* of Hales (1762), p. 217; Van Swieten (1772:1), p. 124; and Quesnay (1774), p. 135.

3: GENERATION AND TAXONOMY: THE SECRETARIES'
PARTI-PRIS

1. A. R. Hall, *The Scientific Revolution, 1500–1800* (Boston: The Beacon Press, 1954), pp. 298–99.

2. Elizabeth B. Gasking, *Investigations into Generation 1651–1828* (Baltimore: Johns Hopkins Press, [1967]), p. 6.

3. Ibid., pp. 29–30, 175.

4. Ibid., pp. 41–43 and Hall, op. cit., p. 292. *Emboîtement*, from *boîte*, box or case, literally means "encasing."

5. Gasking, op. cit., pp. 43–47.

6. Ibid., pp. 51–56.

7. *HARS* (1725), pp. 138–41.

8. Jacques Roger, *Les Sciences de la vie dans la pensée française du XVIIIe siècle* (Paris: Armand Colin, 1963), pp. 731–32.

9. *HARS* (1725), pp. 140–41 and 147–52.

10. Ibid., pp. 146–47 and Roger, op. cit., pp. 432–36.

11. Gasking, op. cit., p. 67.

12. Mairan, "Eloge de M. Lémery," *HARS* (1743), p. 206.

13. *HARS* (1760), p. 175.

14. Ibid. (1743), pp. 206–7.

15. Ibid. (1759), pp. 269, 262.

16. Bentley Glass, "Maupertuis, Pioneer of Genetics and Evolution," in Bentley Glass et al., eds. *Forerunners of Darwin, 1745–1859* (Baltimore: Johns Hopkins University Press, 1959), pp. 82–83, 51–78.

17. Ibid., pp. 77–80.

18. Ibid., p. 62.

19. Fontenelle's *éloges* of Hartsoeker and Poli complete this short list.

20. *HARS* (1759), pp. 270–73, esp. p. 271.

21. Jean Ehrard, *L'Idée de nature en France dans la première moitié du XVIIIe siècle*, 2 vols. (Paris: Ecole Pratique des Hautes Etudes, 1963), 1: 123–25.

22. *HARS* (1777), pp. 136–38.

23. Roger, op. cit., pp. 752–53.

24. In the order of publication of their *éloges*, the natural historians reported as having practiced herborization are: Tournefort, Blondin, Morin de Saint-Victor, C. J. Geoffroy, A. de Jussieu, Hales, B. de Jussieu, Linnaeus, J. de Jussieu, Bergman, Guettard, and Buffon.

25. *HARS*, Fontenelle, "Eloge de Monsieur de Tournefort" (1708), pp. 144–45; Fouchy, "Eloge de M. de Jussieu" (1759), pp. 116–19; Condorcet, *éloges* of B. de Jussieu (1777), pp. 94–95; La Condamine (1774), p. 93, J. de Jussieu (1779), p. 45.

26. Fontenelle, *HARS* (1708), pp. 145–46, 152.

27. Ibid., pp. 147–48.

28. Ibid., p. 148.

29. Ibid., pp. 148–49.

30. René Descartes, *Discours de la Méthode*, pt. 2.

31. *HARS* (1708), p. 148; J. F. Leroy, "Tournefort et la classification végétale,"

in Roger Heim, ed., *Tournefort* (Paris: Muséum National d'Histoire Naturelle, 1957), pp. 202–4.

32. *HARS* (1708), p. 149.

33. S. F. Mason, *Main Currents of Scientific Thought* (New York: Abelard-Schuman, 1956), p. 265; John C. Greene, *The Death of Adam: Evolution and Its Impact on Western Thought* (Ames: The Iowa State University Press, 1959), pp. 129–30.

34. *HARS* (1758), pp. 120–21; Paul Crestois, *L'Enseignement de la botanique au Jardin Royal des Plantes de Paris* (Cahors: A. Coueslant, 1953), p. 100.

35. *HARS* (1758), pp. 121–22.

36. Ibid. (1777), pp. 110–11.

37. Ibid. (1778), pp. 67–69.

38. Ibid., pp. 69–72.

39. Ibid., pp. 72–75.

40. Greene, op. cit., pp. 132–37.

4: SCIENCE AND UTILITY: FROM COLBERT TO FRANKLIN

1. Thomas Sprat, *History of the Royal Society*, ed. Jackson I. Cope and Harold Whitmore Jones, (St. Louis, Mo.: Washington Univ. Press, 1958) pp. 345–62.

2. Ibid., pp. 378–403, 419–27.

3. Fontenelle, *Préface*, 1: i–ii.

4. *HARS* (1720), p. 123.

5. Ibid. (1771), p. 147.

6. Ibid., Bélidor's treatises on ballistics and military fortifications, 1761, pp. 169–73; d'Arcy's and Nollet's improvements of the efficacy of gunpowder, 1779, pp. 60–63 and 1770, pp. 133–34; Chazelles's amelioration of the navigational capacity of galley-ships, 1710, pp. 144–50; Duhamel du Monceau's simplification of the art of rigging, 1782, pp. 137–39, 141–42; and sundry contributions to naval technology by Bouguer, 1758, pp. 133–34, Clairaut, 1765, p. 157, and Mairan, 1771, pp. 94–95. In addition, a goodly proportion of the honoraires and associés libres that the government had selected for membership in the Paris Academy of Sciences had either distinguished themselves in battle—e.g., Amelot, La Faye, Milly, Renau d'Elissagaray, Ressons, Valincourt, Vauban—or had, as ministers of state, labored to improve France's military strength. Thus, Jean-Florent de Vallière required all candidates to the artillery to learn mathematics and ballistics at the schools he himself had instituted for that purpose (1759, p. 253ff.); Rouillié founded the Royal Naval Academy at Brest (1761, pp. 185–86); Albert and La Galissonnière enlarged the Naval Depot of Surveys, Maps, and Journals (1751, pp. 199–200 and 1756, pp. 150–53); and Maurepas, as Minister of the Navy and Minister of the Learned Academies, bridged the gap between the scientific and military realms by supervising the collection and correction of naval maps, giving financial support to the geodesic expeditions to Peru and Lapland, and founding a state school for shipbuilders, headed by Duhamel du Monceau (1781, pp. 79–102 passim).

7. HARS, Fontenelle, *éloges* of J. B. Duhamel (1706), pp. 94–97, and Galloys (1707), pp. 176–80.

8. Hahn, *Anatomy*, p. 21, referring to *HARS* (1666–99), I, 50, 144, 200, 320, 428.

9. Hahn, *Anatomy*, p. 119.

10. E.g., *HARS* (1707), p. 178, and (1730), p. 26.

11. Ibid. (1718), pp. 80–81.

12. See esp. ibid. (1707), pp. 168–69 and (1721), pp. 102–4.

13. Ibid. (1770), pp. 145–46.

14. Ibid. (1766), pp. 174, 177.

15. *Eloges* of d'Aiguillon (1750), d'Aguesseau (1751), Albert (1751), La Galissonnière (1756), Jean-Florent de Vallière (1759), Séchelles (1760), Rouillié (1761). d'Argenson II (1764), Daniel-Charles Trudaine (1769), Chaulnes (1769), and Joseph-Florent de Vallière (1776).

16. *HARS* (1764), pp. 191–92.

17. Baker, *Social Mathematics*, p. 47.

18. *HARS* (1777), pp. 71, 78, 82, 86–88.

19. Charles G. Stricklen, Jr., "The *philosophe's* political mission: the creation of an idea, 1750–1789," *Studies in Voltaire and the Eighteenth Century* 86 (1971): 181–84.

20. *HARS* (1782), pp. 117–18; see also his *éloge* of Haller, *ibid.* (1777), p. 148.

21. *Ibid.*, *éloge* of Tronchin (1782), p. 113.

22. *Ibid.*, *éloges* of La Condamine (1774), pp. 97–98, 105, d'Arcy (1779), pp. 68–70, Turgot (1789), pp. 33–36, and Maurepas (1781), p. 94. Because K. M. Baker's prize-winning *Condorcet: From Natural Philosophy to Social Mathematics* (1975) has analyzed Condorcet's political views in great depth, I felt it unnecessary to develop these views in this study.

23. *HARS, éloges* of La Condamine (1774), pp. 85–87; Trudaine de Montigny (1777), pp. 70–71; L. C. Bourdelin (1777), p. 119; Pringle (1782), p. 57; Vaucanson (1782), pp. 167–68; Hunter (1783), p. 31; Buffon (1788), p. 80; and Condorcet, *Oeuvres complètes de Condorcet* (Paris: Heinrichs, 1804), 2:202–5; Baker, *Social Mathematics*, pp. 26–27.

24. *HARS* (1789), p. 42.

25. Ibid. (1782), p. 134.

26. Ibid., pp. 135–37; André J. Bourde, *Agronomie et agronomes en France au XVIIIe siècle* (Paris: Ecole Pratique des Hautes Etudes, 1967), pp. 260–63.

27. Ibid. (1782), pp. 112–14.

28. Ibid. (1782), pp. 161–64.

29. Alfred Owen Aldridge, *Franklin and his French Contemporaries* (New York: New York University Press, 1957), p. 6.

30. Condorcet, *Oeuvres complètes de Condorcet* (Paris: Heinrichs, 1804), 2:163–65.

31. Baker, *Social Mathematics*, pp. 293–99; Condorcet, *Oeuvres de Condorcet* (Paris: Firmin Didot, 1847–49), 7: 171–95, 247–85, 468–70, 493–4, 552–53.

32. *HARS* (1783), p. 69; see also Condorcet's *éloge* of Guettard (1786), p. 49.

5: ESTATE, EDUCATION, AND EMPLOYMENT

1. The 115 Academicians studied in this chapter include 107 "working" members, 7 honoraires, and the associé étranger Abraham de Moivre, who was born and educated in France but was forced to flee to England because of his Protestant faith. Excluded from the list of native working members who received *éloges* between 1699 and 1791 are the following who did no significant mathematical, scientific, or medical work: the secretaries J. B. Duhamel and Fontenelle; the philosopher Régis, the scholar Terrasson, the journalist Galloys, the treasurer Couplet, and the associés libres Albert, La Galissonnière, Jean-Florent and Joseph-Florent de Vallière, Tressan, and E.-F. Turgot. Condorcet's "written" *éloges* and notices of Academicians who died before 1699 contain little or no biographical information pertinent to this chapter.

2. For an extensive list of biographical studies of these scientists, consult Hahn, *Anatomy,* pp. 331–73.

3. Suzanne Delorme, "La vie scientifique à l'époque de Fontenelle d'après les éloges des savants," *Archeion,* 19 (1937): 217–35.

4. In order of their dates of birth, they are: Ozanam, Chirac, Varignon, Saurin, Tournefort, Lagny, Poupart, Amontons, Carré, Parent, Louville, Chicoyneau, Louis Lémery, Montmort, Nicole, Hellot, Antoine de Jussieu, Ferrein, Malouin, Joseph Lieutaud, Fontaine, Vaucanson, Hérissant, Montigny, Fourcroy de Ramecourt, Bézout, and Bucquet.

5. *HARS* (1717), pp. 86–87; (1708), pp. 143–44; (1719), pp. 83–84; (1771), p. 105; (1711), p. 102; (1782), pp. 156–58.

6. Pierre Huard, "L'Enseignement Médico-Chirurgical," in René Taton, *Enseignement et diffusion des sciences en France au XVIIIe siècle* (Paris: Hermann, 1964), pp. 171–72, 184.

7. In order of their dates of birth, they are: Fagon, Du Verney, Chirac, Littre, Poupart, F. Petit, Claude (II) Bourdelin, Tauvry, Winslow, Chicoyneau, Tuillier, Helvétius, Ferrein, Quesnay, S. F. Morand, Hunauld, Lieutaud, Bertin, Brémond, Hérissant, Lassone, Bouvard, and J. F. C. Morand.

8. The botanists are Dodart, Morin de St. Victor, Tournefort, Blondin, Antoine, Bernard, Joseph de Jussieu, and Guettard.

9. Excepting Homberg, who obtained nearly all his education abroad, the nine French chemists with M.D.'s are: Nicolas Lémery, E. F. Geoffroy, Louis Lémery, Berger, Louis-Claude Bourdelin, Malouin, Baron, Macquer, and Bucquet.

10. Claude (Ier) Bourdelin, J. F. Boulduc, C. J. Geoffroy, Hellot, Rouelle, and Milly.

11. *HARS,* Fouchy (1766), pp. 167–68.

12. The mathematicians include de Moivre, who was educated in France but as a Protestant resided in England; L'Hopital, admitted as an *Académicien géomètre* in 1693 but made an honoraire with the Renouvellement of 1699; and, in the order of their years of birth, P. de La Hire, Ozanam, Rolle, Varignon, Reyneau, Saurin, Lagny, Carré, Parent, Molières, Montmort, Nicole, Bragelongne, Camus, Deparcieux, Fontaine, Gua de Malves, Clairaut, d'Alembert, and Bézout. Because of the variegated nature of their scientific work, Mairan, Réaumur, and Buffon, although

contributing important mémoires on mathematics, have been excluded from this study on education. Most of the mathematicians discussed here devoted their entire career to that subject alone while some did mostly fundamental work in rational and celestial mechanics, which, until this century in both France and England, were viewed as branches of applied mathematics.

13. *HARS* (1711), pp. 102–3; (1744), p. 65; (1719), pp. 83–84; (1758), p. 107; (1754), pp. 176–77; (1768), p. 145.

14. In addition to Cassini I and his nephew G. F. Maraldi, both born in Italy, the eleven astronomers include Chazelles, Louville, Cassini II, J. N. Delisle, Godin, Fouchy, La Caille, Cassini de Thury, and Chappe.

15. By the règlement of January 20, 1699, the scientists of the Academy (that is, all its members but the honoraires, the foreign associates, the secrétaire, and the treasurer) were grouped into six classes of specialization: mathematics, astronomy, mechanics, anatomy, chemistry, and botany. Each class was comprised of three senior pensionnaires, two associés, and three élèves (renamed adjoints in 1716). In that year, too, were created the positions of associés libres "for prominent French scientists unable to attend meetings regularly, but not sufficiently high on the social ladder to be made honorary members." Though the number of members within each rank increased in 1716, 1731, 1762, 1765, and 1785, the number of classes of specialization only increased twice between the renouvellement of 1699 and the demise of the ancient Academy on August 8, 1793. One seat for a geographer was created in 1730 while on April 23, 1785, the Academy belatedly acknowledged the transformation that had occurred in a dozen sciences by raising the number of classes from six to eight: mathematics, astronomy, mechanics, general physics, anatomy, chemistry and metallurgy, botany and agriculture, natural history and mineralogy. (See Hahn, *Anatomy*, pp. 77–78 and Institut de France, *Index biographique des membres et correspondants de l'Académie des Sciences du 22 décembre 1666 au 15 décembre 1967* [Paris: Gauthier-Villars, 1968], pp. I–III.)

16. *HARS*, Fontenelle (1716), p. 79.

17. The ten "working" instrumentalists and technologists were Des Billettes, Ressons, Amontons, Belidor, Vaucanson, Montigny, Fourcroy de Ramecourt, Courtivron, Jars, and Fougeroux de Bondaroy, and the four honoraires Renau, d'Onsenbray, Courtanvaux, and Truchet, the last by virtue of belonging to the Carmelite Order.

18. *HARS*, Fouchy (1769), pp. 174–75.

19. Maurice Crosland, "The Development of a Professional Career in Science in France," *Minerva*, 13 (Spring 1975): 41–45.

20. The court physicians and surgeons were Bourdelin II, Chicoyneau, Chirac, Fagon, Ferrein, Helvétius, Hunauld, La Peyronie, Lassone, Lieutaud, Mery, J. F. C. Morand, S. F. Morand, F. Petit, Quesnay, and Tuillier.

21. The surgeons were La Peyronie and Mery, and the physicians, L. C. Bourdelin, Chicoyneau, Chirac, Dodart, Fagon, Ferrein, E. F. Geoffroy, Helvétius, Hunauld, A. Jussieu, B. Jussieu, L. Lémery, Lieutaud, S. F. Morand, Morin, Quesnay, and Tournefort.

22. *HARS*, Fouchy (1773), pp. 131–32.

23. Jacques Proust, *L'Encyclopédie* (Paris: Armand Colin, 1965), p. 81.

24. Denis I. Duveen and Roger Hahn, "Laplace's Succession to Bézout's Post of *Examinateur des Elèves de l'Artillerie*," *Isis* 48 (December 1957): 418.

25. The Academicians who earned military commissions were d'Arcy, Bélidor, Chaulnes, Courtivron, Courtanvaux, Du Fay, Fourcroy, Godin, La Condamine, La Faye, L'Hopital, Louville, Renau, and Ressons. Those who held clerical offices were Bragelongne, Carré, Chappe, Gua de Malves, La Caille, Molières, Montmort, Reyneau, and Truchet.

26. Marcel Marion, *Dictionnaire des Institutions de la France aux XVIIe et XVIIIe siècles* (Paris: A. & J. Picard, 1972), p. 2.

27. Duveen and Hahn, op. cit., pp. 416–17.

28. Roger Hahn, "Scientific Research as an Occupation in Eighteenth-Century Paris," *Minerva* 13 (Winter 1975): 507, n. 17.

6: SCIENCE AND MORALITY: ANCIENT AND MODERN SOURCES

1. Dorinda Outram, "The Language of Natural Power: The 'Eloges' of Georges Cuvier and the Public Language of Nineteenth Century Science," *History of Science* 16 (1978): 153–78.

2. Ibid., pp. 153–57.

3. Ibid., pp. 153–55.

4. Ibid., pp. 153, 161.

5. Ibid., pp. 154–56.

6. Ibid., pp. 160–61.

7. Martha Walling Howard, *The Influence of Plutarch in the Major European Literatures of the Eighteenth Century* (Chapel Hill: University of North Carolina Press, 1970), pp. 195–96. New French translation of Plutarch's *Lives* appeared in 1711 and 1721, and of his *Works* in 1759, 1783–87, and 1784 (ibid., p. 22).

8. Ibid., pp. 50–51, 54–55.

9. Ibid., p. 6.

10. Plutarch, "Timoleon," in *Plutarch's Lives of Illustrious Men*, original trans. by John Dryden et al., in 1683–86, rev. by A. H. Clough in 1876 (New York: The Modern Library, [n.d.]), p. 293.

11. Howard, op. cit., pp. 33–34.

12. Plutarch, op. cit., "Aemilius Paulus," p. 342.

13. C. A. Sainte-Beuve, "Fontenelle," (January 27, 1851), *Causeries du Lundi* 3d ed. (Paris: Garnier, [1858]). 3: 314–15; Abel-François Villemain, *Cours de littérature française*, new ed. (Paris: Perrin, 1891), 1: 305–29; A. L. Thomas, *Essai sur les éloges* (Paris: Auguste Delalain, 1829), 1: 508.

14. Francisque Bouillier, ed., *Eloges de Fontenelle* (Paris: Garnier, [1883]); J.-R. Carré, *La Philosophie de Fontenelle ou le sourire de la raison* (Paris: Félix Alcan, 1932); Suzanne Delorme, "Des Eloges de Fontenelle et de la psychologie des savants," in *Mélanges Georges Jamati* (Paris: Centre National de la Recherche Scientifique, 1956), pp. 95–100, and "La Vie scientifique à l'époque de Fontenelle d'après les éloges des savants," *Archeion* 19 (1937): 217–35; Amédée Fayol, *Fontenelle* (Paris: Nouvelles editions Debresse, 1961); P. Flourens, *Fontenelle ou de*

la philosophie moderne (Paris: Paulin, 1847); F. Grégoire, *Fontenelle: Une "philosophie" désabusée* (Paris: J. Vrin, 1947); Werner Krauss, *Fontenelle und die Aufklärung* (Munich: Wilhelm Fink, 1969); A. Laborde-Milaa, *Fontenelle* (Paris: Hachette, 1905); and Louis Maigron, *Fontenelle. L'homme, l'oeuvre, l'influence* (Paris: Plon, 1906).

15. Eugene F. Rice, Jr., *The Renaissance Idea of Wisdom* (Cambridge: Harvard University Press, 1958), pp. 9-10.

16. Ibid., pp. 149-57 and 178-207 passim.

17. Condorcet, *Morts depuis 1666*, "Eloge de Roëmer," p. 151.

18. *HARS* (1719), pp. 113, 115; (1731), p. 93; (1744), p. 65; (1746), p. 130; (1750), p. 176; (1756), p. 148; (1757), p. 195; (1769), p. 145; (1770), p. 146.

19. Outram, op. cit., p. 155.

20. The names of these teachers and their students (in parentheses) are: Buot (Couplet), Cassini I (Chazelles, his nephew Maraldi, and E. F. and C. J. Geoffroy), Régis (Simon Boulduc), Malebranche (Carré, Montmort, Bragelongne, Mairan), Ozanam (de Moivre), N. Lémery (Baron, Hérissant), J. G. du Verney (Hunauld and E. F. and C. J. Geoffroy), Chirac (Antoine de Jussieu), Homberg (E. F. and C. J. Geoffroy), Simon Boulduc (J. F. Boulduc), Littre (J. L. Petit), Varignon (Cassini II, Camus), Tournefort (Blondin), Chazelles (Cassini II), Carré (Montmort), Maraldi (Cassini de Thury), Bourdelin II (Baron), Johann I Bernoulli (Maupertuis, Haller, Daniel Bernoulli, Euler), Boerhaave (Tronchin), Winslow (Hunauld, Hérissant, Haller), Guisnée (Montmort, Maupertuis), Chicoyneau (Antoine de Jussieu), G. F. Boulduc (Baron, Hérissant), G. Delisle (Godin), La Peyronie (Antoine de Jussieu), Montmort (Nicole), Réaumur (Nollet), A. de Jussieu (Hérissant, Haller, and his brothers Bernard and Joseph de Jussieu), Du Fay (Nollet), Duhamel du Monceau (his nephew Fougeroux de Bondaroy), Hunauld (Baron), Fontaine (Montigny), Buffon (Montigny), and Fouchy (La Caille).

21. Orinda Outram, "Scientific Biography and the Case of Georges Cuvier," *History of Science* 14 (1976): 102.

22. Gilbert Highet, *The Classical Tradition* (London: Oxford University Press, 1949), p. 162; W. W. Greg, "Pastoral: A Literary Inquiry," in Eleanor Terry Lincoln, ed., *Pastoral and Romance* (Englewood Cliffs, New Jersey: Prentice-Hall, 1969), pp. 8-9.

23. James L. Calderwood and Harold E. Toliver, *Forms of Poetry* (Englewood Cliffs, New Jersey: Prentice-Hall, 1968), pp. 171, 175-76; Robert Mauzi, *L'Idée du bonheur dans la littérature et la pensée françaises au XVIIIe siècle* (Paris: Armand Colin, 1969), p. 364.

24. Outram, "The Language of Natural Power," op. cit., pp. 160-61.

25. In the order of publication of their *éloges,* the men so eulogized are: Viviani, L'Hopital, Amontons, Cassini I, Homberg, Ozanam, Des Billettes, Varignon, Littre, Hartsoeker, Newton, Reyneau, Truchet, Maraldi, Ruysch, Lagny, Boerhaave, Halley, Chicoyneau, Cassini II, Antoine de Jussieu, Bouguer, Winslow, Bélidor, Hales, Baron, Deparcieux, Jars, Fontaine, Bernard de Jussieu, Malouin, Linnaeus, Daniel Bernoulli, Duhamel du Monceau, Euler, Guettard, and Lassone.

26. *HARS* (1705), p. 15.

27. Honesty or sincerity was the hallmark of L'Hopital, Bourdelin II, Blondin,

N. Lémery, Ozanam, Des Billettes, Maraldi, Crousaz, J. L. Petit, Terrasson, C. J. Geoffroy, Winslow, Poleni, Hellot, Baron, Camus, Deparcieux, Rouelle, Pitot, Van Swieten, Huyghens, Fontaine, Bernard de Jussieu, Duhamel du Monceau, d'Alembert, Cassini de Thury, Guettard, and Gua de Malves.

28. *HARS* (1729), p. 120; (1706), p. 152; and (1722), p. 145, all translated and cited by Leonard M. Marsak, in "Bernard de Fontenelle: The Idea of Science in the French Enlightenment," *Transactions of the American Philosophical Society*, new ser., vol. 49, pt. 7 (1959), p. 43.

29. *HARS*, Fontenelle (1705), p. 152; (1707), pp. 168, 184; (1710), p. 150; (1719), p. 96; (1720), pp. 122−23; Fouchy (1750), p. 206; (1752), p. 163; (1760), p. 179; (1768), pp. 142−43, 166; (1772:1), pp. 117, 149; and (1776), p. 60.

30. Fontenelle specifically called attention to these traits in Dodart, Tschirnhaus, Poupart, Bourdelin II, Morin de St. Victor, Ozanam, Fagon, Rolle, Couplet, Lagny, and Boerhaave; Mairan in F. Petit; and Fouchy in Chicoyneau, Wolff, Nicole, Winslow, Baron, Chappe, Pitot, and Van Swieten.

31. *HARS* (1715), p. 93.

32. [Fontenelle], *Poésies pastorales, Avec un Traité sur la Nature de l'Eglogue, & une Digression sur les Anciens & les Modernes* (Paris: Michel Guérout, 1688), pp. 142−46, 154−55, 158−67, 198−211.

33. Niderst, pp. 588−89, 374−75, 611−12.

34. *HARS*, "Eloge de M. Ruysch" (1731), p. 104.

35. Article 26 reads as follows: "The Academy will take rigorous care to ensure that whenever some Academicians are of differing opinions they do not express any terms of contempt or of animosity against each other, either in their speech or their writing; and even when they combat the views of any savant whatsoever the Academy will exhort them to speak of them only with circumspection." The twenty-seven disputatious native scientists are: Tauvry, Régis, Galloys, Cassini I, Poli, P. de La Hire, Rolle, Mery, Varignon, G. J. du Verney, Chirac, Louville, Saurin, L. Lémery, C. J. Geoffroy, Bouguer, Winslow, Ferrein, Mairan, Fontaine, La Condamine, Quesnay, Lieutaud, Duhamel du Monceau, d'Alembert, Bouvard, and Buffon.

36. *HARS* (1743), pp. 197, 200.

37. Mauzi, op. cit., p. 527.

38. Hahn, *Anatomy*, pp. 36−37.

39. Thomas Sprat, *History of the Royal Society*, ed. Jackson I. Cope and Harold Whitmore Jones, Washington University Studies (St. Louis, Mo.: Washington Univ. Press, 1958), p. 18.

40. R. M. Wenley, *Stoicism and Its Influence* (New York: Cooper Square Publishers, 1963), pp. 80−98. See also E. Vernon Arnold, *Roman Stoicism* (New York: The Humanities Press, 1958), and G. Pire, *Stoïcisme et Pédagogie de Zénon à Marc Aurèle, de Sénèque à Montaigne et à J. J. Rousseau* (Paris: J. Vrin, 1958), pp. 26−27, 112−21, 150−59.

41. Seneca coined as his motto "*Vivere militare est*" ("Life is like a military exercise"), Epictetus adopted this motto as his own, and Marcus Aurelius altered it to: "To live is to struggle."

42. *HARS* (1730), p. 129; (1752), p. 168; (1769), pp. 164−71; (1783), p. 4.

43. Ibid. (1711), p. 106; (1727), p. 169; (1782), p. 120; (1750), p. 178.

44. Wenley, op. cit., pp. 25−26.

CONCLUSION: THE MORAL PHILOSOPHERS OF NATURE

1. *HARS* (1748), p. 132.

2. Ernst Robert Curtius, *European Literature and the Latin Middle Ages,* trans. Willard R. Trask (New York: Pantheon Books, 1953), pp. 59–60.

3. O. B. Hardison, *The Enduring Monument* (Chapel Hill: University of North Carolina Press, 1962), pp. 52, 57–58.

4. This quotation is taken from Robert Mauzi, *L'Idée du bonheur dans la littérature et la pensée françaises au XVIIIe siècle* (Paris: Armand Colin, 1969), p. 16.

5. Dorinda Outram, "Scientific Biography and the Case of Georges Cuvier," *History of Science* 14 (1976): 102, 108.

6. These qualities were collected from the *éloges* delivered at the Académie des Inscriptions et Belles-Lettres in commemoration of men (all but one of whom were not scientists) who also happened to be members of the Paris Academy of Sciences. These Academicians, with their years of death, are: the abbé Louvois (1718), the honorary Academician Valincourt (1730), Cardinal de Polignac (1741), Cardinal de Fleury (de facto ruler of France between 1726 and 1743) (1743), the abbé Jean-Paul Bignon (first president of the Academy of Sciences) (1743), Fontenelle (1757), the minister Comte d'Argenson (1764), the minister Comte de Maurepas (1781), the geographer d'Anville (1782), and the minister Marquis de Paulmy d'Argenson (1787).

7. G. Pire, *Stoicïsme et Pedagogie de Zénon . . . à J. J. Rousseau* (Paris: J. Vrin, 1958), pp. 40–41 and 136–38.

8. Ibid., pp. 112–21; E. Vernon Arnold, *Roman Stoicism* (New York: The Humanities Press, 1958), pp. 295–96.

9. Arnold, op. cit., pp. 41–42.

10. The quotation is taken from R. M. Wenley, *Stoicism and Its Influence* (New York: Cooper Square Publishers, 1963), p. 79.

11. *HARS,* Fontenelle, *éloges* of Tschirnhaus (1709), p. 124; and Leibniz (1716), p. 127; Fouchy, *éloges* of J. L. Petit (1750), p. 202; and Wolff (1754), p. 166.

12. *HARS,* Fouchy (1750), pp. 206–7.

13. *HARS* (1777), p. 90. See also Condorcet, *Oeuvres complètes de Condorcet* (Paris: Heinrichs, 1804): "Eloge de M. de Fourcroy," 2: 199–200.

14. Ira O. Wade, "The 'Philosophe' in the French Drama of the Eighteenth Century" (Ph.D. Diss. Princeton University, 1926), p. viii.

15. Cited in ibid., p. viii, nn. 1, 2.

16. Herbert Dieckmann, *Le Philosophe: Texts and Translation,* Washington University Studies, n. s., Language and Literature, no. 18, 1948, pp. 69, 81–82.

17. Jean Le Rond d'Alembert, "Essai sur les Elémens de Philosophie," *Oeuvres de d'Alembert* (Paris: A. Belin, 1821), 1: 231–32.

18. These are two of the many definitions or connotations of the term "philosophe" that Ira Wade found in the characterizations of French plays (Ira Wade, op. cit., pp. ix and 4).

19. The first definition is found identically in the *Dictionnaire de l'Académie Française,* 1694, 1718, and 1740 editions, and the second definition, in the first two

editions of the *Dictionnaire de Trévoux*, 1732 and 1743, before the Jesuits took on the parti encyclopédique or parti des (so-called) philosophes. Both definitions are cited in Dieckmann, op. cit., pp. 72–73.

20. Roger Hahn, "Scientific Research as an Occupation in Eighteenth-Century Paris," *Minerva* 13 (Winter 1975): 504. Sydney Ross, in "*Scientist*: The Story of a Word," *Annals of Science* 18 (June 1962): 65–85, shows that in England the term "scientist" was first propounded by William Whewell in 1834 but was not fully accepted there until c. 1910. The natural philosopher was loath to drop his ideal "of a man liberally educated, whose avocation was science as an intellectual *cum* philanthropic recreation, to which he might indeed devote most of his time without ever surrendering his claim to be a private gentleman of wide culture."

21. With the exception of Huyghens, Roemer, Perrault, Mariotte, and Roberval, the original membership of the Academy was comprised not only of scientists of the second rank but also of men who were not at all scientists by our or the late eighteenth-century definition. In addition to the two secretaries J. B. Duhamel and his successor Fontenelle, the Academy admitted between its founding in 1666 and its renewal in 1699 thirteen out of fifty-three savants who appear to have been admitted solely on the basis of their interest (rather than activity) in science (Carcavi, Pivert, Galloys, J. Marchant, Lannion, Bessé, Thevenot, Cusset, La Coudraye, G. P. La Hire, S. Boulduc, Couplet de Tartreaux, and Langlade). This practice was largely dropped from 1700 on. Men without scientific achievements to their credit were admitted from 1716 on, but as associés libres. Although they formally differed from the other working Academicians in being unable to attend meetings regularly and from honoraires in not being sufficiently high on the social scale (Hahn, *Anatomy*, p. 78), they also differed informally from the former group in that out of 17 elected to that position between 1716 and 1784 (and who died before 1792), six were scholars, science patrons, or writers of one, and only one, relatively insignificant memoir (Reyneau, Albert, Tressan, La Galissonnière, Etienne-François Turgot, and Joseph-Florent de Vallière).

Various forces combined to make the criteria for admission more stringent after 1699. There was an increase in the number of qualified candidates, spurred by an increasingly favorable climate of opinion and by increasingly evident rewards in being among the Academic elect. As K. M. Baker puts it, the Academician "had a social and legal status in the old regime—and, to some extent, an income—that derived from recognition of his scientific achievements" (*Social Mathematics*, p. 12). Since one of the most important aspects of that status was the jealously-guarded right to "determine the eligibility of candidates for admission," the Academicians insured that their future colleagues would meet the same strict requirement of "outstanding scientific achievement" that they had had to fulfill (ibid.). And as the scientific achievements of the Academicians grew in power, scope, and utility, the Renaissance ideal of *scientia* was rapidly transformed into the modern ideal of science. Indeed, whereas natural scientists before 1700 had to sit next to learned, but not scientifically-minded, scholars, after the mid-eighteenth century they had to sit next to men, like Jars or Montigny, whose predilections were unabashedly utilitarian.

22. Priestly was admitted to the Paris Academy of Sciences as a foreign associate on February 26, 1784, and his *éloge* was read by Cuvier on June 24, 1805.

23. Joseph Priestley, *The History and Present State of Electricity, with Original*

Experiments, 2 vols., 3d ed. (London: C. Bathurst, T. Lowndes, 1775); 1:xxiii.

24. Outram, op. cit., p. 113.

25. H. L. Nieburg, *In the Name of Science* (Chicago: Quadrangle Books, 1966), p. 103.

26. Ibid., p. 105.

27. Ross, op. cit., p. 83.

28. *The Christian Science Monitor*, May 7, 1968, 12, and *Newsweek* 71 (February 26, 1968): 88.

29. *The Saturday Review* 51 (March 16, 1968): 36.

30. Herbert Butterfield, *The Origins of Modern Science* rev. ed. (New York: Collier Books, 1957), pp. 172–76. See also the concurrent judgment by Jean Rostand in "Fontenelle, 'Homme de vérité,'" *Revue de Synthèse*, 3d ser., 21 (January–March 1961): 57.

NOTES TO APPENDIXES

1. L'Hopital had originally been elected to the Paris Academy of Sciences on June 17, 1693, as a mathematician, but his status changed to that of honoraire with the Renouvellement of January 28, 1699.

2. This roll includes de Moivre, a French Protestant refugee in London.

3. Roger Hahn uses the term "working Academicians" to designate all those who were neither honoraires nor associés étrangers. (*The Anatomy of a Scientific Institution,* p. 331).

4. Jean-Baptiste Enguehard and Daniel-Louis Vieussens in 1712, Aubert and Pierre du Verney in 1714, and François-Joseph de Camus in 1723.

5. Those Academicians were de Langlade, first physician to the Queen of Spain; Claude Burlet, first physician to the King of Spain; M. G. Bernard de Rézay, resident of Munich; the anatomist Pierre-Simon Rouhault, first surgeon to the King of Sardinia and professor of surgery at the University of Turin; and Raymond Vieussens, who elected to do his medical practice in Montpellier.

6. Cited in Condorcet, *Oeuvres de Condorcet* (Paris: Firmin Didot, 1847–49), 2: 156.

7. "Eloge de M. de Fontenelle," *HARS* (1757), p. 192.

8. Hahn, *Anatomy,* p. 82 n. 62.

9. André-Francois-Boureau-Deslandes (1712–57), Claude-François Geoffroy (1752–53), Jean Grosse (1731–44), Jean-Henri Imbert (1712–22), Jean Marius (1718–20), Louis Nicollic (1746–51), Poli the younger (1715), Jacques Trant (1722–39), and Christophe du Verney (1699–1748).

10. Beauvillier, Bomie, Delisle de La Croyère, Pierre Maheu, Jean-Baptiste Senac, Michel de Senne, and Simon de Valhebert.

11. See n. 16, chap. 5 above.

12. De Beaufort, Joseph Le Paute Dagelet, Pierre-Elisabeth de Fontanieu, Jacques Lémery, and Sébastien Vaillant.

13. André Dalesme, Etienne-Simon de Gamaches, Antoine-Tristan Danty d'Isnard, Jacques Jaugeon, and Pierre Le Monnier.

14. In addition to Pierre du Verney (n. 4 above), C. F. Geoffroy, Poli the younger,

Christophe du Verney (n. 9), and Jacques Lémery (n. 12), this roster includes Johann II Bernoulli, Simon Boulduc, François Chevallier (a nephew of Sauveur), Couplet de Tartreaux, Gabriel-Philippe and Jean-Nicholas de La Hire, G. D. Maraldi, Jean Marchant, and Charles Penot de Tournière (a son-in-law of Jean-Florent de Vallière).

15. These members are: the honoraires Joseph-Antoine d'Aguesseau; Victor-Marie, duc d'Estrées; the Jesuit mathematician and astronomer Thomas Gouye; Henry-Jacques-Nompar de Caumont, duc de La Force; Michel-Robert Le Peletier, comte de Saint-Fargeau; and Louis-François-Armand Duplessis, duc de Richelieu; the foreign associés Joseph Cervi, first physician to Philip V of Spain; the duke of Escalona, viceroy of Naples; the Polish prince, Joseph-Alexander Jablonowski; prince Charles Thomas von Löwenstein-Wertheim-Rochefort, ruler of the German principality of the same name; George Parker, second Earl of Macclesfield; and Thomas Herbert, 8th Earl of Pembroke. The working *régnicoles* include Jean-Baptiste-Antoine Andouille; Charles *le géomètre*; Pierre-Jean-Baptiste Chomel, Guisnée, La Chevalleraye, Jacques Lieutaud, Pierre Maloët, Michel-Louys Reneaume, and Saulmon.

16. Ernest Maindron, *L'Académie des Sciences* (Paris: Felix Alcan, 1888), p. 93.

17. Paris Academy of Sciences, Archives: Dossiers of Bernard de Jussieu, Joseph de Jussieu, and of Fouchy; Bibliothèque de l'Institut (Paris): Ms. 855, folios 54, 62, 66—90, 106—22; Ms. 1786, folios 43—179.

18. *HARS* (1716), p. 128; (1738), pp. 115, 117; (1723), p. 146.

19. Ibid. (1742), p. 181; (1743), n., p. 178.

20. Ibid. (1754), p. 185; (1755), p. 153; (1754), p. 167; (1744), p. 65; (1769), n., p. 135.

21. Ibid. (1782), p. 110; (1787), n., p. 75; (1781), p. 62; (1783), p. 96; (1774), pp. 85—88; (1785), pp. 135—36; (1778), p. 81.

22. Ibid, (1715), pp. 74—82; read at the public session of the Paris academy of Sciences on November 13, 1715.

23. The *Démonstrateur* assisted the Professor with his experiments or demonstrations.

24. In the Middle Ages the Faculty of Medicine at Montpellier was reputed one of the best in Europe. It had not entirely lost this reputation by the seventeenth century, as attested by the fact that the Academicians Littre, E. F. Geoffroy, Chirac, F. Petit, La Peyronnie, Chicoyneau, A. de Jussieu, and B. de Jussieu studied medicine or received their medical degrees there.

25. Louis II, *prince* de Condé (1621—86), called the Grand Condé, one of the two leading generals of the early part of Louis XIV's reign and best known for his victory at Rocroi (1643), which repulsed a Spanish invasion of France. Pierre-Michon Bourdelot founded an academy, a quasi-forerunner of the Paris Academy of Sciences, where amateurs met to discuss sundry topics, including scientific experiments. Justel was a wealthy Protestant and a former royal councillor, at whose house erudite men met weekly to discuss "the beautiful, the curious, and the solid in all the *sciences, especially literature*" (Niderst, pp. 113—14).

26. The hero is the Grand Condé, whose country residence at the Chateau de Chantilly, northwest of Paris, has been rebuilt and presently houses the collections of the Institut de France (the collective name for the five leading French academies).

27. The astronomer Auzout, the philosopher Régis, and the botanist Tournefort

subsequently were admitted to the Paris Academy of Sciences. Jacques Rohault was a popular lecturer on Cartesian physics. François Bernier, a traveler and physician, wrote an abridgment of Gassendi's Epicurean philosophy.

28. On the popularity of Du Verney's eloquent lectures on anatomy, see Fontenelle's *éloge* of him in HARS (1730), pp. 123–24.

29. In the margin of the *éloge* of Lémery, Fontenelle has added, "See the *Histoire* [of the Academy of Sciences] of 1708, p. 124."

30. In the 1680s close to 150,000 French Protestants emigrated to Brandenburg-Prussia, where they were received with open arms by the Great Elector Frederick Wilhelm (1640–88).

31. The Edict of Nantes was promulgated by Henri IV in 1598, at the end of the French religious wars. It guaranteed the Huguenots or French Protestants (mostly Calvinists) the free exercise of their faith and certain special rights. The revocation of this edict by Louis XIV in 1685 culminated nearly a decade of attempted conversions by force or persuasion and officially revoked the profession of Protestant faith, prohibited Huguenots from emigrating, and forcibly placed their children in Catholic schools.

32. The Marquis de Seignelay (1651–90), a minister of the navy, was the son of the famous minister Jean-Baptiste Colbert.

33. During the seventeenth and eighteenth centuries the Parlement of Paris, the highest judicial body in France, claimed to share with the monarch "truly universal and unlimited" authority over such matters as "the police, legislation, finances, public assistance, public instruction." Physicians and apothecaries formed two distinct and rival corporations. The Guards of corporations were responsible for enforcing the corporative rules (Marcel Marion, *Dictionnaire des Institutions de la France aux XVIIe et XVIIIe siècles*, pp. 123 and 253).

34. The Chancellor, the highest official of the kingdom, since 1626 had been nominally entrusted with the task of granting *privilèges* or licenses, without which books could not be sold. In practice, the function of licensing had been handed over to a *Directeur de Librairie,* who was assisted by a number of book censors.

35. Claude (Ier) Bourdelin (1621–99), the subject of Fontenelle's first *éloge* (*HARS*, 1699, pp. 151–52).

36. Louis Lémery (1677–1743) was appointed Pensionnary Chemist on March 18, 1715 (*Eloge* in *HARS*, 1743, pp. 195–208). His younger brother, Jacques (1678–1721), did not receive an *éloge*.

37. Cartesian philosopher and member of the Academy of Sciences.

38. The translation of the last sentence was borrowed from Leonard M. Marsak, "Bernard de Fontenelle," *Transactions of the American Philosohpical Society*, new ser., vol. 49, pt. 7 (1959), p. 43.

39. *HARS* (1762), pp. 231–42; read at the public session of the Paris Academy of Sciences on May 2, 1764.

40. Actually in March 1693.

41. In 1711 he entered Balliol College, from which he received his B.A. in 1714 and his M.A. in 1717.

42. Near Ross, Monmouthshire.

43. Reverend James Pound, rector of Wanstead, Essex, was one of the most skillful amateur astronomers in England.

44. George Parker, Second Earl of Macclesfield (1697–1764) was at one time president of the Royal Society and in 1755 took his seat as Foreign Associate at the Paris Academy of Sciences. He received no *éloge*. The *éloges* of Isaac Newton and Edmund Halley can be found in *HARS* (1727), pp. 151–72, and (1742), pp. 172–88, respectively.

45. Keill was noted for his defense of Newtonian attractionism and his application of that theory to the hypothesis of chemical affinities.

46. Sir Henry Savil (1549–1622) endowed two special chairs at Oxford in 1619.

47. The abbé Jean Picard (1620–82), admitted to the Academy of Sciences in 1666, was best known for his geodesic work. His short *éloge* is included in Condorcet, *Morts depuis 1666*, pp. 36–48.

48. Thanks to Picard, the Danish astronomer Claus Rømer (1644–1710) was admitted to the Paris Academy of Sciences in 1672. He returned to his homeland in the early 1680s as a result of the increasingly anti-Protestant climate in France (see n. 31 above). His *éloge* is found in Condorcet, *Morts depuis 1666*, pp. 141–52.

49. Alexis-Claude Clairaut (1713–65), a child prodigy in mathematical physics, was admitted to the Academy of Sciences in 1731 by special exemption at the age of eighteen. His *éloge*, by Fouchy, is in *HARS* (1765), pp. 144–59.

50. George Graham constructed a twenty-four-foot zenith section while his pupil John Bird, with a one-thousand-pound grant from the Admiralty, built two mural quadrants and a transit instrument.

51. The Royal Society of London was governed by a Council of twenty-one members, which included the president, a treasurer, and two secretaries.

52. Giuseppe Cervi (1663–1748), first physician to Philip V of Spain, was a member of the Academy of Sciences from 1739 to 1748. He received no *éloge*.

53. An academy founded in 1652 at Schweinfurt, Germany, for the purpose of promoting medicine and pharmacy by observation.

54. *HARS* (1788), pp. 37–49; read at the public session of the Paris Academy of Sciences on November 14, 1789.

55. The Chambre des Comptes was a branch of the royal administration in charge of the revenues of the royal domain and other fiscal matters pertaining to the kingdom. The duc d'Orléans was the grandson of Louis XIV's only brother and the son of the notorious *Régent* who governed France during Louis XV's minority.

56. Fouchy held the position of perpetual secretary from January 8, 1744, to July 24, 1776 (during which period he wrote all his *éloges*), those of honorary perpetual secretary and pensionnary veteran from July 24, 1776 to April 23, 1785, and only that of pensionnary veteran from that last date until his death in 1788.

57. Upon the death of the childless Charles II of Spain in 1700, Louis XIV was successful in placing his grandson the Duc d'Anjou upon the Spanish throne under the name of Philip V, but not before embroiling a good part of Europe in the devastating and exhausting War of the Spanish Succession (1701–14).

58. Fouchy *fils* was only eight years old when Louis XIV died in 1715.

59. Clairaut, de Gua, La Condamine, Nollet (and Quesnay) were future members of the Paris Academy of Sciences. The Rameau mentioned here is probably the composer and musical theorist Jean-Philippe Rameau, who devoted more than forty years to finding the scientific basis of musical harmony. Henry Sully was a famous English clockmaker and the Le Roy family were famous French clockmakers. For

further information on the Society of Arts see Roger Hahn, "The Application of Science to Society: the Societies of Arts," *Studies on Voltaire and the Eighteenth Century* 24–25 (1963): 829–36. On Rameau the theorist see Charles B. Paul, "Jean-Philippe Rameau (1683–1764), the Musician as *Philosophe*," *Proceedings of the American Philosophical Society,* 114 (April 13, 1970): 140–54.

60. To be more precise, Fouchy was appointed supernumerary assistant astronomer on April 24, 1731, but received a regular appointment, as assistant mécanicien, only on March 30, 1733. He was appointed assistant astronomer on December 16 of the same year, associate astronomer on February 5, 1741, and was nominated perpetual secretary on September 2, 1743, a position he occupied only on January 8, 1744.

61. Less than a year prior to the time this *éloge* was delivered, Jean-Sylvain Bailly (1736–93) had become president of the Constituant Assembly during the famous scene of the Oath of the Tennis Court (June 20, 1789), and then mayor of Paris. Sixteen years earlier he had, with the support of Buffon, applied for the position of assistant secretary of the Academy of Sciences but had lost out to Condorcet, who had been supported by d'Alembert, Lagrange, and others (see n. 65 below).

62. Mairan held the position of secretary from January 7, 1741, to August 23, 1743.

63. Fontenelle's mother, Marthe Corneille, was the sister of the two brothers Pierre, the great tragedian, and Thomas, the lyrical poet and librettist.

64. The life of Fontenelle spanned the century (February 11, 1657–January 9, 1757) that began with the religious quarrels led, among others, by the Jansenist Antoine Arnauld (1612–94), and with the defense of the divine right of kingship by the Catholic bishop, orator, and writer Jacques-Bénigne Bossuet (1627–1704), and that ended with the systematic criticism of absolute monarchy by Montesquieu (1689–1755) and of established religions by Voltaire (1694–1778).

65. For a nonpartisan appraisal of Condorcet's appointment as associate secretary on March 8, 1773, see K. M. Baker's "Les débuts de Condorcet au secrétariat de l'Académie royale des sciences (1773–1776)," *Revue d'histoire des sciences et de leurs applications*, 20 (1967): 229–80.

66. The physicist, of course, is Benjamin Franklin (1706–90).

67. Immanuel Kant, in "What is Enlightenment?" (1784).

68. "Observation anatomique," *MARS* (1784), pp. 399–401.

BIBLIOGRAPHY

A. COLLECTIONS OF "ÉLOGES"

Two-hundred sixty-four members of the Paris Academy of Sciences died between its official renouvellement on January 20, 1699, and the reading of Condorcet's last *éloge* on November 12, 1791. Of these, 193 received official eulogies: 69 by Fontenelle between 1699 and 1739, 10 by Mairan between 1741 and 1743, 64 by Fouchy between 1744 and 1776, and 50 by Condorcet between 1773 and 1791. These *éloges*, referred throughout this book as the "public" *éloges*, were, with the exception of the last two, published in the *Histoire* section of nearly every issue of the yearly *Histoire et Mémoires de l'Académie Royale des Sciences* (see appendices A and C). In addition, Condorcet published in a separate volume in 1773 the *Eloges des Académiciens de l'Académie Royale des Sciences, Morts depuis 1666, jusqu'en 1699*. These encomiums, which I entitle "written" *éloges*, since they were never delivered at the biyearly public sessions of the Academy, are composed of eleven eulogies and twenty short notices (see appendix B).

Most of these 224 eulogies were also published separately, either in collections of *éloges* or in the "complete" works of Fontenelle and Condorcet. The ones I consulted at the *Bibliothèque Nationale* are, along with their catalog numbers:

Bernard le Bovier de Fontenelle

8^0Ln^91	*Histoire du renouvellement de l'Académie Royale des Sciences en M.DC.XCIX. et les éloges historiques de tous les Académiciens morts depuis ce Renouvellement*. Paris: Jean Boudot, 1708. Contains the *éloges* of Bourdelin, Tauvry, Tuillier, Viviani, de l'Hopital, Jacques Bernoulli, d'Amontons, Du Hamel, Régis, Vauban, Galloys, and Dodart. A variant, possibly pirated (8^0Ln^91A), bears the publishing data Amsterdam: Pierre de Coup, 1709.
8^0Ln^91B	*Histoire du renouvellement de l'Académie Royale des Sciences en M.DC.XCIX. et les éloges historiques de tous les Académiciens morts depuis ce Renouvellement*. Paris: Michel Brunet, 1716. This appears to be volume two of the 1708 edition, since it contains the *éloges* of Tournefort, Tschirnhaus, Poupart, Chazelles, Guglielmini, Carré, Bourdelin II, Berger, Cassini I, Blondin, Poli, Morin, N. Lémery, Homberg, Malebranche, Sauveur, and Parent.

Z. 24193   *Oeuvres diverses de M. de Fontenelle contenant l'Histoire du Renouvellement de l'Académie Royale des Sciences*. Vol. 8. New, aug. ed. Paris: Michel Brunet, 1715. Contains the same *éloges* as listed in the 1708 edition.

8^0Ln^{9}1C   *Histoire du Renouvellement de l'Académie des Sciences & éloges historiques*. 3 vols. Paris: Michel Brunet. Vol. 1 (1719): *éloges* from Bourdelin through Dodart; Vol. 2 (1717): *éloges* from Tournefort through Parent; Vol. 3 (1722): *éloges* of Leibniz, Ozanam, La Hire, La Faye, Fagon, Louvois, Montmort, Rolle, Renau, Dangeau, and des Billettes.

Z.24196.   *Oeuvres diverses de M. de Fontenelle*. Vol. 3. New, aug. ed. Paris: Michel Brunet, 1724. Contains all the *éloges* given in the above edition, plus those of d'Argenson, Couplet, Méry, and Varignon. Two variant printings of volume 3 are: La Haye: Gosse & Neaulme, 1728−29, and Amsterdam: F. Changuion, 1743.

8^0Ln^{9}2.   *Suite des Eloges des Académiciens de l'Académie Royale des Sciences morts depuis l'an MDCCXII*. Paris: Brunet, 1733. Contains the *éloges* of Peter I, Littre, Hartsoeker, Delisle, Malézieu, Newton, Reyneau, Tallard, Truchet, Bianchini, Maraldi, Valincourt, Marsigli, and Du Verney. A variant copy of this edition bears the Parisian booksellers' names of Osmont, Hourdel, Huart, Grissby, David le jeune, Chaubert, & Clousier.

Z.24201−Z.24202. *Oeuvres de Monsieur de Fontenelle*. Vols. 5 and 6. Paris: Bernard Brunet, 1742. Contains all 69 *éloges*.

Z.24207−Z.24208. A variant of the above, also of 1742.

Z.24216−Z.24217. *Oeuvres de Monsieur de Fontenelle*. Vols. 5 and 6. New ed. Paris: Bernard Brunet, 1752. Contains all 69 *éloges*.

Z.24224−Z.24225. A variant, with different pagination and format, published presumably in Amsterdam in 1754.

Z.24230−Z.24231. *Oeuvres de Monsieur de Fontenelle*. Vols. 5 and 6. New ed. Paris: Bernard Brunet, 1758. Contains all 69 *éloges*.

8^0L^{9}99.   *Eloges des Académiciens de l'Académie Royale des Sciences, Morts depuis l'an 1699*. 2 vols. New ed. Paris: Chez les Libraires associés, 1766. Contains all 69 *éloges*.

Z.24243−Z.24244. *Oeuvres de Monsieur de Fontenelle*. Vols. 5 and 6. New ed. Paris: Chez les Libraires associés, 1766. Contains all 69 *éloges*.

Z.24261−Z.24262. *Oeuvres de Monsieur de Fontenelle*. Vols. 5 and 6. New ed. Paris: Saillant, Desaint, Regnard, de la Doue, 1767. Contains all 69 *éloges*.

Z.24274−Z.24275. *Oeuvres de Fontenelle, précedées d'une notice historique sur sa vie et ses travaux*. Vols. 1 and 2. Paris: Salmon, Peytieux, 1825. Contains all 69 *éloges*.

X.19219.   *Choix d'Eloges français les plus estimés* (Paris: D'Hautel, 1812). Vol. 3. Contains *éloges* of Newton, Tournefort, Vauban, Leibniz, d'Argenson, and Peter I.

8⁰G.6087.   *Choix d'Eloges*. Edited by Paul Janet. Paris: Charles Delagrave, 1888. Contains *éloges* of L'Hopital, Bernoulli, d'Amontons, Régis, Vauban, Tournefort, Chazelles, Carré, Cassini, Lémery, Malebranche, Leibniz, Ozanam, Fagon, Dangeau, Varignon, Peter I, Newton, Du Verney, Boerhaave, and Du Fay.

8⁰Ln⁹180A.   *Eloges de Fontenelle, avec une introduction et des notes.* Edited by Francisque Bouillier. Paris: Garnier, [1883]. Contains *éloges* of d'Amontons, Du Hamel, Régis, Vauban, Galloys, Dodart, Tournefort, Chazelles, Carré, Bourdelin, Morin, Malebranche, Sauveur, Leibniz, Montmort, Renau, d'Argenson, Couplet, Varignon, Peter I, Delisle, Malézieu, Newton, Truchet, Du Verney, Marsigli, Geoffroy, Chirac, Ressons, Boerhaave, and Du Fay.

8⁰Z.17539.   *Pages choisies des écrivains: Fontenelle.* Edited by Henri Potez. Paris: Armand Colin, 1909. Contains, in part or in whole, the *éloges* of Viviani, Vauban, Tournefort, Carré, Morin, Lémery, Malebranche, Leibniz, Fagon, Montmort, Dangeau, d'Argenson, Peter I, Newton, Truchet, Valincourt, Du Verney, Marsigli, Ruysch, Chirac, Louville, Saurin, and Du Fay.

In addition to these, there is a facsimile reprint, put out by Culture et Civilisation (Brussels, 1969) of the two-volume edition of the *Eloges des Académiciens avec l'Histoire de l'Académie Royale des Sciences en M.DC.XCIX. avec un discours préliminaire sur l'utilité des Mathématiques* (The Hague: Isaac vander Kloot, 1740). These two volumes contain all the *éloges* composed between 1699 (Bourdelin I) and 1730 (Du Verney). The first volume opens with Fontenelle's "Préface sur l'utilité des Mathématiques et de la Physique et sur les Travaux de l'Académie des Science" and the "Règlement ordonné par le Roi pour l'Académie Royale des Sciences" upon its "renewal" in 1699.

Jean-Jacques Dortous de Mairan

8⁰Ln⁹4.   *Eloges des Académiciens de l'Académie Royale des Sciences, Morts dans les Années 1741, 1742, 1743* Paris: Durand, 1747. Contains all the 10 *éloges* written by Mairan.

Jean-Paul Grandjean de Fouchy

8⁰Ln⁹5.   *Eloges des Académiciens de l'Académie Royale des Sciences, Morts depuis l'an 1744.* Paris: V. Brunet, 1761. Contains only the *éloges* of Bragelongne, Torcy, La Peyronie, Jean Bernoulli, d'Amelot, d'Aiguillon, Crousaz, Petit le Chirurgien, Terrasson, d'Aguesseau, d'Albert, Geoffroy, Chicoyneau, Sloane, d'Onsenbray, Wolff, Folkes, de Moivre, Lowendal, Helvétius, and Boyer. Apparently, no separately-published work containing all of Fouchy's *éloges* was ever published.

Marie-Jean-Antoine-Nicolas Caritat de Condorcet

8⁰Ln⁹6A.   *Eloges des Académiciens de l'Académie Royale des Sciences, Morts depuis l'an 1666 jusqu'en 1790*. 5 vols. Paris: Viewig et Fuchs, 1799. Contains all of Condorcet's "written" and "public" *éloges*.

Z.28829−Z.28832.   *Oeuvres complètes de Condorcet*. Edited by A. A. Barbier, P.-J.-G. Cabanis, and D.-J. Garat. 21 vols. Paris: Heinrichs, 1804. The first four volumes contain all the "written" and "public" *éloges*.

Z.28850−Z.28861.   *Oeuvres de Condorcet*. Edited by A. Condorcet O'Connor and F. Arago. 12 vols. Paris: Firmin Didot, 1847−49. Volume 2 contains the "written" *éloges* and notices, an "Essai d'une histoire des correspondants de l'Académie Royale des Sciences" (pp. 93−138), and 25 "public" *éloges*, while volume 3 contains the remaining "public" *éloges*.

B. MANUSCRIPTS

In addition to the printed *Registre des procès-verbaux des séances* of the Paris Academy of Sciences, I have also consulted the handwritten minutes of the early proceedings of that institution, the plumitifs or original drafts of the Academy's sessions kept by the secretaries and others (especially the indefatigable Réaumur), and the biographical dossiers of over a hundred Academicians. Of special relevance to this study are the materials found in the following dossiers:

Joseph de Jussieu: Typed copy of Antoine-Laurent de Jussieu's "Notes sur la vie de Monsieur Joseph de Jussieu" (original copy in the Bibliothèque du Muséum national d'histoire naturelle).

Bernard de Jussieu: A typed copy of Antoine-Laurent de Jussieu's "Notes sur la vie de M. Bernard de Jussieu" (original copy in the Bibliothèque du Muséum national d'histoire naturelle).

La Condamine: Autobiographical notes on his early life, which are the acknowledged source for Condorcet's *éloge* up to page 88.

Fouchy: Autograph of his life written by his son and sent to Condorcet.

Of no less importance to this monograph are the manuscripts found in the Bibliothèque de l'Institut. Of the voluminous manuscripts of Condorcet in its safekeeping, I have made particular use of:

MS 623*   Correspondance

MS 855   Papiers littéraires et académiques:

        Folio 62.   Drafts of the *éloges* of Trudaine de Montigny and Luynes.

	Folios 66−90.	Drafts of the *éloge* of Linnaeus.
	Folios 106−22.	Draft of the *éloge* of Haller.
MSS 873−874.	Plan for a dictionary of the sciences.	
MS 1962	"Collection des Règlements & Déliberations de l'Académie Royale des Sciences par ordre des Matières."	
MS 1786	Folios 43−104.	D'Alembert. "Notice des éloges de Mrs Malouin et Haller lus par M^r le Marquis de Condorcet, à la rentrée de l'Académie des Sciences le 14 novembre 1778."
	Folios 105−79.	"Extrait de l'Eloge de M. de la Condamine par M. le Marquis de Condorcet."

C. CONTEMPORARY "ÉLOGES" OF OTHER ACADEMIES

Since many members of the Paris Academy of Sciences were also members of one or more of the four Academies referred to in the following bibliographic entries, the *éloges* delivered at their sessions have been consulted for comparisons and contrasts with the *éloges* studied here.

[Académie Française] *Recueil des pièces d'éloquence présentées à l'Académie Françoise*. Paris: Coignard, 1743.

Académie Royale des Inscriptions et Belles Lettres. *Histoires*. 51 vols. Paris: Imprimerie Royale, 1729−88.

Louis, A. *Eloges lus dans les séances publiques de l'Académie Royale de Chirurgie de 1750 à 1792*. Edited by E.-F. Dubois. Paris: J. B. Baillière, 1859.

[Vicq-d'Azyr, Félix.] *Oeuvres de Vicq-d'Azyr*. 6 vols. Edited by Jacques L. Moreau. Paris: Duprat-Duverger, 1805. The first three volumes contain the *éloges* composed by this secretary of the Société Royale de Médecine (1748−94).

D. EIGHTEENTH-CENTURY WORKS ALLUDING TO THE "*ÉLOGES*"

[Bachaumont, Louis Petit de.] *Mémoires sécrets de Bachaumont (1762−1771)*. Edited by Van Bever. 2 vols. Paris: Louis Michaud, [n.d.].

Grimm, Melchior, Denis Diderot, G.-T.-F. Raynal, J.H. Meister et al. *Correspondance littéraire, philosophique et critique*. Edited by Maurice Tourneux. 16 vols. Paris: Garnier, 1877−92.

Journal des Scavans. 1665−1790.

[Marais, Mathieu.] *Journal et Mémoires de Mathieu Marais . . . 1715−1737*. Edited by M. de Lescure. 4 vols. Paris: Firmin Didot, 1864.

Mercure de France. 1700−92.

Thomas, A. L. *Essai sur les éloges*. 2 vols. Paris: Auguste Delalain, 1829. This book was written between 1758 and 1785 by Thomas, a member of the Académie Française.

E. GENERAL SOURCES CONTAINING
BIOGRAPHICAL LISTS OR ENTRIES

Desessarts, N. L. M. et al. *Les Siècles littéraires de la France, ou Nouveau diction-naire historique, critique, et bibliographique*. 7 vols. Paris: Desessarts, 1800–1. No foreign members of the Academy of Sciences are listed, but nearly all the French ones who died before 1792 are. Some of the entries mention the fact that they are paraphrases of the *éloges*; most of them are unacknowledged paraphrases.

Gillispie, C. C., ed. *Dictionary of Scientific Biography*. 14 vols. New York: Charles Scribner, 1970–76. Of the 140-odd "working" Academicians eulogized before 1792, seventy-seven are given notices here.

[Institut de France.] *Index biographique des membres et correspondants de l'Académie des Sciences, du 22 décembre 1666 au 15 décembre 1967*. Paris: Gauthier-Villars, 1968. See appendices A and C above for some corrections of or additions to dates of delivery of *éloges* at the public sessions of the Academy of Sciences.

Hazon, Jacques Albert. *Notice des hommes les plus célèbres de la Faculté de Médecine en l'Université de Paris*. Paris: Benoit Morin, 1778. "Extraite (en plus grande partie) du Manuscrit de feu M. Thomas-Bernard Bertrand, communiqué par M. son fils, rédigée par M. Jacques-Albert Hazon, Docteur-Régent de la même Faculté."

Hoeffer, F., ed. *Nouvelle biographie generale*. 46 vols. Paris: Firmin Didot, 1858–78.

Mascart, Jean. *La Vie et les travaux du chevalier Jean-Charles de Borda (1733–1799): épisodes de la vie scientifique au XVIIIe siècle*. Annales de l'Université de Lyon, n.s., fasc. 33. Paris: Picard, 1919. Each scientist mentioned in the text is given a brief biographical notice in a footnote.

Michaud, Joseph François, ed.. *Biographie universelle, ancienne et moderne*. 83 vols. Paris: Michaud frères, 1811–55. Many of the entries on the Academicians are poorly-disguised paraphrases of the *éloges*.

Poggendorff, Johann Christian, ed.. *Biographisch-literarisches Handwörtenbuch der exakten Naturwissenschaften*. 7 vols. Leipzig: J. A. Barth, 1863–71.

Prévost, M. & R. d'Amat, eds.. *Dictionnaire de biographie française*. 12 vols. Paris: Letouzey et Ane, 1933–70.

Rozier, François. *Nouvelle table des articles contenus dans les volumes de l'Académie Royale des Sciences, depuis 1666 jusqu'en 1770*. 4 vols. Paris: Ruault, 1775. Volume 1 contains lists of members of the Academy of Sciences by classes.

Saigey, Emile. *Les Sciences au XVIIIe siècle*, pt. 2, *L'Ancienne Académie des Sciences et les Académiciens jusqu'en 1795*. Paris: Germer Baillière, 1873. An appendix contains a complete list of Academicians nominated up to 1793, with some brief information, in the order of their nomination.

F. ADDITIONAL WORKS BY THE SECRETARIES

Fontenelle

"Digression sur les anciens et les modernes" (1688) and "Sur l'histoire" (c.1680). *Oeuvres de M. de Fontenelle*. New ed. 11 vols. Paris: Chez les Libraires associés, 1766. 5: 280–90 and 420–43.

Elémens de la géométrie de l'infini, suite des 'Mémoires de l'Académie Royale des Sciences'. Paris: Imprimerie royale, 1727.

Entretiens sur la pluralité des mondes. Edited by Jérôme Lalande. Paris: Janet et Cotelle, 1820.

Krauss, Werner. *Fontenelle und die Aufklärung*. Munich: Wilhelm Fink, 1969.

Poésies pastorales, Avec un Traité sur la Nature de l'Eglogue, & une Digression sur les Anciens & les Modernes. Paris: Michel Guérout, 1688.

Mairan

Camp, [n.n.]. "Lettres inédites de Mairan à Bouillet." *Bulletin de la Société Archéologique de Béziers*. 2d ser. 2 (1860): 1–25.

Dissertation sur la Glace, ou Explication physique de la formation de la Glace et de ses divers phénomènes. Paris: L'Imprimerie royale, 1749.

Condorcet

Delattre, André. "Une lettre inédite de Condorcet à Jean-Robert Tronchin." *Modern Language Notes* 58 (November 1943): 528–32. Requests information for an *éloge* on his brother Théodore.

Discours prononcés dans l'Académie françoise, le Jeudi XXI Février M.DCC.LXXXII, à la réception de M. le Marquis de Condorcet. Paris: Demonville, 1782.

"Esquisse d'un Tableau Historique des progrès de l'esprit humain." Condorcet, *Oeuvres complètes de Condorcet*. Paris: Heinrichs, 1804. Vol. 8.

Henry, Charles, ed. *Correspondance inédite de Condorcet et de Turgot, 1770–1779*. Paris: Charavay, 1882.

G. SECONDARY SOURCES ON THE SECRETARIES

On Fontenelle

Callot, Emile. "Un maitre à penser: Fontenelle." *Six philosophes français du XVIIIe siècle*. Annecy: Gardet, 1963.

Carré, J.-R. *La Philosophie de Fontenelle ou le sourire de la raison*. Paris: Félix Alcan, 1932.

Cosentini, John W. *Fontenelle's Art of the Dialogue*. New York: King's Crown Press, 1952.

Counillon, J.-F. *Fontenelle: écrivain, savant, philosophe.* Fecamp: L. Durand et fils, 1959.

Delorme, Suzanne. "Des Eloges de Fontenelle et de la psychologie des savants." *Mélanges Georges Jamati.* Paris: Centre National de la Recherche Scientifique, 1956.

————. "Tableau chronologique de la vie et des oeuvres de Fontenelle," and "Contribution à la bibliographie de Fontenelle." *Revue d'histoire des sciences et de leurs applications* 10 (1957): 288–309.

————. "La vie scientifique à l'époque de Fontenelle d'après les éloges des savants." *Archeion* 19 (1937): 217–35.

Edsall, H. Linn. "The Idea of History and Progress in Fontenelle and Voltaire." In *Studies by Members of the French Department of Yale University*, edited by Albert Feuillerat. New Haven: Yale University Press, 1941.

Fayol, Amédée. *Fontenelle.* Paris: Debresse, 1961.

Flourens, P. *Fontenelle ou de la philosophie moderne.* Paris: Paulin, 1847.

Grégoire, F. "Le dernier défenseur des tourbillons: Fontenelle." *Revue d'histoire des sciences et de leurs applications* 7 (July–September 1954): 220–46.

————. *Fontenelle: Une "philosophie" désabusée.* Paris: J. Vrin, 1947.

Laborde-Milaa, A. *Fontenelle.* Paris: Hachette, 1905.

Maigron, Louis. *Fontenelle. L'homme, l'oeuvre, l'influence.* Paris: Plon, 1906.

Marsak, Leonard M. "Bernard de Fontenelle: The Idea of Science in the French Enlightenment." *Transactions of the American Philosophical Society*, vol. 49, pt. 7 (1959).

————. "Bernard de Fontenelle: In Defense of Science." In *The Rise of Science in Relation to Society.* Edited by L. M. Marsak. New York: Macmillan, 1964.

————. "Cartesianism in Fontenelle and French Science, 1686–1752." *Isis* 50 (1959): 51–60.

Niderst, Alain. *Fontenelle à la recherche de lui-même (1657–1702).* Paris: A. G. Nizet, 1972.

Revue de Synthèse. 3rd ser. 21 (January–March 1961): Suzanne Delorme, "Fontenelle: L'Homme et son temps," 3–35; Antoine Adam, "Fontenelle, Homme de lettres," 37–42; André Couder, "Fontenelle, homme de science," 43–51; Jean Rostand, "Fontenelle, 'Homme de Vérité'," 53–77; André Robinet, "Malebranche dans la pensée de Fontenelle," 79–86.

Robinet, André. "Considérations sur un Centenaire: Notes soumises aux historiens de Fontenelle." *Revue de métaphysique et de morale* 63 (April–September 1958): 283–298.

Sainte-Beuve, C.-A. "Fontenelle." In *Causeries du Lundi.* 3d ed. Paris: Garnier, [1858], III: 314–35.

Trublet, Abbé. *Mémoires pour servir à l'Histoire de la vie et des ouvrages de Mr. de Fontenelle, tirés du Mercure de France 1756, 1757, 1758.* 2d ed. Amsterdam: Michel Rey, 1759.

Villemain, Abel-François. *Cours de littérature française: Tableau de la littérature au XVIIIe siècle.* 4 vols. New ed. Paris: Perrin, 1891. 1:305–329.

On Mairan

Duboul, J. "Dortous de Mairan: Etude sur sa vie et sur ses travaux." *Actes de l'Académie Impériale des sciences, belles-lettres et arts*. 3d ser. 24:163−97.

Guerlac, Henry. "The Newtonianism of Dortous de Mairan." *Essays and Papers in the History of Science*. Baltimore: Johns Hopkins University Press, 1977.

Kleinbaum, Abby R. "Jean-Jacques Dortous de Mairan (1678−1771): Study of an Enlightened Scientist." Ph.D. dissertation, Columbia University, 1970.

Roche, D. "Un savant et sa bibliothèque au XVIIIe siècle: les livres de Jean-Jacques Dortous de Mairan." *Dix-huitième siècle* 1 (1969): 47−88.

On Condorcet

Asse, Eugène, ed. *Lettres de Mlle. de Lespinasse,* etc. Paris: Charpentier, [n.d.]. Pp. 324−330. Lespinasse's famous portrait of Condorcet.

Arago, François. *Oeuvres de François Arago*. 13 vols. 2nd ed. Paris: Théodore Morgand, 1865. 2: 117−246. His *éloge* of Condorcet.

Baker, Keith Michael. *Condorcet: From Natural Philosophy to Social Mathematics*. Chicago: University of Chicago Press, 1975.

———. "Les débuts de Condorcet au sécrétariat de l'Académie Royale des Sciences (1773−1776)." *Revue d'histoire des sciences et de leurs applications* 10 (1967): 229−80.

———. "Un 'Eloge' Officieux de Condorcet: Sa notice historique et critique de Condillac." *Revue de Synthèse*, 3d ser. 88 (1967): 227−51.

———. "Scientism, elitism and liberalism: the case of Condorcet." *Studies on Voltaire and the Eighteenth Century* 55 (1967): 129−65.

Brooks, Richard A. "Condorcet and Pascal." *Studies on Voltaire and the Eighteenth Century* 55 (1967): 297−307.

Cahen, Léon. *Condorcet et la Revolution française*. Paris: Félix Alcan, 1904.

Charma, Antoine. *Condorcet: sa vie et ses oeuvres*. Caen: A. Hardel, 1863.

Granger, Gilles-Gaston. *La Mathématique sociale du Marquis de Condorcet*. Paris: Presses universitaires de France, 1956.

Laboulle, M.-J. "La Mathématique sociale: Condorcet et ses prédécesseurs." *Revue d'Histoire littéraire de la France* 46 (1939): 33−55.

Lacroix, Sylvestre. *Notice historique sur la vie et les ouvrages de Condorcet*. Paris: J.-B. Sajou, 1813.

Lalande, Jérôme. "Notice sur la vie et les ouvrages de Condorcet." *Le Mercure Francais* 21 (1796): 141−162.

Manuel, Frank E. *The Prophets of Paris*. Cambridge, Mass.: Harvard University Press, 1962. Chap. 2.

Sainte-Beuve, C.-A. "Condorcet." In *Causeries du Lundi*. 3d ed. Paris: Garnier, [1858]. 3: 336−359.

Sergescu, Pierre. "La Contribution de Condorcet à l'*Encyclopédie*." *Revue d'histoire des sciences et de leurs applications* 4 (July−December 1951): 233−237.

H. WORKS BY OTHER ACADEMICIANS

Alembert, Jean le Rond d'. "Eloges académiques" and "Infini géométrique." *Encyclopédie ou Dictionnaire raisonné des sciences, des arts et des métiers.* 17 vols. Paris, 1751–1780. 12: 149–51, and 8: 702–4.

―――. *Oeuvres de d'Alembert.* 5 vols. Paris: A. Belin, 1821.

Malebranche, Nicolas. "Recherche de la Verité, où l'on traite de la nature de l'esprit de l'homme et de l'usage qu'il en doit faire pour éviter l'erreur dans les sciences." *Oeuvres de Malebranche.* 11 vols. Edited by G. Rodis-Lewis. Vols. 1 and 2. Paris: Vrin, 1962.

Nollet, Jean-Antoine. *L'Art des expériences, ou avis aux amateurs de la physique.* 3 vols. 2d ed. Paris: P. E. G. Durand, 1770.

―――. *Lecons de physique expérimentale.* 5th ed., 6 vols. Paris: Hippolyte-Louis Guerin, 1759. 1: v–xciv.

I. WORKS ON OTHER ACADEMICIANS

The following bibliography of Academicians other than the secretaries is in no way designed to take the place of the comprehensive "Biographical Data on Academicians" in Roger Hahn's *The Anatomy of a Scientific Institution,* pp. 330–73. Listed below are only such items as I have cited in this study and those published after Hahn's book went to press.

Ahlers, Willem C. *Un chimiste du XVIIIe siècle, Pierre Joseph Macquer (1718–1784), Aspects de sa vie et de son oeuvre.* University of Paris, Faculté des Lettres et sciences humaines, thèse de troisième cycle, 1969.

Aldridge, Alfred Owen. *Franklin and his French Contemporaries.* New York: New York University Press, 1957.

Le père André. *La Vie du R. P. Malebranche.* Paris: Poussielgue frères, 1886. Written around 1721.

[Bailly, J. S.] *Eloges de Charles V, de Molière, de Corneille, de l'abbé de La Caille, et de Leibniz.* Paris: Deladain, 1770.

Balz, Albert G. "Louis de la Chambre, 1594–1669." *The Philosophical Review* 39 (July 1930): 375–397.

Barber, W. H. *Leibniz in France, from Arnauld to Voltaire.* Oxford: Clarendon Press, 1955.

Bell, A. E. *Christian Huygens and the Development of Science in the Seventeenth Century.* London: Edward Arnold, 1947.

Brunet, Pierre. *Maupertuis.* 2 vols. Paris: Albert Blanchard, 1929.

―――. *La Vie et l'oeuvre de Clairaut (1713–1765).* Paris: Presses universitaires de France, 1952.

Callot, Emile. "L'universalité de Maupertuis." *Six philosophes français du XVIIIe siècle.* Annecy: Gardet, 1963.

Clarke, Jack A. "Abbé Jean-Paul Bignon, 'Moderator of the Academies' and Royal Librarian." *French Historical Studies* 8 (Fall 1973): 213–235.

Coleby, Leslie J. M. *The Chemical Studies of P. J. Macquer*. London: George Allen and Unwin, 1938.

Doyon, André, and Liaigre, Lucien. *Jacques Vaucanson, mécanicien de génie. Mélanges Franco-Italiens de littérature*, vol. 41. Paris: Presses universitaires de France, 1966.

Duveen, Denis I., and Hahn, Roger. "Laplace's Succession to Bézout's Post of 'Examinateur des Elèves de l'Artillerie.' " *Isis* 48 (December 1957): 416–427.

["Eloge de M. Charas."] *Mercure de France*, February 1698, pp. 122–40. Much of Condorcet's "written" *éloge* (1773) seems to be based on this notice.

Glass, Bentley, et al., eds. *Forerunners of Darwin, 1745–1859*. Baltimore: Johns Hopkins University Press, 1959.

Grasse, Pierre-P., *La vie et l'oeuvre de Réaumur (1683–1757)*. Paris: Presses universitaires de France, 1962.

Guédon, Jean-Claude. "Protestantisme et Chimie: Le Milieu intellectuel de Nicolas Lémery." *Isis* 65 (June 1974): 212–28.

Guerlac, Henry. "An Augustan Monument: The *Opticks* of Isaac Newton." *Essays and Papers in the History of Science*. Baltimore: Johns Hopkins University Press, 1977.

Hagberg, Knut. *Carl Linnaeus*. Translated by Alan Blair. London: Jonathan Cape, 1952.

Hankins, Thomas L. "The Influence of Malebranche on the Science of Mechanics during the Eighteenth Century." *Journal of the History of Ideas* 27 (April–June 1967): 193–210.

———. *Jean d'Alembert: Science and the Enlightenment*. Oxford: Clarendon Press, 1970.

Heim, Roger, ed. *Buffon, les grands naturalistes français*. Paris: Muséum national d'histoire naturelle, 1954.

———. ed. *Tournefort*. Paris: Museum national d'histoire naturelle, 1957.

Lindeboom, G. A. *Herman Boerhaave: The Man and His Work*. London: Methuen, 1968.

McKie, Douglas. "Guillaume-François Rouelle (1703–1770)," *Endeavor* 12 (July 1953): 130–133.

Plantefol, Lucien. "Duhamel du Monceau." *Dix-huitième siècle* 1 (1969): 123–137.

Rappaport, Rhoda. "G.-F. Rouelle: An Eighteenth-Century Chemist and Teacher." *Chymia* 6 (1960): 68–101.

Revue d'histoire des sciences et de leurs applications:
   Birembaut, Arthur, "La contribution de Réaumur à la thermométrie," 11 (October–December 1958): 302–329.
   Broglie, Louis de, "Un mathématicien, homme de lettres: d'Alembert," 4 (July–December 1951): 204–212.
   Mayer, Jean, "Portrait d'un chimiste: Guillaume-François Rouelle (1703–1770)," 23 (October–December 1970): 305–332.

Ostoya, Paul, "Maupertuis et la biologie," 7 (January–March 1954): 60–78.

Robinet, André, "Le groupe malebranchiste introducteur de Calcul infinitésimal en France," 13 (October–December 1960): 287–308.

——, "La philosophie malebranchiste des mathématiques," 14 (July–December 1961): 205–54.

——, "La vocation académicienne de Malebranche," 12 (January–March 1959): 1–18.

Taton, René. "Réaumur mathématicien," 11 (April–June 1958): 130–33.

Robinet, André. *Malebranche et Leibniz: Relations personnelles.* Paris: J. Vrin, 1955.

Schneider, Ivo. "Der Mathematiker Abraham de Moivre." *Archive for History of Exact Sciences* 5 (1968–69): 177–317.

Torlais, Jean. *L'Abbé Nollet (1700–1770) et la physique expérimentale au XVIIIe siècle.* Paris: Les Conférences du Palais de la Découverte, [n.d.].

——. *Un Esprit Encyclopédique en dehors de l'Encyclopédie: Réaumur.* Paris: Albert Blanchard, 1961.

Tressan, Comte de. "Eloge de M. Moreau de Maupertuis . . . prononcé dans l'Assemblée publique de la Société royale de Nancy, le 30 janvier 1760." In *Oeuvres posthumes du comte de Tressan.* Paris: Desray, 1791, 2: 309–41.

J. STUDIES ON LEARNED AND TEACHING INSTITUTIONS

Barrière, P. *L'Académie de Bordeaux: Centre de culture internationale au XVIIIe siècle (1712–1792).* Bordeaux, Paris: Biere, [n.d.].

Bertrand, Joseph. *L'Académie des Sciences et les Académiciens de 1666 à 1793.* Paris: J. Hetzel, 1869.

Contant, Jean-Paul. *L'Enseignement de la chimie au Jardin Royal des Plantes de Paris.* Cahors: A. Coueslant, 1952.

Crestois, Paul. *L'Enseignement de la botanique au Jardin Royal Des Plantes de Paris.* (Cahors: A. Coueslant, 1953.

Dainville, François de. "L'Enseignement des mathématiques dans les collèges jésuites de France du XVIe au XVIIIe siècles." *Revue d'histoire des sciences et de leurs applications* 7 (1954): 6–21, 109–23.

Gauja, Pierre. *L'Académie des Sciences de l'Institut de France.* Paris: Gauthier-Villars, 1934.

Hahn, Roger, *The Anatomy of a Scientific Institution: The Paris Academy of Sciences, 1666–1803.* Berkeley, Los Angeles, London: University of California Press, 1971.

——. "The Application of Science to Society: the Societies of Arts." *Studies on Voltaire and the Eighteenth Century* 25 (1963): 829–36.

Huard, Pierre. *L'Académie royale de chirurgie (1731–1793).* Paris: Palais de la Découverte, 1967.

Jourdain, Charles. *Histoire de l'Université de Paris, au XVIIe et au XVIIIe siècle.* 2 vols. Paris: Firmin Didot, 1888.

Maindron, Ernest. *L'Académie des Sciences* Paris: Felix Alcan, 1888.

Marion, Marcel. *Dictionnaire des Institutions de la France aux XVIIe et XVIIIe siècles.* Paris: A. & J. Picard, 1972. Originally published in 1923.

Maury, L.-F. Alfred. *L'Ancienne Académie des Sciences.* Paris: Didier, 1864.

————. *L'Ancienne Académie des Inscriptions et Belles Lettres.* Paris: Didier, 1864.

Ornstein, Martha. *The Role of Scientific Societies in the Seventeenth Century.* 3d ed. Chicago: University of Chicago Press, 1938.

Schimberg, André. *L'Education morale dans les collèges de la Compagnie de Jésus en France sous l'Ancien Régime.* Paris: Honoré Champion, 1913.

Snyders, Georges. *La Pédagogie en France aux XVIIe et XVIIIe siècles.* Paris: Presses universitaires de France, 1965.

Sprat, Thomas. *History of the Royal Society.* Edited by Jackson I. Cope and Harold Whitmore Jones. Washington University Studies. St. Louis, Mo.; Washington University Press, 1958. Originally published in 1667.

Taton, René, ed. *Enseignement et diffusion des sciences en France au XVIIIe siècle.* Paris: Hermann, 1964.

K. STUDIES ON LITERATURE AND RHETORIC

Basso, Louis. "Le problème de la vulgarisation scientifique." *Revue philosophique de la France et de l'étranger* 97 (1924): 104–39, 268–305.

Burgess, Theodore C. *Epideictic Literature*, Studies in Classical Philology. Chicago: University of Chicago Press, 1902. 3:89–261.

Calderwood, James L., and Toliver, Harold E. *Forms of Poetry.* Englewood Cliffs, N. J.: Prentice-Hall, 1968.

Campbell, George. *The Philosophy of Rhetoric.* Edited by Lloyd F. Bitzer. Carbondale: Southern Illinois University Press, 1963. Originally published in 1776.

Caussade, François de. *Notions de rhétorique et étude des genres littéraires.* Paris: Masson, [1906].

Curtius, Ernst Robert. *European Literature and the Latin Middle Ages.* Translated by Willard R. Trask. New York: Pantheon Books, 1953.

Dainville, Francois de. "L'Evolution de l'enseignement de la rhétorique au XVIIe siècle." *Dix-septième siècle* 80–81 (April 1968): 19–43.

France, Peter. *Rhetoric and Truth in France: Descartes to Diderot.* Oxford: Clarendon Press, 1972.

Garrison, James D. *Dryden and the Tradition of the Panegyric.* Berkeley, Los Angeles, London: University of California Press, 1975.

[Gibert, B.] *De la Veritable Éloquence, ou Réfutation des Paradoxes sur l'Eloquence, avancez par l'Auteur de la Connoissance de soi-même.* Paris: Michel David, 1703.

Hardison, O. B. *The Enduring Monument: A Study of the Idea of Praise in Renaissance Literary Theory and Practice.* Chapel Hill: University of North Carolina Press, 1962.

Highet, Gilbert. *The Classical Tradition: Greek and Roman Influences on Western Literature*. New York and London: Oxford University Press, 1949.

Lincoln, Eleanor Terry, ed. *Pastoral and Romance: Modern Essays in Criticism*. Englewood Cliffs, N. J.: Prentice-Hall, 1969.

[Ortigues de Vaumorières, P. d'.] *Harangues sur toutes sortes de sujets, avec l'art de composer*. Paris: Jean Guignard, 1687.

Quintilian. *The Institutio Oratorio*. Translated by H. E. Butler. 4 vols. London: William Heinemann, 1933.

L. OTHER WORKS WRITTEN BEFORE 1800

Benot, Yves, ed. *Diderot et Falconet: Le Pour et le Contre; Correspondance polémique sur le respect de la posterité, Pline et les Anciens*. Paris: Editeurs Français Réunis, 1958.

Diderot, Denis. *Oeuvres complètes de Diderot*. Edited by J. Assézat and M. Tourneux. 20 vols. Paris: Garnier, 1875–1879.

[Lagrange, Joseph-Louis.] *Oeuvres de Lagrange*. 14 vols. Edited by J. A. Serret and Gaston Darboux. Vols. 13 and 14. Paris: Gauthier-Villars, 1892.

Montucla, J. F. *Histoire des Mathématiques*. 4 vols. Paris: Henri Agasse, [1799].

Perrault, Charles. *Mémoires de ma vie*. Edited by Paul Bonnefon. Paris: Renouard, H. Laurens, 1909.

Plutarch. *Plutarch's Lives of Illustrious Men*. Translated by John Dryden and corrected from the Greek and revised by A. H. Clough. New York, New York: The Modern Library, [n.d.].

Priestley, Joseph. *The History and Present State of Electricity, with Original Experiments*. 2 vols. 3d ed. London: C. Bathurst et al., 1775.

Voltaire. *Oeuvres complètes de Voltaire*. 52 vols. Edited by Louis Moland and G. Bengesco. Vol. 22. Paris: Garnier, 1877–1885.

M. OTHER WORKS WRITTEN AFTER 1800

Arnold, E. Vernon. *Roman Stoicism*. New York: The Humanities Press, 1958.

Bessmertny, Bertha. "Les principaux ouvrages sur l'histoire des sciences parus en France pendant le XVIIIe siècle." *Archeion* 16 (1934): 325–28

Birn, Raymond. "Le Journal des Savants sous l'Ancien Régime." *Journal des Savants*, January–March 1965, pp. 15–35.

Bouillier, Francisque. *Histoire de la philosophie cartésienne*. 2 vols. 3d ed. Paris: Delagrave, 1868.

Bourde, André J. *Agronomie et agronomes en France au XVIIIe siècle*. Paris: Ecole Pratique des Hautes Etudes, 1967.

Brunet, Pierre. *L'Introduction des théories de Newton en France au XVIIIe siècle*. Paris: Albert Blanchard, 1931.

————. *Les Physiciens hollandais et la méthode expérimentale en France au XVIIIe siècle*. Paris: Albert Blanchard, 1926.

Bury, J. B. *The Idea of Progress*. New York: Dover, 1955.

Butterfield, Herbert. *The Origins of Modern Science*. Rev. ed. New York: Collier Books, 1957.

Cassirer, Ernst. *The Philosophy of the Enlightenment*. Translated by F. C. A. Koelln and J. P. Pettegrove. Boston: Beacon Press, 1955.

Cattell, J. McKeen. "A Statistical Study of American Men of Science: The Selection of a Group of One Thousand Scientific Men." *Science* 24 (1906): 658–65, 699–707, 732–42.

————. "A Further Statistical Study of American Men of Science." *Science* 32 (1910): 633–48, 672–88.

Chapin, Seymour L. "The Academy of Sciences during the Eighteenth Century: An Astronomical Appraisal." *French Historical Studies* 5 (Fall 1968): 371–404.

Crosland, Maurice. "The Development of a Professional Career in Science in France." *Minerva* 13 (Spring 1975): 38–57.

Cuvier, Georges. *Histoire des Sciences naturelles, depuis leur origine jusqu'à nos jours, chez tous les peuples connus*. 5 vols. Paris: Fortin, Masson et Cie., 1841–45. Vols. 3 and 4.

Daumas, Maurice, ed. *Histoire de la science*. Paris: Gallimard, 1957.

Delambre, J.-B.-J. *Histoire de l'astronomie au dix-huitième siècle*. Paris: Bachelier, 1827.

Dieckmann, Herbert. *Le Philosophe: Texts and Translation*. St. Louis, Mo.: Washington University Studies, n.s., Language and Literature, no. 18, 1948.

Ehrard, Jean. *L'Idée de nature en France dans la première moitié du XVIIIe siècle*. 2 vols. Paris: Ecole Pratique des Hautes Etudes, 1963. An abridged version of this work, entitled *L'Idée de nature en France à l'aube des Lumières*, was published by Flammarion in Paris in 1969.

Gasking, Elizabeth B. *Investigations into Generation 1651–1828*. Baltimore: Johns Hopkins University Press, [1967].

Gay, Peter. *The Enlightenment: An Interpretation*. 2 vols. New York: Vintage Books, 1966–69.

Greene, John C. *The Death of Adam: Evolution and Its Impact on Western Thought*. Ames: The Iowa State University Press, 1959.

Hahn, Roger, "Scientific Research as an Occupation in Eighteenth-Century Paris." *Minerva* 13 (Winter 1975): 501–13.

Hall, A. R. *The Scientific Revolution, 1500–1800*. Boston: Beacon Press, 1954.

Howard, Martha Walling. *The Influence of Plutarch in the Major European Literatures of the Eighteenth Century*. Chapel Hill: University of North Carolina Press, 1970.

Iltis, Carolyn. "The Decline of Cartesianism in Mechanics: The Leibnizian-Cartesian Debates." *Isis* 64 (September 1973): 356–73.

Knight, David M. "The Scientist as Sage." *Studies in Romanticism* 6 (Winter 1967): 65–88.

Kristeller, Paul Oskar. *The Classics and Renaissance Thought*. Vol. 15 Martin Classical Lectures Cambridge, Mass.: Harvard University Press, 1955.

Mason, Stephen F. *Main Currents of Scientific Thought: A History of the Sciences*. New York: Abelard-Schuman, 1956.

Maurois, André, *Aspects of Biography*. Translated by S. C. Roberts. Cambridge: University Press, 1929.

Mauzi, Robert. *L'Idée du bonheur au XVIIIe siècle*. Paris: Armand Colin, 1960.

Metzger, Héléne. *Les doctrines chimiques en France du début du XVIIe à la fin du XVIIIe siècle*. Paris: Presses universitaires de France, 1923.

———. "La Littérature scientifique française au XVIIIe siècle." *Archéion* 16 (1934): 1–17.

———. *Newton, Stahl, Boerhaave et la doctrine chimique*. Paris: Félix Alcan, 1930.

Mornet, Daniel. *Les Origines intellectuelles de la Révolution française, 1715–1787*. 4th ed. Paris: Armand Colin, 1947.

———. *Les Sciences de la nature en France, au XVIIIe siècle*. Paris: Armand Colin, 1911.

Mouy, Paul. *Le Développement de la Physique Cartésienne, 1646–1712*. Paris: J. Vrin, 1934.

Munteano, B. *Constantes dialectiques en littérature et en histoire: problèmes, recherches, perspectives*. Paris: Didier, 1967.

Nieburg, H. L. *In the Name of Science*. Chicago: Quadrangle Books, 1966.

Outram, Dorinda. "The Language of Natural Power: The 'Eloges' of Georges Cuvier and the Public Language of Nineteenth Century Science." *History of Science* 16 (1978): 153–78.

———. "Scientific Biography and the Case of Georges Cuvier: With a Critical Bibliography." *History of Science* 14 (1976): 101–37.

Partington, J. R. *A Short History of Chemistry*. New York: Harper Torchbooks, 1957.

Pire, G. *Stoïcisme et Pédagogie de Zénon à Marc Aurèle, de Sénèque à Montaigne et à J. J. Rousseau*. Paris: J. Vrin, 1958.

Proust, Jacques. *L'Encyclopédie*. Paris: Armand Colin, 1965.

Ranum, Orest. *Paris in the Age of Absolutism*. New York: John Wiley, 1968.

Rice, Eugene F., Jr. *The Renaissance Idea of Wisdom*. Cambridge: Harvard University Press, 1958.

Rigault, Hippolyte. *Histoire de la querelle des anciens et des modernes*. Paris: Hachette, 1856.

Roger, Jacques. *Les Sciences de la vie dans la pensée française du XVIIIe siècle*. Paris: Armand Colin, 1963.

Ross, Sydney. "Scientist: The Story of a Word." *Annals of Science* 18 (June 1962): 65–88.

Schofield, Robert. "What is Modern in the Eighteenth Century?—*Not* Science." *Studies in Eighteenth-Century Culture*. Edited by Louis T. Milic. Cleveland: The Press of Case Western Reserve University, 1971.

Smith, Preserved. *A History of Modern Culture*. Vol. 2, *The Enlightenment*. New York: Crowell-Collier, 1962.

Stock, Hyman. *The Method of Descartes in the Natural Sciences*. New York: The Marion Press, 1931.

Stricklen, Jr., Charles G. "The *philosophe's* political mission: the creation of an idea." *Studies in Voltaire and the Eighteenth Century*. 86 (1971): 137–228.

Todhunter, I. *A History of the Mathematical Theory of Probability*. New York: Chelsea, 1949. Originally published in 1865.

Vartanian, Aram. *Diderot and Descartes, A Study of Scientific Naturalism in the Enlightenment*. Princeton: Princeton University Press, 1953.

Wade, Ira O. "The 'Philosophe' in the French Drama of the Eighteenth Century." Ph.D. Dissertation, Princeton University, 1926.

Wenley, R. M. *Stoicism and Its Influence*. New York: Cooper Square Publishers, 1963.

Woolf, Harry. *The Transits of Venus: A Study of Eighteenth-Century Science*. Princeton: Princeton University Press, 1959.

INDEXES

Index of Names

Subject Index

Designer:	U.C. Press staff
Compositor:	Trend Western Corp.
Printer:	Braun-Brumfield, Inc.
Binder:	Braun-Brumfield, Inc.
Text:	Linocomp Times Roman
Display:	Linocomp Times Roman and Bold